24 95/80E

Principles of Integrated Electronics

Edward Pasahow
San Diego Community Colleges
San Diego, California

Breton Publishers
A Division of Wadsworth, Inc.
North Scituate, Massachusetts

For Joan and Dave

Principles of Integrated Electronics was prepared for publication by the following people: **Carol Beal**, copy editor; **Trisha Hanlon**, interior text designer; **Stephen Wm. Snider**, cover designer; **Jay's Publishers Services, Inc.**, illustrator. **Ellie Connolly** supervised production. The book was set in **Century Schoolbook** by **A & B Typesetters, Inc.**; printing and binding was by **The Alpine Press, Inc.**

Breton Publishers
A Division of Wadsworth, Inc.

Library of Congress Cataloging in Publication Data

Pasahow, Edward.
  Principles of integrated electronics.
  Includes index.
  1. Integrated circuits. 2. Digital electronics. I. Title.
TK7874.P39   621.381'73   81-10119
ISBN 0-534-01055-5   AACR2

Printed in the United States of America
1 2 3 4 5 6 7 8 9 — 86 85 84 83 82

Contents

Preface

Chapter Six
TTL Output Stages_____ 65

Chapter Seven
MOS Logic_____ 79

Chapter Eight
Number Systems _____ 93

Chapter Nine
Digital Arithmetic _____ 109

Chapter Ten
Data Selection and Comparison

Chapter Eleven
Flip-Flops

Chapter Twelve
Registers and Counters

Chapter Thirteen
Operational Amplifiers —————— 169

Chapter Fourteen
Signal Conditioning —————— 191

Chapter Fifteen
Data Conversion

Chapter Sixteen
Timers, Oscillators, and Triggers

Chapter Seventeen
Phase-locked Loops _____ 245

Chapter Eighteen
Optoelectronics _____ 257

Chapter Nineteen
Power Supply and Control

Chapter Twenty
Construction and Troubleshooting

Appendix
Transistors

Preface

Integrated circuit applications are the most rapidly growing area of electronics. More than three-quarters of the electrical equipment being manufactured today is partially or entirely digital. Many of the analog circuits, which only recently were built of discrete components, are now available as low-cost chips. The number of technicians qualified to work on these devices falls far short of the industrial demand. Moreover, technicians who have been on the job a few years are finding that their knowledge and skills are becoming obsolete with the introduction of the new equipment.

The purpose of this book is to provide a broad basis for a basic course in modern electronics. It is aimed at the community or technical college student who is primarily interested in digital and analog integrated circuits. A prerequisite course in dc theory and a corequisite of ac theory are the background necessary to understand this material.

By presenting electronics principles from the perspective of integrated circuits, this text prepares students for advanced studies of logic circuits, microcomputers and microprocessors, and digital communications systems. Coverage is divided between digital and analog devices, with supplementary topics on discrete transistors and diodes, optoelectronics, power supplies and controls, and construction techniques.

The material is readily adaptable to a two-semester course in electronics fundamentals. The first semester would deal with digital functions, and the following semester would take up linear and analog devices. The subjects of optoelectronics, power supplies, and troubleshooting would be taught at the points most appropriate to the students' needs. Courses accompanied by laboratory experiments would probably profit from that material quite early; other course curricula might find those subjects more suitable later in the school year.

The study of two-state devices begins with simple inverter concepts. Consideration of diodes and transistors as switching circuit elements is a natural consequence of this beginning. (Transistor amplifiers are covered in the Appendix.) A strong foundation in logic analysis is provided by an early introduction to Boolean algebra, truth tables, and basic gates. An in-depth look into TTL and CMOS devices demonstrates how these principles apply to real devices in widespread use. The emphasis is on the standard logic families, which the student is most likely to encounter. The basics of digital theory conclude with binary arithmetic circuits, data selectors and digital comparators, flip-flops, and registers and counters.

A parallel analysis of analog and linear devices begins with the concept of operational amplifiers and demonstrates how they form the foundation for more complex circuits. The op amp is shown in comparator, integrator, differentiator, summing, and high-speed configurations. Schmitt triggers, timers, and converters serve as additional examples of linear circuits. This section is completed by study of both digital and analog forms of phase-locked loops and timers.

As on my previous books, the assistance and understanding of two people were a major factor in the writing of this book. Rosemarie Pasahow helps just by being there at the right time, and Myrna Davis types the manuscript. Thank you both.

Edward Pasahow
San Diego, California

Chapter One

Introduction to Modern Electronic Analysis

Technicians today are confronted with third- and fourth-generation components in the equipment they work with. In addition to individual resistors, capacitors, and transistors, electronic components frequently encountered include integrated circuits, operational amplifiers, fiber optics, and phase-locked loops. Even power supplies are often modular packages, providing overtemperature protection, voltage regulation, and current limiting, all within a single subunit.

This growth in the quantity and diversity of electronic components can often be confusing to the technician. Yet, with the proper perspective, modern electronic circuits can be analyzed in a straightforward manner. The techniques presented in this book are applicable to individual and integrated components, and they also work with both digital and analog circuits.

This chapter introduces the basic concepts of circuit analysis, which are applied in a variety of circumstances throughout the remainder of the book. Once you can gain an understanding of this approach to circuit analysis, you will find that it offers insight into the workings of any circuit that you are likely to come across on the job.

Chapter Objectives

Upon completion of this chapter, you should be able to:

☐ Distinguish between digital and analog signals.
☐ Describe the characteristics of each level in the scale of integrated circuits.
☐ Determine the direction of conventional current flow in a circuit.
☐ Model discrete resistors and capacitors by using functional analysis.
☐ Analyze the action of bipolar and field effect transistors by using graphical analysis.
☐ Explain the switching nature of transistors.

☐ CIRCUIT COMPONENTS

You are already familiar with *passive, discrete circuit elements* from your study of dc circuit analysis. Each of these devices has *two ports*; one port is used as an input terminal and the other is used as an output terminal. Examples of passive, discrete components are resistors, capacitors, and inductors (coils); see Figure 1–1a. In passive circuits, inverting the component so that the input becomes the output, and conversely, does not change the voltages or currents in the circuit, as shown in Figure 1–1b. But we will see that, in general, electronic components *cannot* be in-

verted without affecting both currents and voltages. (Perhaps you already know about electrolytic capacitors, which must always be installed with one terminal at positive polarity relative to the other in order to protect the capacitor against damage.)

The *active, discrete circuit elements* must always be installed in a circuit with the proper orientation. Reversing the leads incorrectly will prevent the circuit from operating and could result in failures. For this reason, you must be very careful to note the proper pin positions when installing these components. Another characteristic of active devices is their ability to *amplify* or *attenuate* the incoming signal. For these circuits, then, we can no longer write an equation relating the output voltage and current to the inputs. Instead we use *graphical analysis* or *models* of these components to determine the results of any combination of inputs. Transistors and diodes are typical active, discrete components.

Figure 1–2 shows a circuit board with capacitors, resistors, transistors, and diodes. The tubular resistors in the figure are easily recognized by their color-coded bands. The capacitors are the disks near the bottom of the figure and seen from the top, they appear as circular packages with two leads. There are also two other light-colored capacitors located in the center of the board. The four transistors are the shiny "cans" aligned in a row in the center of the figure. Below the row of transistors are four partially transparent diodes. All these devices working together form two complete *flip-flops* (which will be discussed in Chapter 11).

An **integrated circuit** is, in effect, an entire circuit board in a single component. The integrated circuit is made from a semiconductor, most often silicon. The semiconducting material is treated in various ways so that both active and passive devices can be included in one package. This process alters the crystalline structure of the silicon in such a way that all the individual components exist in a *monolithic* (single-crystal) form. Figure 1–3 shows a silicon wafer that has been processed into integrated circuits (note size of circuit in relation to the dime shown). Each square on the wafer is a complete circuit (a flip-flop, for example). In the manufacturing process, the squares are cut apart. Each square, called a **chip**, is then put in a separate package that protects it against damage. Also, each package is provided with pins so that it can be mounted on a circuit board.

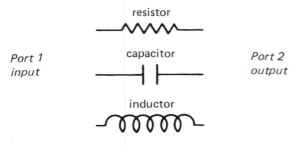

(a) Symbols

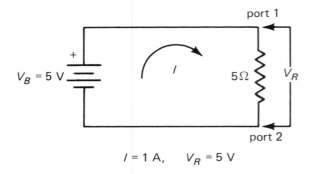

$I = 1\ A,\quad V_R = 5\ V$

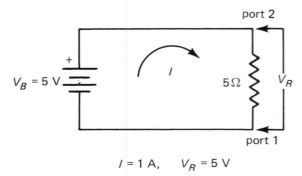

$I = 1\ A,\quad V_R = 5\ V$

(b) Inverting the Component

FIGURE 1–1. Passive, Discrete Components

FIGURE 1-2.
Discrete Component
Circuit Board

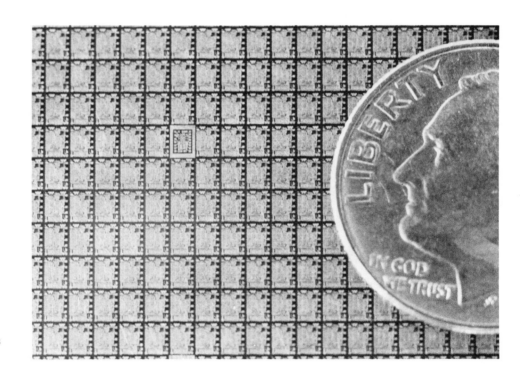

FIGURE 1-3.
Integrated Circuit
Wafer with Hundreds
of Chips

☐ DIGITAL AND ANALOG CIRCUITS

In the past, all electronic circuits used continuous, or **analog**, voltages and currents. In an analog circuit, the values for currents and voltages can take on any reading within the valid range of the circuit. Figure 1-4a shows a voltage that varies between a low of −3 V and a high of 3.69 V. At some time the voltage takes on *every*

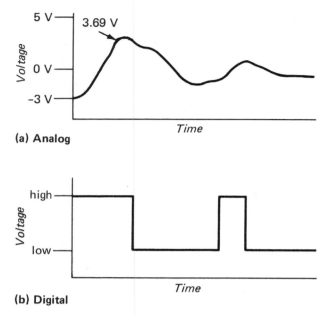

FIGURE 1-4. Analog and Digital Voltages

value between these limits at least once. An analog circuit will react to each of these values as their characteristic equations predict.

A different way of treating the voltage (or current) variations is used in **digital circuits**. Here there are only two *levels*, or steps, of interest, as shown in Figure 1-4b. The voltage is either at the high or the low level. Digital circuits, therefore, deal with only two values of voltage. Should the voltage be neither high nor low, an undetermined situation occurs and circuit action is not predictable. Thus, digital voltages are designed to stabilize at high or low levels.

□ SCALE OF INTEGRATION

The earliest integrated circuits were quite simple and contained only a few components. As manufacturing techniques became more sophisticated, chips with thousands of transistors could be produced on a piece of silicon the size of your fingernail. Integrated circuits are sometimes referred to as *third-generation devices*. The preceding generations of electronic circuits were vacuum tubes (first-generation) and discrete-component transistors (second-generation). Today you may hear reference to fourth-generation components, which are the highly complex chips used in microcomputers, though this terminology is not universally applied.

Integrated circuits are classified by the complexity of their internal units. The basic building block is the **logic gate**, which is the simplest digital component. (Chapters 2 and 3 fully describe logic gates.) An integrated circuit that has less than 10 logic gates on the chip is ranked as **small-scale integration (SSI)**. The next level of complexity, from 10 to 100 logic gates, is **medium-scale integration (MSI)**. A major subsystem of from 100 to 1000 logic gates fabricated in a single microcircuit is called **large-scale integration (LSI)**. At the highest level, above 1000 gates, the circuits are classified as **very large-scale integration (VLSI)**. Even though analog integrated circuits do not use logic gates in their construction, analog circuit complexity is still classified in this way. This classification is used because the analog microcircuit can be compared with a digital circuit with the same number of active and passive components.

Table 1-1 lists many of the integrated circuits that will be covered in this book. Each of the microcircuits is identified as digital or analog, and the scale of integration is specified. Interestingly enough, the same analytical methods used in studying SSI circuits apply directly to VLSI. The only difference is that the VLSI circuits involve more logic gates than the simpler circuits.

□ ANALYTICAL MODELS OF PASSIVE ELEMENTS

When you were studying resistors and capacitors in your earlier courses, you may have thought that the actual device was being considered. This was not the case, however. Instead, you were simplifying the analytical problem by considering a *model* of the device. For example, if you were interested in the voltages and currents in a resistor network, you ignored the effects of temperature, gravity, solar radiation, and cosmic ray bombardment. Yet, in certain applications, each of these factors could become overriding, and the voltages and currents would be quite different from those predicted by the simpler model.

How do you know which model to use? The answer to this question is sometimes difficult to decide, and much of the research in electronics is aimed at finding that answer. This difficulty rarely arises for the technician, though, because the manufacturers provide handbooks describing

TABLE 1-1. Applications of Integrated Circuits

	Scale of Integration			
Application	SSI	MSI	LSI	VLSI
Digital				
Arithmetic and logic components	Logic gate	Four-bit adder, digital multiplexer	Arithmetic logic unit	Microprocessor
Memory	Flip-flop	Eight-bit latch	Static RAM	Dynamic random-access memory, read-only memory
Analog				
Frequency control	Fixed divider	Variable divider	Frequency synthesizer	Digital synthesizer
Conversion	Operational amplifier, sample-and-hold	Digital-to-analog converter	Successive-approximation, analog-to-digital converter	Flash analog-to-digital converter
Signal switching and timing	Simple analog multiplexer	Timers	Phase-locked loops	

the models to be used with their circuits and the limits within which these models are valid. Thus, to acquaint you with the concept of modeling electronic circuits, we will consider some of the methods that you learned in dc circuit analysis by using several alternative models.

Resistor Model

This is the simplest model of all. It is just **Ohm's law**, which states

$$R = \frac{V_R}{I} \qquad (1\text{-}1)$$

That is, the resistance (R) is equal to the voltage (V_R) across the resistor divided by the current (I) flowing through it. Figure 1-5a shows a resistor circuit as it is normally depicted. (Note that *conventional current flow* is used in all the schematics in this book. The direction of conventional current flow is from the positive potential, produced by a chemical reaction within the battery, through the resistor, and back to the negative terminal of the battery. Electrons flow in the direction *opposite* to that of conventional current flow.)

The functional model of the resistor (see Figure 1-5b) may appear to be the same circuit,

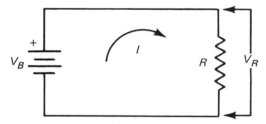

(a) Traditional Model

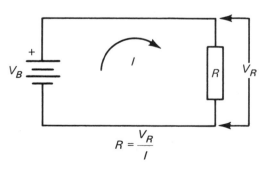

$$R = \frac{V_R}{I}$$

(b) Functional Model

Note:
V_B = *battery voltage*

FIGURE 1-5. Traditional and Functional Models of a Resistor

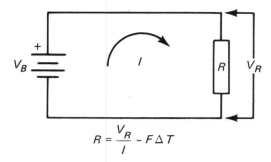

$$R = \frac{V_R}{I} - F\Delta T$$

FIGURE 1-6. Temperature-compensated Resistor Model

but there is a significant difference. The model explicitly states that resistance is defined by Equation 1-1. That is, the model assumes that no other factors ever enter into consideration. If some other parameter (temperature, for example) is to be used in the calculations, the model must be changed accordingly.

To show how a model can be adapted to take other factors into consideration, we will modify the model that uses Ohm's law. Figure 1-6 shows our new model. Now the resistance is

$$R = \frac{V_R}{I} - F\Delta T \qquad (1-2)$$

where

F = temperature coefficient for the resistive material

$\Delta T = 20° - T$, the difference between ambient Celsius temperature and 20°C

The resistance is a factor not only of the voltage and current but also of the ambient (surrounding) temperature.

□ **EXAMPLE 1-1**

Find the value of a 1 percent resistor that is to be used in a space satellite operating at −270°C if the current flow is to be 100 mA and the voltage drop across the resistor is to be 15 V.

Solution Both models will be applied to show the difference in the resistance each predicts. The Ohm's law model gives

$$R - \frac{V_R}{I} = \frac{15}{100 \times 10^{-3}}$$
$$= 150 \ \Omega$$

Now we will apply the model with temperature compensation. Suppose a carbon resistor is to be used. The temperature coefficient for the resistive material is −0.05 per degree Celsius change from 20° (the minus sign means that resistance decreases with increasing temperature). Then we have

$$R = \frac{V_R}{I} - F\Delta T$$
$$= \frac{15}{100 \times 10^{-3}} - (-0.05)(20 - 270)$$
$$= 150 - 12.5$$
$$= 137.5 \ \Omega$$

The Ohm's law model results in a resistor that is 12.5 Ω too large. This error is significant, because 1 percent of a 150-Ω resistor is just ±1.5 Ω. Therefore, the Ohm's law model is not adequate for selecting resistors for these conditions. The temperature-compensated model should be applied. (The values used in this example were selected to emphasize a point. In aerospace equipment, resistors with much smaller temperature coefficients would be used; typical values are at least 100 times less than the one specified. In addition, designers must also consider many other factors such as acceleration, radiation, and reliability. Thus, the resistor model would have to be further modified to account for these effects.)

Capacitor Model

The capacitor model depends on the physical composition of the device. One formula that can be used to calculate the capacitance (C) is

$$C = \frac{KA(n - 1)}{d} \qquad (1-3)$$

where

K = dielectric constant of the insulator between the plates

A = area of each plate

d = separation between plate surfaces

n = number of plates

This model allows us to predict the way changing one or more of these parameters will affect the overall capacitance. The capacitance will be increased if we do any of the following:

1. Select an insulator with a higher dielectric constant,
2. Increase the area of plates,
3. Increase the number of plates.

The capacitance will increase because all these variables appear in the numerator of the equation. On the other hand, increasing the distance between the plates will decrease the capacitance, because that variable is in the denominator.

□ EXAMPLE 1-2

The insulator in a capacitor is changed from dry air ($K = 0.224$) to mica ($K = 1.21$). If the original capacitance was 4 pF with air for insulation, what will it become when mica is used?

Solution From Equation 1-3, the original capacitance is

$$C_O = \frac{K_{air}A(n-1)}{d}$$

The new capacitance will be

$$C_N = \frac{K_{mica}A(n-1)}{d}$$

Then

$$\frac{C_N}{C_O} = \left[\frac{K_{mica}A(n-1)}{d}\right] \bigg/ \left[\frac{K_{air}A(n-1)}{d}\right]$$

Canceling like terms gives the simplified equation

$$\frac{C_N}{C_O} = \frac{K_{mica}}{K_{air}}$$

Multiplying both sides by C_O gives

$$C_N = C_O \left(\frac{K_{mica}}{K_{air}}\right)$$
$$= (4 \times 10^{-12})\left(\frac{1.21}{0.224}\right)$$
$$= 21.6 \text{ pF}$$

The capacitance increases by the ratio of the two dielectric constants.

Dynamic *RC* Model

So far the discussion of resistors and capacitors has been limited to *static* (steady state) *operation*. As you know, they function differently in a *dynamic transient* (time-varying) *condition*. Figure 1-7 shows an *RC* circuit with a switch that opens at a time that we will call $t = 0$. How does the voltage across the capacitor change with time?

From dc circuit theory, we recall that the equation that describes the dynamics of this circuit is

$$V_C = V_i e^{-t/RC} \tag{1-4}$$

where

V_C = time-varying voltage across the capacitor
V_i = initial voltage across the capacitor
R = resistance
C = capacitance
t = time since the switch opened
e = base of natural logarithms

An important measure of how quickly an *RC* circuit reaches steady state is the **time constant**, usually designated by the Greek letter τ (tau) and defined as

$$\tau = RC \tag{1-5}$$

Note from Figure 1-8 that the voltage on the capacitor is almost zero after five time constants. Table 1-2 lists the capacitor voltages at 1, 2, 3, 4, and 5 time constants. Example 1-3 shows how these values were calculated.

TABLE 1-2. Variation of Capacitor Voltage with Time

Time after Switch Opens		
In *RC* Time Constants	In ms	V_C (V)
1	5	1.10
2	10	0.41
3	15	0.15
4	20	0.05
5	25	0.02

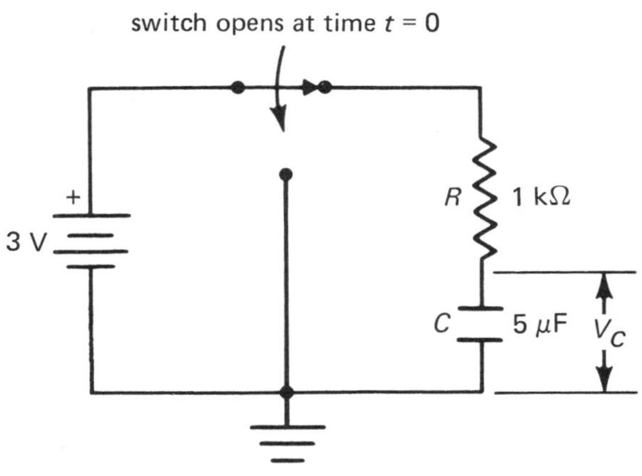

FIGURE 1-7. Schematic of *RC* Circuit

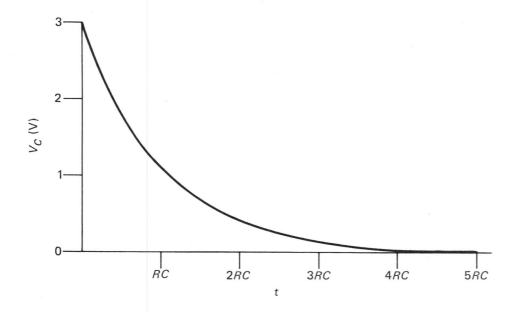

FIGURE 1-8.
Voltage Across the
Capacitor in the
RC Circuit

□ EXAMPLE 1-3

Find the voltage across the capacitor at the following times: τ, 2τ, 3τ, 4τ, and 5τ.

Solution From Equation 1-5, we have

$$\tau = RC$$
$$2\tau = 2RC$$
$$3\tau = 3RC$$
$$4\tau = 4RC$$
$$5\tau = 5RC$$

Then we substitute each value for τ in Equation 1-4

$$V_C = V_i e^{-t/RC}$$

When the switch is first opened, $t = 0$. So

$$V_C = 3e^{-0/RC} = 3(1) = 3$$

At $t = \tau$, we have

$$V_C = 3e^{-RC/RC}$$
$$= 3e^{-1}$$
$$= 3(0.368)$$
$$= 1.10 \text{ V}$$

At $t = 2\tau$, we have

$$V_C = 3e^{-2RC/RC}$$
$$= 3e^{-2}$$
$$= 3(0.135)$$
$$= 0.41 \text{ V}$$

At $t = 3\tau$, we have

$$V_C = 3e^{-3RC/RC}$$
$$= 3e^{-3}$$
$$= 3(0.05)$$
$$= 0.15 \text{ V}$$

At $t = 4\tau$, we have

$$V_C = 3e^{-4RC/RC}$$
$$= 3e^{-4}$$
$$= 3(0.02)$$
$$= 0.05 \text{ V}$$

And, finally, when $t = 5\tau$, we have

$$V_C = 3e^{-5RC/RC}$$
$$= 3e^{-5}$$
$$= 3(0.007)$$
$$= 0.02 \text{ V}$$

□ ANALYTICAL MODELS OF ACTIVE ELEMENTS

Models can also be used to describe active elements. In this section, we will take an initial look at two types of transistors. In later chapters, transistors will become the basis for both digital and analog circuits. For now, we will develop a general model that can be used in the analysis of transistor action in the circuits to follow.

Bipolar Transistors

A **transistor** is a three-terminal circuit element that is fabricated from a single crystal. As Figure 1-9a shows, two portions of the crystal are chemically changed so that they have an excess of electrons (labeled *n*, negative). A process called **doping** is used to diffuse a small amount of another element (often arsenic or antimony) that readily supplies valence electrons into the silicon crystal lattice. These elements are called **donors.** Because electrons are negative charge carriers, this portion of the crystal is said to be doped with *n*-**type impurities.**

The center area of the transistor is doped with an element (typically boron or indium) that can easily accept valence electrons. These **acceptor atoms** in the crystal create an area that is deficient in electrons. Hence, the area appears to have an excess of positive charge carriers. This portion of the crystal is *p*-**type** (positive-type) **material.** The positive charge carriers are called **holes.** The interface between the *p* and *n* areas is referred to as the **junction.** There are two junctions in a **bipolar transistor.**

npn Transistor

The structure described above is called an *npn* **transistor** because of the sequence (*n, p, n*) of semiconductor materials in the crystal. (It is worth emphasizing here that the transistor is a *single* crystal; it is *not* formed by joining different types of semiconductors.) The symbol for an *npn* transistor is shown in Figure 1-9b. The first *n* area is called the **emitter** and the second *n* area is called the **collector.** In between is the **base,** which is *p* material.

Since a transistor has three terminals, it has three currents, one associated with each terminal, and three voltages between these terminals. Figure 1-10 shows how the currents and voltages of a transistor are designated. The direction of positive current flow for I_B (*B* designates *base*), I_E (*E* for emitter), and I_C (*C* for collector) is *into* the device. The voltages are measured in the direction (polarity) indicated by the order of the letters in the subscript. That is:

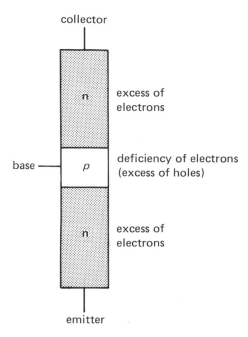

(a) Structure

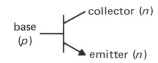

(b) Symbol

FIGURE 1-9. *npn* Transistor

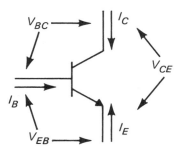

FIGURE 1-10. Designation of *npn* Transistor Voltages and Currents

- $\square$ V_{EB} is positive if the emitter is more positive than the base.
- $\square$ V_{BC} is positive if the base is more positive than the collector.
- $\square$ V_{CE} is positive if the collector is more positive than the emitter.

pnp **Transistor**

The *npn* sequence of the transistor in Figure 1–9a is not the only way to arrange the *p* and *n* areas, of course. If we start with material that is doped

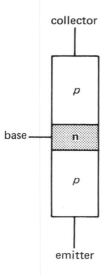

(a) Structure

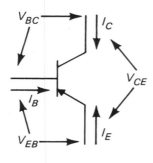

(b) Symbol

FIGURE 1–11. *pnp* Transistor

with *p* material at the emitter, we arrive at the configuration of Figure 1–11a. This transistor is a *pnp* **transistor**. Once again note that there are currents for each terminal, and voltages can be measured between the emitter-base, base-collector, and collector-emitter. The symbol, shown in Figure 1–11b, is like that of the *npn* transistor except that the direction of the arrow on the emitter is reversed.

☐ **TRANSISTOR CIRCUITS**

This introduction to transistor circuits will not consider all possible transistor circuit configurations. We will limit the discussion to the widely used **common-emitter circuit**. The name indicates the common return point for the two power supplies, which join at the emitter (see Figure 1–12).

Both batteries in this circuit are provided with potentiometers so that V_{EB} and V_{CE} can be varied. The operation of this circuit can be best understood by considering the family of common-emitter characteristic curves shown in Figure 1–13. The procedure used to generate these curves with the circuit of Figure 1–11 is as follows:

1. Adjust potentiometer R_1 to produce a base current of 50 μA (microamperes).
2. Adjust R_2 to a collector-emitter voltage of 0 V. Measure the collector current; then increase V_{CE} slightly. Again measure I_C. Continue in this manner until V_{CE} is equal to V_{CC}.
3. Adjust potentiometer R_1 to produce a base current of 10 μA less than the previous one; then go to step 2. Continue in this way until $I_B = 0$.

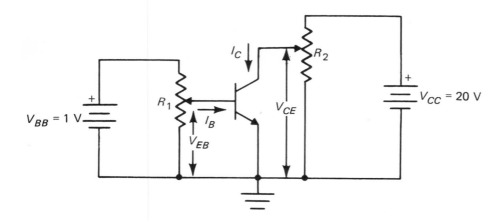

FIGURE 1–12.
npn Common-
Emitter Circuit

☐ EXAMPLE 1-4

The plot in Figure 1-13 shows how the collector current varies with a change in V_{CE} for a constant value of base current. For example, if $I_B = 50 \mu A$, an increasing V_{CE} from 5 V to 15 V causes I_C to change from 4 mA to 4.5 mA—the points labeled A and B in the figure. (Be sure to observe the relative magnitudes of the currents. The collector current is measured in *milliamperes*, while base current is in *microamperes*.)

☐ EXAMPLE 1-5

Another way to use the plot in Figure 1-13 is to predict how a change in base current will affect collector current at a constant value for V_{CE}. On this graph for a constant V_{CE} of 10 V, a change in I_B from 20 μA to 30 μA boosts the collector current by 0.8 mA—from point C to point D. This last example shows the *amplifying* ability of the common-emitter transistor; a change in base current of 10 μA causes collector current to increase by 0.8 mA. The amplification factor is

$$\frac{0.8 \times 10^{-3}}{10 \times 10^{-6}} = 80$$

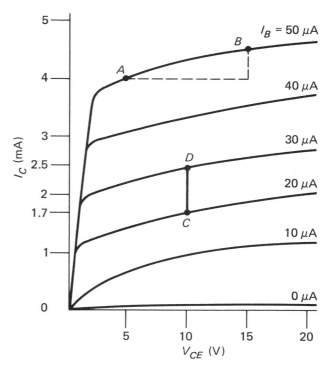

FIGURE 1-13. *npn* Common-Emitter Circuit Characteristic Curves

A helpful way to remember the **biasing** (polarity of the batteries) for the *npn* transistor in any of its possible configurations is shown below:

$n \qquad p \qquad 'n$

Second letter is the polarity of the collector with respect to the base.

First letter is the polarity of the emitter with respect to the base.

For normal biasing, therefore, the emitter of an *npn* transistor should be more negative than the base, and the collector should be more positive than the base.

The same memory aid also serves for the *pnp* transistor:

$p \qquad n \qquad p$

Second letter is the polarity of the collector with respect to the base.

First letter is the polarity of the emitter with respect to the base.

The emitter of a *pnp* transistor should be positive relative to the base potential, and the collector should be negative with respect to the base.

☐ LOAD LINE

The transistor is limited in the portion of the characteristic curve that it can operate in by its load line. The **load line** represents the resistance of the load between the collector and emitter. Figure 1-14 shows a common-emitter transistor with a load resistance of 5 kΩ.

To plot the load line for this circuit, we use a combination of Ohm's law and linear graph theory. Remember that a straight line can be plotted if one point on the line and its slope are known. From the fact that V_{CC} is 20 V, we know that the maximum collector-to-emitter voltage is 20 V. Furthermore, when V_{CE} is maximum, the collector current is zero. This condition is called **transistor cutoff**. These two facts give us the intersection of the load line with the horizontal axis:

$$V_{CE} = 20 \text{ V}$$
$$I_C = 0$$

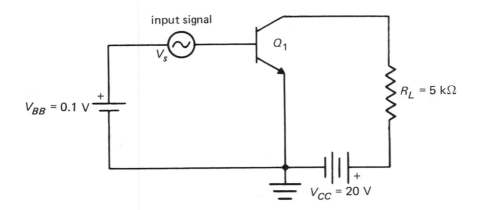

FIGURE 1–14. Loading of Common-Emitter Transistor Circuit

The slope of the load line is equal to $1/R_L$ and

$$\text{slope} = \frac{\text{rise (along } I_C \text{ axis)}}{\text{run (along } V_{CE} \text{ axis)}}$$

Substituting $1/R_L$ for the slope and V_{CC} for the run (the range of values along V_{CE} is from 0 V to V_{CC}), we obtain

$$\frac{1}{5 \times 10^3} = \frac{\text{rise}}{20}$$

Then the intercept on the I_C axis is

$$\text{rise} = \frac{20}{5 \times 10^3} = 4 \text{ mA}$$

As shown on the characteristic curve in Figure 1–15, the load line is drawn from $I_C = 4$ mA to $V_{CE} = 20$ V.

□ EXAMPLE 1-6

Now we can find the operating point of the transistor, given V_{CE} alone. If V_{CE} is 10 V, the base current is slightly above 20 μA and collector current is 2 mA (shown by the broken line on the plot in Figure 1–15).

□ TRANSISTOR OPERATING MODES

The load line restricts the transistor to three operating modes. One of them, the cutoff mode, was described above. The second operating mode occurs as the input signal changes, causing the base current to increase. Now the transistor is taken out of the cutoff mode and into the **active region** on the load line. There the collector current increases with increasing base current, but V_{CE} is falling. The third operating mode occurs if the base current continues to increase. Now the collector-emitter voltage becomes quite small. Eventually, the collector-emitter junction becomes forward-biased, and the transistor is **saturated**. At this point, collector current reaches its maximum.

Digital circuits operate transistors in the

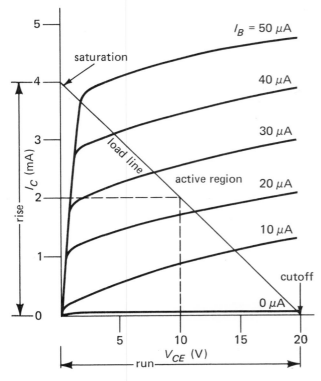

FIGURE 1–15. Common-Emitter Circuit Transistor Load Line

TABLE 1–3. Bipolar Transistor Modes

Parameter	Cutoff	Active	Saturated
		Mode	
V_{CE}	Maximum	Medium	Minimum (about 0.2 V)
I_C	0	Medium	Maximum
V_{BC}	Reverse-biased	Reverse-biased	Forward-biased
Digital switching condition	Open	Not applicable	Closed
Linearity	Poor (distorted)	Good to excellent	Poor (distorted)

saturated and cutoff regions. At these points, the transistor is like a switch:

saturation = closed switch
cutoff = open switch

A transistor moves from one extreme of the load line to the other in a very short time, so rapid response to a new input is possible.

Transistors used in analog circuits are usually operated in the active region on the load line. By restricting the movement so that cutoff and saturation are never reached, one keeps the response of the collector current output proportional to the base current input. Thus the output is *linearly* related to the input.

Table 1–3 summarizes key voltages and currents of a common-emitter circuit in each of these three modes. Of primary interest in digital applications are the switching conditions, while linearity is of primary concern in analog circuits.

☐ FIELD EFFECT TRANSISTORS

Bipolar junction fabrication is not the only way to build transistors. Another technology heavily used in digital circuits and of growing importance in analog circuits is the **field effect transistor (FET)**. As the name implies, the FET depends on electrical fields for its operation instead of junction potentials. Figure 1–16 shows an FET transistor fabricated by *metal-oxide-semiconductor*

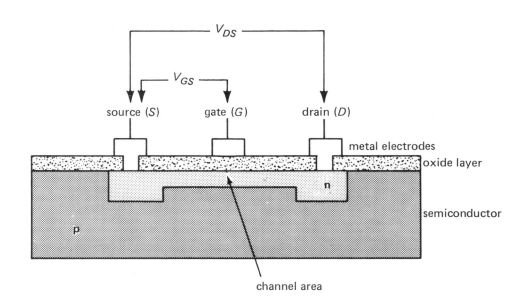

FIGURE 1–16. Depletion, *n* Channel MOSFET Cross Section

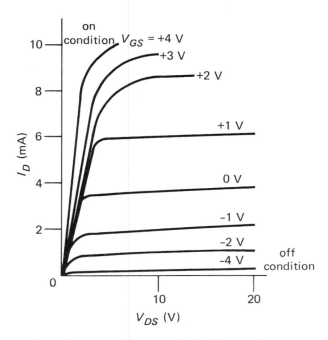

FIGURE 1-17. Characteristic Curves for Depletion, n Channel MOSFET

(MOS) technology; hence, these devices are called **MOSFETs**. They are also called **IGFETs** because of their *insulated gate*, which is one of the three terminals. The other terminals are denoted as the *source* and the *drain*.

In the FET, the current flows from the drain to the source and is controlled by the gate. As it becomes more negative, the gate *depletes* the charge carriers in the "channel" area, so this type of transistor structure is called a **depletion MOSFET**. If the channel is n material, the charge carriers are electrons, and we have an **NMOS transistor**. A channel fabricated from p material uses holes for charge carriers and forms a **PMOS transistor**.

The characteristic curves for a depletion, n channel MOSFET are shown in Figure 1-17. When the gate has a positive potential relative to the source (V_{GS}), the drain current (I_D) is maximum and the transistor is equivalent to a closed switch. In this condition, the transistor is said to be *on*. When V_{GS} becomes negative, the drain-to-

TABLE 1-4. Field Effect Transistor Characteristics

Parameter	Types	Depletion MOS	Enhancement MOS
V_{DS} polarity	NMOS	Drain more positive	Drain more positive
	PMOS	Drain more negative	Drain more negative
V_{GS} polarity	NMOS	Any	Gate more positive
	PMOS	Any	Gate more negative
Off (open-switch condition)	NMOS	V_{GS} negative	$V_{GS} = 0$ V
	PMOS	V_{GS} positive	$V_{GS} = 0$ V
On (closed-switch condition)	NMOS	V_{GS} positive	V_{GS} positive
	PMOS	V_{GS} negative	V_{GS} negative

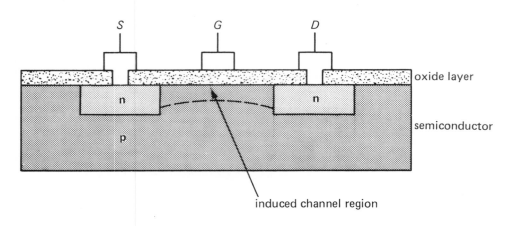

FIGURE 1-18. Enhancement, n channel MOSFET Cross Section

source voltage (V_{DS}) can increase to its maximum, but I_D becomes zero. This is the *off*, or open-switch, condition of the transistor. An important point to note about depletion MOS is that a *significant drain current flows* when the voltage on the gate is 0 V.

Another structure for the FET is used for **enhancement MOS**, as Figure 1–18 shows. There is no channel built into the transistor between the source and drain. Instead, a voltage on the gate *induces* charge carriers into the region between the source and drain.

The characteristic curves for the enhancement MOSFET are shown in Figure 1–19. When the gate-to-source voltage is positive, the transistor is *on*, as in the depletion NMOS transistor. But the transistor is *off* when the gate-to-source voltage is 0 V. This is an important difference between enhancement and depletion MOS. Further details on the operation of MOSFETs are provided in Chapter 7. Table 1–4 summarizes key parameters of these devices.

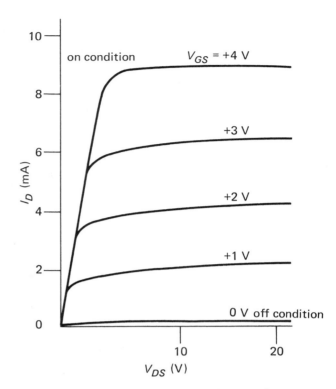

FIGURE 1–19. Characteristic Curves for Enhancement, *n* Channel MOSFET

Chapter Summary

☐ Passive discrete components can be treated as two-port devices. One port is used for input and the other for output. With passive components the input and output ports can be interchanged without affecting voltages or currents. But active components must always be installed with the proper orientation. Active elements amplify or attenuate the incoming signals.

☐ Integrated circuits combine the components in a monolithic structure made from a semiconductor. The circuit is manufactured in a single package.

☐ Analog voltages and currents vary in a continuous manner, while digital signals change in discrete steps, or levels.

☐ The scale of integration of an integrated circuit depends on the number of gates in the package.

☐ Analytical models allow us to ignore physical conditions that do not enter into the circuit action that we are concerned about.

☐ Conventional current flow direction is from the more positive potential to the less positive potential. Electron flow is in the direction opposite to conventional current flow.

☐ Models for resistors and capacitors operating under a variety of conditions have been developed.

☐ In dynamic models, the time at which events occur becomes an important variable in the equation.

□ Transient conditions in *RC* circuits are most dependent on the time constant of the circuit.

□ The models of active elements are often shown in the form of graphs.

□ A bipolar transistor has two junctions between the emitter, base, and collector areas of the crystal. Areas that have an excess of valence electrons, supplied by donor atoms, are called *n* material. Areas with a deficiency of valence electrons, resulting from acceptor atoms, are *p* material. The arrangement of the *p* and *n* materials can be used to form *npn* or *pnp* transistors.

□ The transistor must operate along its load line. Consequently, it will be in the cutoff, active, or saturated condition.

□ Digital circuits use transistors as switches in the cutoff and saturated modes, but analog circuits require linear operation in the active region.

□ Field effect transistors differ from bipolar devices in that electric fields control current flow instead of junction voltages.

Problems

1-1. Compare the resistor value of the Ohm's law model with that of the temperature-compensated model if the voltage drop across the resistor is 10 V and the current is 250 mA. The operating temperature is 100 °C and the temperature coefficient is -0.06 per degree Celsius change from 20 °C.

1-2. How much would a capacitor value of 15 pF be changed if the area of the plates is increased by a factor of 3? How would increasing the number of plates from 6 to 9 affect the capacitance?

1-3. What would the voltage across the capacitor be in Figure 1-7 at 7.5 ms after the switch is opened?

1-4. If V_{CE} is increased from 10 to 15 V, how much does the collector current change if base current is 30 μA? Refer to Figure 1-13.

1-5. If the collector-emitter voltage is held constant at 15 V, how much must the base current be increased from 10 μA to cause a 1-mA rise in collector current? Use the transistor characteristic curves of Figure 1-13.

1-6. The load resistor in Figure 1-14 is changed to 4 kΩ. Draw the new load line. What is the maximum collector current when the transistor is saturated? What is an approximate value for collector-to-emitter voltage in the saturated condition?

1-7. For each of the conditions listed below, state whether the FET is on or off.

Type	V_{GS}	V_{DS}
NMOS depletion	-4 V	20 V
PMOS depletion	-4 V	-20 V
NMOS enhancement	0 V	20 V
PMOS enhancement	-4 V	-20 V

1-8. What is the load resistance of an *npn* common-emitter resistor if V_{CC} is 15 V and I_C is 4 mA at saturation?

1-9. For each case below, state whether the transistor is in the cutoff, saturated, or active mode for a common-emitter transistor circuit.

Type	V_{CE}	I_C
npn	20 V	0 mA
npn	10 V	2.7 mA
npn	0.2 V	6 mA
pnp	-15 V	0 mA

1-10. The resistor and capacitor values in the *RC* circuit of Figure 1-7 are changed to 3 MΩ and 65 pF, respectively. How long after the switch opens will the voltage across the capacitor first drop to 0 V?

Chapter Two
Inverters

Possibly the simplest digital device, the **inverter,** is also one of the most widely used. Not only are inverters used alone to shift signal levels, but they are also combined with other circuits to perform more powerful operations. In this chapter, we will show how two-state signals are developed and how the inverter affects them. The analysis begins with the switching characteristics of diodes and transistors. Then it evolves into a functional analysis of inputs and outputs to circuit elements.

Chapter Objectives

Upon completion of this chapter, you should be able to:

- [ ] Distinguish among the levels of two-state signals.
- [ ] Draw an idealized, diode switching curve.
- [ ] Explain how a transistor performs as a switch.
- [ ] Explain inverter action on input signals.
- [ ] Construct a timing diagram for the output waveform of an inverter.
- [ ] Show how inverters can be cascaded.

☐ TWO-STATE SIGNALS

Stop and think for a minute how often you are confronted with choices that exist only as opposites. Such examples as "yes and no" or "true and false" will probably occur to you. Other examples might be "hot and cold," "high and low," and "black and white." One similar relationship that you will find used extensively in digital ap-

plications is that between the digits 1 and 0, which are considered opposites. The foundation of all digital circuits, sometimes called **logic circuits**, is the two-state condition of signal levels.

As Figure 2-1 indicates, the amplitude of a signal may span a range of values. For digital circuits, our interest will primarily be on the voltage levels of the signal. Given a signal such as the one shown in the figure, a band of voltage levels can be established. In this case, any voltage between 2.0 and 5.5 V is *high*. A level between −1.5 and 0.8 V is *low*. Whenever the signal amplitude is between high and low, the level is *undefined*. Finally, any level above 5.5 V or below −1.5 V is *forbidden*.

These forbidden bands are obviously arbitrary; you know that a signal can exceed the high level and drop below the low level. However, for the purpose of the circuits we are interested in, these events cannot be permitted. In that sense, they can be thought of as forbidden. Similarly, a signal moving between the high and low levels must pass through the undefined zone. Eventually, though, the level must stabilize within either the high or the low bounds for proper operation of digital circuits. The purpose of this explanation has been to help you visualize **two-state voltage levels**.

All two-state circuits do not use the same bounds for high and low levels. For instance, the voltages shown in Figure 2-1 are only appropriate for certain types of devices. However, the manufacturer will specify limits on the high or low voltages for normal operation of the circuits. Also, keep in mind that the signals are analog voltages, which do not instantaneously change from high to low. Furthermore, it is just when the voltages do not stay within the established bounds that a technician is most needed. For example, a faulty power supply could produce the wrong levels. At those times, you should remember that the amplitude of the signals could be outside the normal limits and thus are worth checking before starting a more elaborate series of tests.

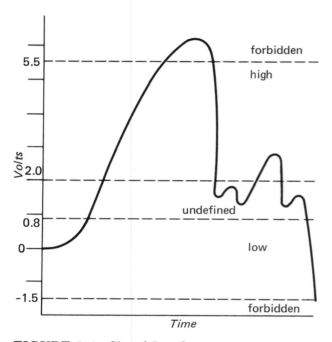

FIGURE 2-1. Signal Levels

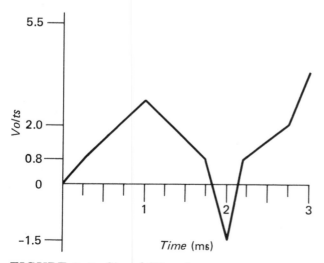

FIGURE 2-2. Signal Waveform

☐ EXAMPLE 2-1

Refer to the signal in Figure 2-2. Assuming that the definitions for high and low levels are the same as given in Figure 2-1, list the time intervals when the signal is high, low, and undefined.

Solution From the figure, we observe the following relationships:

High	Low	Undefined
0.75–1.25 ms	0–0.25 ms	0.25–0.75 ms
2.75–3 ms	1.75–2.25 ms	1.25–1.75 ms
		2.25–2.75 ms

□ SWITCHES

Another set of opposites that could have been listed in the last section is the pair "off and on." A switch is often used to establish these conditions for electrical signals. A switch can be considered a functional element, as defined and shown in Figure 2–3.

Whenever the switch in Figure 2–3 is closed, the output voltage is 5 V. It is 0 V when the switch is open. That is, a complete circuit must exist in order for current to flow. This condition also implies that the proper battery orientation and voltages are supplied.

□ EXAMPLE 2–2

An oscilloscope is connected to the output terminals of the circuit in Figure 2–3. The trace on the scope is shown in Figure 2–4. From the information shown, determine when the switch was open and when it was closed.

Solution Because the output voltage is zero between 0 and 100 ms, the switch must have been open then. The voltage rises to 5 V during the interval 100 to 300 ms. Then it falls again to 0 V. The conclusion is that the switch was closed for the 100-to-300-ms period and then opened.

Diode Switches

The **diode** is an *active* circuit element that acts as a switch. Figure 2–5 shows a typical semiconductor diode.

The schematic diagram of the diode in Figure 2–6 conveys information about the device. For instance, the anode terminal is distinguished from the cathode. As you might expect, a diode will not work in a circuit if the device is rotated by 180°. Then the anode would be in the position of the cathode and vice versa. Contrasting this

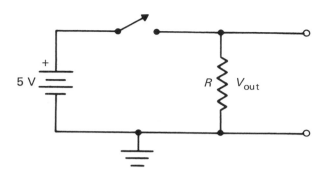

Function Table

Condition	V_{out}
open	0 V
closed	5 V

FIGURE 2–3. Switch Functions

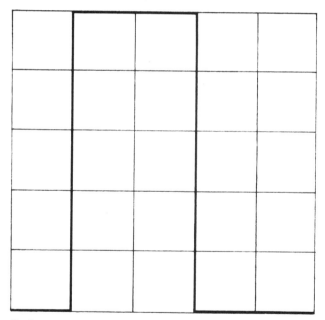

Scale:
1 V *per vertical division*
100 ms *per horizontal division*

FIGURE 2–4. Oscilloscope Waveform

situation with passive elements such as resistors and capacitors, you will note an important difference between active and passive elements. Terminals of active elements cannot be interchanged, while those of passive elements can be. (One exception to this general rule for passive elements is the electrolytic capacitor. This device has polar-

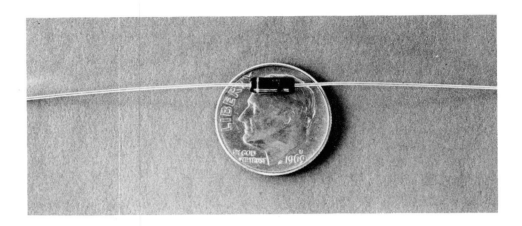

FIGURE 2-5.
Typical Diode

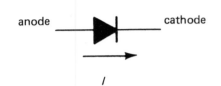

anode   cathode

I

FIGURE 2-6. Diode Symbol

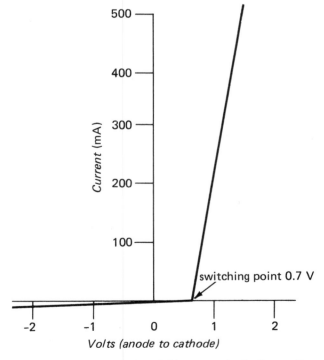

FIGURE 2-7. Idealized Characteristic Curve for Silicon Diode

ized leads; the lead marked with a plus sign must always be more positive than the other.) Note in Figure 2-6 that the arrowhead of the diode symbol points in the direction of current flow.

The functions of a diode are characterized by the curve shown in Figure 2-7. This curve is somewhat idealized in that actual diode switching curves are less linear. However, as a model in understanding circuit operation, this curve is quite acceptable.

Immediately obvious from the figure is the fact that current flows quite easily through the diode in the forward direction and hardly at all in the reverse direction. The voltage scale shows the potential difference between the anode and cathode. When the anode is more negative than the cathode, essentially no current flows. There is no current flow when there is a zero voltage across the diode, either. As the anode becomes more positive than the cathode, there is a significant change in the current flow. When the forward bias exceeds 0.7 V, the current increases to several milliamperes.

The 0.7-V value given in Figure 2-7 is a good approximation for diodes made of silicon. For other materials, such as germanium, the switching voltage may be some other value. Even so, all semiconductor diodes exhibit similar characteristic curves, differing only in the amount of current or voltage at any point on the curve. In this book, silicon diodes will be used in many examples because they are most common.

Diode action can be summarized by observing that with negative biasing little or no reverse current flows. Forward biasing produces increasing current with increasing voltage after the switching voltage is exceeded. Thus, a semiconductor diode can function much like the switch of the previous section.

□ EXAMPLE 2-3

Consider the circuit in Figure 2-8. Here a 5-V battery forward-biases the diode by an amount in excess of the switching potential. Ignoring the slight slope of the diode curve, how much voltage is dropped across the diode and the resistor in this circuit?

Solution Only the 0.7 V necessary to forward-bias the diode drops across it. The remainder is the resistor voltage drop. Therefore V_{out} must be 4.3 V. The current flowing in the circuit is readily found:

$$I = \frac{5 - 0.7}{100} = 43 \text{ mA}$$

The diode is turned on by a potential of 0.7 V.

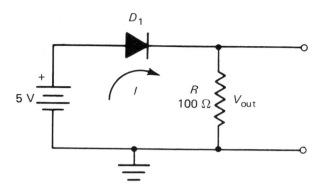

FIGURE 2-8. Forward-biased Diode

□ EXAMPLE 2-4

Now look at the reverse-biased diode in Figure 2-9. Everything is the same as in the previous example except that the battery terminals are reversed. Now the current flow is zero, so V_{out} must also be 0 V.

From these two examples, a functional description of diode action can be written. This functional description is given in Table 2-1.

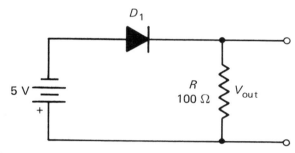

FIGURE 2-9. Reverse-biased Diode

TABLE 2-1. Output Voltages for a Diode

Condition	V_{out}
Voltage less than switching potential	0 V
Voltage greater than switching potential	IR_{out}

Transistor Switches

As you recall from the last chapter, the transistor is a three-terminal device that can also be described in terms of a characteristic curve. Such a curve is shown in Figure 2-10. To review the earlier material, we have drawn a load line on the plot, which shows how collector current varies with base current and collector-to-emitter voltage.

As shown in the figure, when a collector-to-emitter voltage is maximum—5 V in this case—the transistor is *cutoff* and no current flows. With a minimum V_{CE}—0.2 V here—collector current is maximum and the transistor is *saturated*. In between these two points, the transistor is in the *active* region; values for V_{CE} and I_C are then in the range between the two extremes.

In digital circuits, we are most interested in the cutoff or saturated states of the transistor. The active region is acknowledged only because the transistor passes through it in changing from cutoff to saturation, or in changing the other way. When the transistor is in the cutoff mode, it acts as an open switch. When it is operating in saturation, it acts as a closed switch.

□ EXAMPLE 2-5

The transistor circuit in Figure 2-11a will be used to illustrate the switching concepts. Here the input and output voltages are measured with

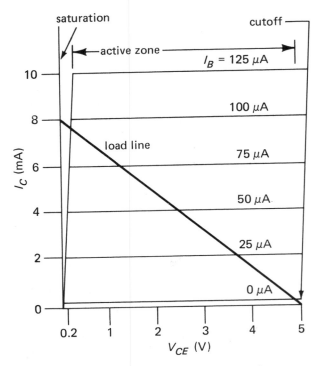

FIGURE 2-10. Idealized Characteristic Curve for Transistor

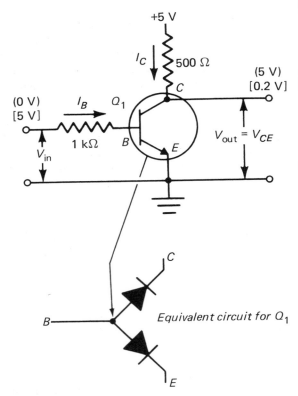

(a) Transistor Circuit

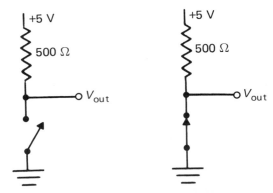

(b) Input Voltage of 0 V   (c) Input Voltage of 5 V

FIGURE 2-11. Transistor Switching

respect to ground. This convention is normally followed in all digital circuits.

Assume that 0 V is applied to the input of the circuit. Where on the load line is the transistor operating? To find out, observe in Figure 2-10 that with a 0-V input, the base current must be zero. Now find the intersection of the zero I_B curve with the load line. The intersection is at the cutoff point. Thus, the output voltage is the potential across the collector and emitter terminals, which is 5 V.

Another way to think about this situation is to realize that the transistor acts as an open switch when in the cutoff mode, as shown in Figure 2-11b. The output terminal is pulled up to 5 V by the power supply. (There is no voltage drop across the 500-Ω resistor because no current flows in the output circuit.)

Now let 5 V be applied to the input. Clearly the base current will be more than adequate to saturate the transistor. Note that both the 1-kΩ resistor and the base-emitter junction of the transistor limit the current. The equivalent circuit of the base-emitter junction of the transistor, found in Figure 2-11a, shows how this portion of the transistor acts as a diode. From the discussion on

diode switches, you know that the voltage between the base and emitter will be 0.7 V when forward-biased, which is the case here. Furthermore, the diode of the base-collector is reverse-biased.

On the transistor characteristic curve, trace the load line up to maximum base current. Here the transistor is in saturation. The voltage drop across the collector and emitter is a few tenths of a volt. The transistor is functioning as a closed switch; Figure 2–11c shows the equivalent circuit. (There is a minor difference between the actual circuit and the equivalent with a switch. The output of Figure 2–11c is obviously 0 V, but from the characteristic curves you can see that V_{CE} in saturation is about 0.2 V. For the applications of interest, 0.2 V is close enough to zero to be considered a low-level signal.)

The relationship of corresponding input and output levels is indicated on Figure 2–11a with parentheses and square brackets. The 0-V input produces a 5-V output, and a 5-V input yields a 0.2-V output. These results are expressed in tabular form in Table 2–2.

Notice in the table that a low input causes a high output. Applying a high input causes the output to switch to the low state. This circuit acts as a simple **inverter**; the input is changed to the opposite state. In the next section, we will investigate inverters that are built as integrated circuits rather than from discrete components, as in this example.

☐ INTEGRATED CIRCUIT INVERTERS

Modular integrated circuits (ICs), which provide signal inversion, are based on the principles of diode and transistor switches. And just as in the previous examples, the active devices permit current flow or prevent it. Figure 2–12 illustrates a circuit suitable for use in an integrated inverter. It differs from the discrete component version

TABLE 2–2. Transistor Switching Function

V_{in}		V_{out}	
Voltage	Level	Voltage	Level
0 V	Low	5 V	High
5 V	High	0.2 V	Low

not in the method of operation but in the method of construction. In an **integrated circuit**, such as the one in Figure 2–12, all the components are formed on a single chip of silicon. In contrast, discrete circuits such as those described previously, are built of separate transistors, diodes, and resistors.

Analysis of the IC inverter proceeds in exactly the same way as that for the discrete circuit. A high and low voltage are applied to the input terminal in turn, and the resulting output voltages are found.

This time we will begin with a high input. The question we are concerned with is whether each diode (D_1, D_2, D_3) and the transistor (Q_1) of Figure 2–12 act as open or closed switches. Working from left to right, let's examine D_1 first. It has the 5-V input on its cathode, and the power supply voltage, through the 5-kΩ resistor, is on its anode. Consequently, the diode is reverse-biased and no current flows through it.

Now look at the string D_2, D_3, and Q_1. Just as in the last example, the base-emitter of Q_1 can be treated as a diode also. The voltages necessary to forward-bias all three of these diodes must be added, because they are in series. In other words, it requires

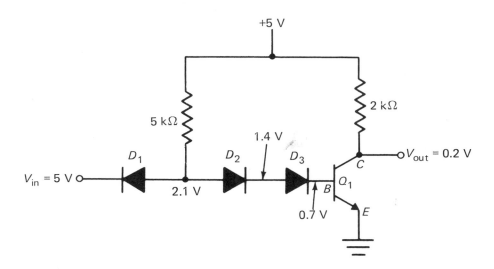

FIGURE 2–12.
Integrated Circuit
Inverter with a
High Input

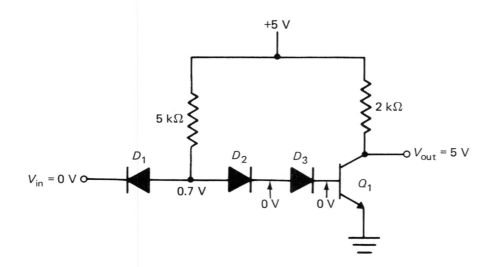

FIGURE 2-13.
Integrated Circuit
Inverter with a
Low Input

$$3 \times 0.7 \text{ V} = 2.1 \text{ V}$$

to forward-bias this leg of the circuit. Is sufficient voltage available? The answer is yes. The power supply voltage is 5 V. The remaining voltage,

$$5 \text{ V} - 2.1 \text{ V} = 2.9 \text{ V}$$

is dropped across the 5-kΩ resistor. The transistor is saturated, thus pulling the output down to a low level of 0.2 V.

Next the input is changed to 0 V, as shown in Figure 2-13. With its cathode at ground potential, D_1 will switch on because the power supply is forward-biasing that diode. The voltage on the anode will become 0.7 V. Is there enough forward bias for the other diodes and transistor, though? As calculated above, this bias must be at least 2.1 V, but the voltage is only 0.7 V on the anode of D_2. We conclude that the forward bias is not enough for the series of three diodes, so Q_1 must be cut off. The power supply will then pull the output level up to 5 V through the 2-kΩ resistor.

Now the need for the series of diodes becomes apparent. If D_2 and D_3 were removed from the circuit, the 0.7 V on the anode of D_1 might be enough to saturate Q_1 when the input is low. And if the transistor saturates, the output will be pulled low and no inversion would occur.

Integrated circuits that use this construction technique for inverters are referred to as **diode-transistor logic (DTL) circuits**. DTL circuits were the first type of ICs used in a large number of applications. Other families of ICs have now replaced the DTL in new equipment, but many DTL chips remain in service for existing applications.

□ **EXAMPLE 2-6**

Find the current through the 5-kΩ resistor of the DTL inverter when the input is high.

Solution From Figure 2-12, we see that the drop across the resistor is

$$5 \text{ V} - 2.1 \text{ V} = 2.9 \text{ V}$$

From Ohm's law, then,

$$I = \frac{2.9}{5 \times 10^3} = 580 \ \mu\text{A}$$

□ **INVERTER LOGIC**

The functional description for an inverter has already been developed in Table 2-2, which applies equally well to the DTL integrated circuit inverter. That table relates voltages on the input and output terminals. However, another type of table can be derived from the voltages. Called a **truth table**, this arrangement replaces voltage levels with the digits 0 and 1. If the low level is replaced with a 0 and the high level with a 1, we have the description shown in Table 2-3.

TABLE 2-3. Inverter Truth Table

Input	Output
0	1
1	0

Instead of drawing the separate components of the inverter, we can represent the entire function in schematic diagrams by using the symbol of Figure 2-14. The symbol for an amplifier is shown in Figure 2-14a. In Figure 2-14b, a small circle, or bubble, is added to the symbol for an amplifier to show that inversion is performed by that circuit element.

In terms of the truth table, the 1 and 0 values are the only **logic levels** that the inverter can accept. They are analogous to the two-state voltage levels used in voltage tables. The inverter converts a 0 to a 1, so the **inverse** of 0 is 1.

Because inverters are so frequently used in digital circuits, a short way of writing *the inverse of* has come into use. A bar over the value means that it is to be inverted. For example:

$\overline{0} = 1$ The inverse of 0 is 1.
$\overline{1} = 0$ The inverse of 1 is 0.

The inverse bar may also be used with variables as well as constants. Let k be a variable that can take on the values of 0 or 1. Then $\overline{k}$ is the inverse of k. The inverse function is also called the **not** or **complement function**. (Don't confuse the latter with the word *compliment*, meaning to praise, and pronounced the same way.) Then we may read $\overline{k}$ in any of the following ways:

☐ the inverse of k
☐ not k
☐ the complement of k

All three terms convey the same message.

☐ EXAMPLE 2-7

Let the input waveform to an inverter be as shown in Figure 2-15a. What output waveform does the inverter produce?

Solution By complementing each segment of the input, we obtain the output shown in Figure 2-15b.

☐ COMBINATION OF INVERTERS

Inverters need not be used singly. More than one can be cascaded, as shown in Figure 2-16. If the

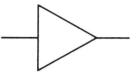

(a) Amplifier

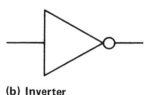

(b) Inverter

FIGURE 2-14. Amplifier and Inverter Symbol

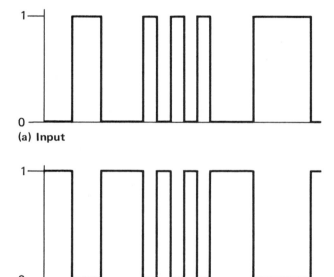

FIGURE 2-15. Inverter Waveforms

two-inverter circuit is used, how is the input changed? Assume that a 0 is the input to Figure 2-16a. The output of inverter 1 is

$$\overline{0} = 1$$

the complement of the input. This value is now the input to inverter 2, which converts it to

$$\overline{1} = 0$$

As you no doubt have already concluded,

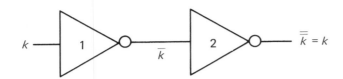

(a) Two Inverters

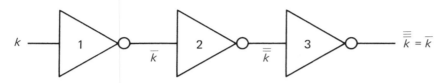

(b) Three Inverters

FIGURE 2-16.
Cascaded Inverters

any value complemented twice is logically equivalent to no inversion at all. That is,

$$\bar{\bar{k}} = k$$

where two bars indicate a double inverse.

What if three inverters are used, as in Figure 2-16b? The output of the second inverter will be the same as the original input, and inverter 3 complements that value. The final output is $\bar{k}$. In general, an even number of complementing stages is logically the same as no inversion; an odd number is equivalent to one inversion.

☐ EXAMPLE 2-8

A circuit with an input of m produces an output of $\bar{\bar{\bar{m}}}$. If the input is a 1, what is the output?

Solution An even number of inversion steps produces a 1 output, which is equal to the input.

☐ LOGIC SIGNALS

Logic levels can represent physical events. Often sensors will produce one level if a condition is true and a different level for false. Usually, a true condition is represented by 1, false by 0.

☐ EXAMPLE 2-9

Consider a digital fire alarm system in an oil tank. The system uses two sensors, one for light and the other for heat. By monitoring these signals, one can detect all possible combinations of light and heat conditions that exceed the threshold of the sensors. In this system, the fire alarm will sound only if both sensors produce a logic signal of 1. The possibilities include these:

Light Sensor	Heat Sensor
0	0
0	1
1	0
1	1 (indication of fire)

All we need now is a circuit that can detect that both sensor signals are 1s and output a trigger to the fire alarm. Such circuits are called *gates* and are the subject of Chapter 3.

Chapter Summary

- ☐ Signal levels may be grouped into high, low, undefined, and forbidden bands. Two-state voltage levels only have two stable ranges: high and low.
- ☐ Switches turn signals on or off. The state of the switch can be detected by noting the output level of the circuit.

□ Diodes are active elements that permit current flow only when forward-biased. In this way, diodes operate as switches. Characteristic curves are used to analyze diode operation.

□ In the saturated or cutoff regions of the load line, a transistor also acts as a switch. When saturated, a transistor is like a closed switch; when cut off, it is like an open switch. Inverters can be built from discrete transistors and other circuit elements.

□ Integrated circuit inverters are widely used and practical circuit elements. Principles similar to those for discrete components also apply to IC inverter functions. DTL logic is one type of integrated circuit used for inverters.

□ Truth tables explain circuit functions by using the digits 0 and 1 in place of the voltage levels used in a voltage table.

□ Inverter functions are defined by a truth table.

□ The terms *inverse*, *complement*, and *not* can all be used to define the function of an inverter.

□ Inverters may be cascaded to produce several cycles of complementing of the input. If an even number of inverters is used, the input and output are equal. An odd number of inverters complements the input.

□ Logic levels can be used to represent physical events. Often a value of 1 means that the event is true and 0 means that it is false.

Problems

2-1. Given the input voltage shown in Figure 2-17, determine when the level is high, low, undefined, or in a forbidden region. Use the ranges given in this chapter for each region (see Figure 2-1).

2-2. What is the output voltage for each of the circuits shown in Figure 2-18? All diodes are made of silicon.

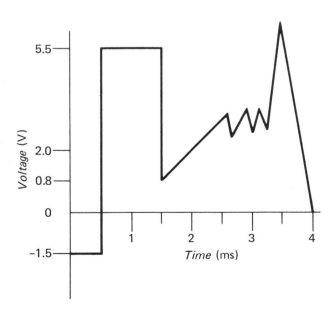

FIGURE 2-17.

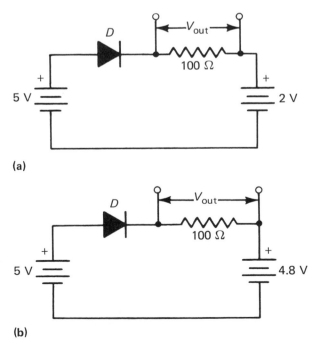

(a)

(b)

FIGURE 2-18.

2-3. An inverter accepts signals in the range of 2.0 to 5.5 V as high levels and -1.5 to 0.8 V as low. What is the output of this inverter if the input is the portion of the waveform shown in Figure 2-17 between 2 ms and 3 ms?

2-4. Use the inverter described in Problem 2-3. What would be its output for the waveform in Figure 2-2 during the period 0.1 to 0.2 ms? During 1.0 to 1.1 ms?

2-5. Draw the oscilloscope trace for a switching circuit like the one in Figure 2-4 for the following sequence of events:

Switch Condition	Duration (ms)
open	950
closed	420
open	760
closed	840
open	1000

2-6. In Example 2-2, what change would be observed in the oscilloscope trace if the interval for each switch transition were doubled?

2-7. What current is produced by a bias of 1 V across a diode? A bias of -0.8 V? Use the characteristic curve, Figure 2-7.

2-8. If the diode current is 250 mA, what do you conclude about the anode to cathode potential? Use Figure 2-7 to answer this question.

2-9. If the resistor in Figure 2-8 is replaced with one with a value of 500 Ω, what is the output voltage?

2-10. Repeat Problem 2-9 but use the circuit in Figure 2-9.

2-11. What is the current through the 500-Ω resistor in Figure 2-11a with a high input? A low input?

2-12. What is the current flowing through the 1-kΩ resistor in Figure 2-11a when the input is low? When the input is high?

2-13. What is the resulting current through the 5-kΩ resistor of the DTL inverter in Figure 2-13 when the input is low?

2-14. Find the current flowing in the 2-kΩ resistor of the DTL inverter for both high and low input levels. (See Figures 2-12 and 2-13.)

2-15. Let the input to a DTL inverter be a square wave that varies between the high and low levels at an interval of 100 ms. That is, the wave is high at 100 ms and then becomes low in another 100 ms; then the cycle repeats. Sketch the output wave of the circuit.

2-16. Evaluate these expressions when n is equal to zero.

$$\bar{n} = \underline{\qquad} \qquad \bar{\bar{n}} = \underline{\qquad}$$

$$\bar{\bar{\bar{n}}} = \underline{\qquad} \qquad \bar{\bar{\bar{\bar{n}}}} = \underline{\qquad}$$

2-17. Draw the schematic for the expressions below, using cascaded inverter symbols.

   a. $\bar{\bar{f}}$
   b. $\bar{\bar{\bar{g}}}$

2-18. The table below lists the number of inverters cascaded in series, like those in Figure 2-16. For the input given, find the output.

Number of Inverters	Input Value
4	0
6	1
5	0

2-19. Draw the output of an inverter if the input is as described below.

Level	Duration (ms)
0	20
1	50
0	40
1	30
0	80

Chapter Three
Logic Gates

A logic gate produces an output that depends on the combination of inputs to the gate. Two-state signals are used exclusively with gates. Inputs and outputs are limited to high or low levels. The most useful aid in analyzing gate networks is Boolean algebra. Similar in many ways to the form of algebra that you are already familiar with, Boolean algebra allows you to represent complicated circuits as equations that can be readily manipulated or simplified. The principles of these operations will be important in any work that you do involving digital equipment. An understanding of fundamental Boolean algebra rules will assist you in reading logic diagrams, interpreting schematics, and simplifying circuits.

Chapter Objectives

Upon completion of this chapter, you should be able to:

☐ Define AND and OR gates by means of truth tables.
☐ State the fundamental laws of Boolean algebra.
☐ Show how gates can be combined to generate new functions.
☐ Explain the significance of DeMorgan's theorem.
☐ Demonstrate how gates can be used to select the correct response for the given inputs.

☐ SIMPLE GATES

Gates are used to provide the switching in digital circuits. Just as with inverters, transistors and diodes internal to the gate route the proper electrical signals. There is no need to delve into a gate to see what's inside in order to understand its

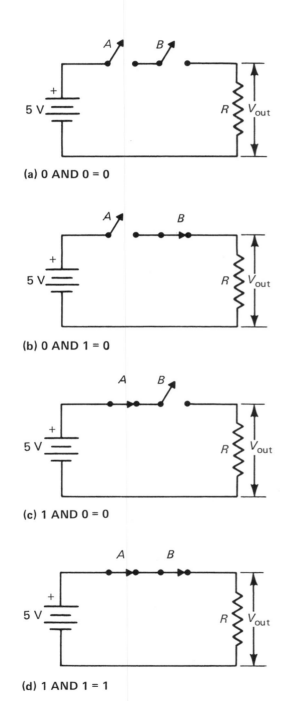

(a) 0 AND 0 = 0

(b) 0 AND 1 = 0

(c) 1 AND 0 = 0

(d) 1 AND 1 = 1

FIGURE 3-1. AND Switching Function

purpose. A **functional analysis** is a much more powerful method. Functional analysis treats a combination of circuit elements as a block that performs a mathematical operation. Analysis of digital circuits by consideration of the internal components would be impossible; some of these devices consist of thousands of transistors and diodes. Another reason for choosing a functional analysis is that even if only one transistor in a gate fails, there is no way to repair it. The entire gate must be replaced.

☐ AND GATES

The AND gate provides an output that is determined by the inputs. The gate can have two or more inputs. A switching operation that represents the AND function is shown in Figure 3-1. As shown in the figure, the AND function is equivalent to a series of switches.

If we label each switch to represent a variable, the value of that variable depends on whether the switch is open or closed. Let a value of 0 mean that the switch is open and let a value of 1 mean that the switch is closed. Then from your experience with series circuits, you can find the value of the output voltage for any given setting of the switches.

☐ EXAMPLE 3-1

For the circuit in Figure 3-1, the output voltage depends on the state of switches A and B. If both switches are open (Figure 3-1a), the output voltage is zero because no current flows in the circuit. Closing switch B but leaving A open (Figure 3-1b) still results in an output of zero. In the same way, closing A and opening B (Figure 3-1c) produces a V_{out} of zero. Only when both switches are closed (Figure 3-1d) does the output change to the high level.

The performance of the circuit in Figure 3-1 can be summarized as a truth table (Table 3-1). This table shows how the output varies for each input condition. The output is represented by a 0 value if the voltage level is low and by a 1 if high. Note that the output is 1 only if both A and B are 1s.

TABLE 3-1. AND Gate Truth Table

Input		Output
A	B	
0	0	0
0	1	0
1	0	0
1	1	1

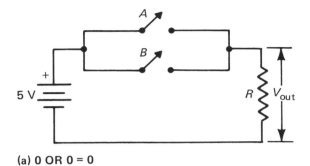

(a) 0 OR 0 = 0

☐ OR GATES

The **OR gate** is another basic function. Like the AND gate, the OR has two or more inputs. It can be modeled as a parallel circuit of two or more switches, as shown in Figure 3-2. The OR function produces its output from the combination of inputs in a manner analogous to the AND function.

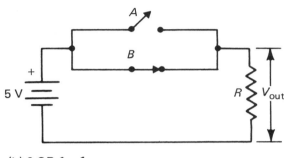

(b) 0 OR 1 = 1

☐ EXAMPLE 3-2

Using the switching configuration of Figure 3-2, we can analyze the OR function. When both switches are open (in the zero state; Figure 3-2a), no current flows, so the output is zero. If one of the switches is closed (Figure 3-2b, c), current will flow in the complete circuit, producing a voltage drop across the resistor. Only one switch need be closed to complete the circuit because the switches are in parallel. Obviously, then, closing both switches (Figure 3-2d) will also result in an output voltage that is high.

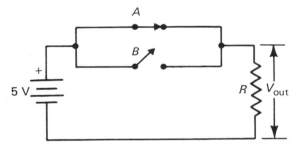

(c) 1 OR 0 = 1

The truth table (Table 3-2) for an OR function will have an output of 1 if either input A *or* input B is a 1. If both inputs are 1, then the output is also equal to 1.

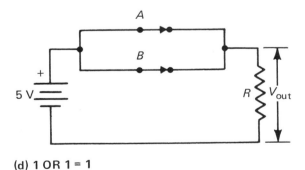

(d) 1 OR 1 = 1

FIGURE 3-2. OR Switching Function

TABLE 3-2. OR Gate Truth Table

Input		Output
A	B	
0	0	0
0	1	1
1	0	1
1	1	1

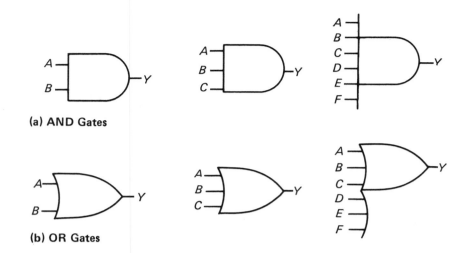

(a) AND Gates

(b) OR Gates

FIGURE 3-3. Logic Gate Symbology

□ NOTATION AND SYMBOLOGY

As you might imagine, the AND and OR gates are used over and over again in digital circuits. So that these words need not be repeatedly written, special symbols have been devised to replace the words.

The symbol most often used for AND is a dot—for example,

$$A \cdot B \qquad (3-1)$$

This expression is read, "A and B." Other symbols for AND that you may find in other books include $\wedge$, $\cap$, and &.

When there is no possibility of confusion, AND functions can also be written without the dot. In such cases, you should mentally supply the dot to interpret the expression.

□ AB is the same as $A \cdot B$.
□ ABC is the same as $A \cdot B \cdot C$.
□ KLM is the same as $K \cdot L \cdot M$.

A common symbol for the OR operation is the plus sign, as in

$$A + B \qquad (3-2)$$

which is read, "A or B." Other symbols for OR that are sometimes used are $\vee$ and $\cup$.

Just as these symbols make written expressions shorter, other symbols for the AND and OR gates make the drawing of schematic diagrams easier. These symbols are shown in Figure 3-3. As shown in the figure, the symbols can be ex-

panded to accommodate as many inputs as needed. For example, the AND gates shown in Figure 3-3a (reading from left to right) represent the logic equations

$$Y = AB$$
$$Y = ABC$$
$$Y = ABCDEF$$

Similarly, for the OR gates in Figure 3-3b, we have

$$Y = A + B$$
$$Y = A + B + C$$
$$Y = A + B + C + D + E + F$$

□ EXAMPLE 3-3

Read the expressions below. Remember that the dot between terms in an AND operation need not be explicitly shown.

1. $C \cdot D$
2. $E + F$
3. GH
4. $(XZ) + Q$

Solution

1. C and D
2. E or F
3. G and H
4. the *quantity* X and Z or Q

Notice that in the last case, parentheses are used to group the terms to show the sequence of operations. More will be said on this topic in the next section. For now, it is sufficient to know that parentheses usage for gate symbols is much like that of ordinary algebra.

☐ BOOLEAN ALGEBRA

Boolean algebra is sometimes also referred to as *switching algebra*. Any circuit elements, or other devices that operate in only two states, can be studied with this technique. The values in Boolean algebra are limited to 0 or 1, so you can expect to see some differences from the mathematics you are already familiar with. But in spite of this seeming dissimilarity, the underlying principles of Boolean algebra are the same as the ones you know from other mathematics.

The need for Boolean algebra may be best appreciated by taking a look at a switching network that consists of both AND and OR functions. Such a network is shown in Figure 3-4. As you can see from the figure, the operation of this circuit is not as clear as that of the single-gate networks. The logic equation for these switches is

$$\text{output} = (A + B) \cdot C \cdot D \qquad (3\text{-}3)$$

To obtain this equation, we observe that switches A and B are in parallel as well as being in series with C and D. Clearly network complexity can grow to the point where understanding it just from the schematic becomes impossible. That is why we use Boolean algebra, which has a set of rules that allows us to write logic equations for switching networks and thus to interpret those networks more easily.

Postulates and Laws

If we use Boolean algebra, it is much easier to decide the value of Equation 3-3 than if we laboriously trace circuit paths on the schematic. The basis of Boolean algebra is a set of rules. These rules are called postulates, laws, or theorems.

From the last section and the chapter on inverters, you already know some of the **postulates** of Boolean algebra. These postulates are summarized in Table 3-3.

Now we will examine the **laws** that allow us to manipulate the terms in an expression.

The **commutative law** permits the terms of an operation to be written in any order.

$$A \cdot B = B \cdot A$$
$$K + M = M + K \qquad (3\text{-}4)$$

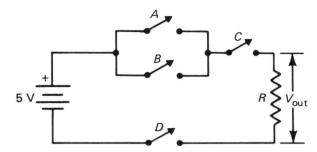

FIGURE 3-4. Switching Network

TABLE 3-3. Postulates of Boolean Algebra

AND	OR	NOT
$0 \cdot 0 = 0$	$0 + 0 = 0$	$\overline{0} = 1$
$0 \cdot 1 = 0$	$0 + 1 = 1$	$\overline{1} = 0$
$1 \cdot 0 = 0$	$1 + 0 = 1$	
$1 \cdot 1 = 1$	$1 + 1 = 1$	

Refer to the switching circuits for the AND and OR gates (Figures 3-1 and 3-2). The commutative law states that the labels on the switches could have been interchanged without altering the outcome. That is, we could have called the left switch of Figure 3-1 the B switch and the right one the A switch. This labeling would not have affected the AND gate truth table. Similarly, the labels on the top and bottom switches of the OR gate in Figure 3-2 could have been interchanged without changing the OR gate truth table. In fact, all Boolean operations prove their validity by demonstrating that the truth table for the expression to the left of the equal sign is the same as that for the expression on the right.

The **associative law** allows us to group terms of one operation in any way we like.

$$A \cdot (B \cdot C) = (A \cdot B) \cdot C = A \cdot B \cdot C$$
$$A + (B + C) = (A + B) + C = A + B + C \qquad (3\text{-}5)$$

In terms of switching elements, this law says that variables can be combined two at a time or all at once. In any case, the order does not matter. Figure 3-5a illustrates some of the equivalent AND gate combinations, and Figure 3-5b shows some of the equivalent OR gate combinations.

The associative law offers the possibility of an important cost advantage. For instance, one

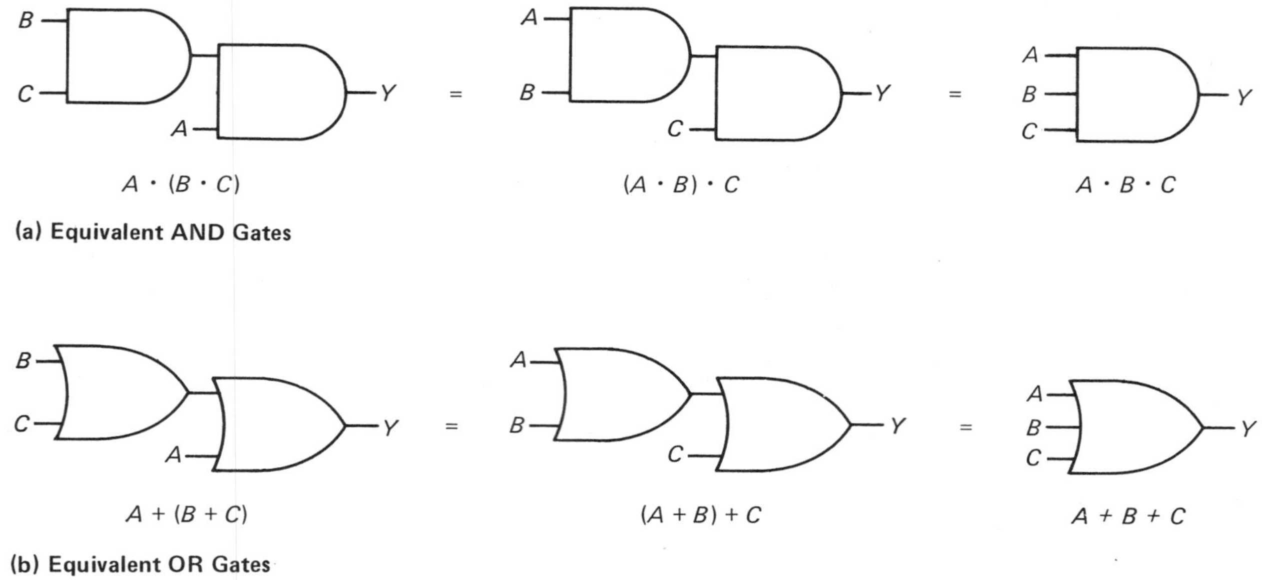

(a) Equivalent AND Gates

(b) Equivalent OR Gates

FIGURE 3-5. Circuits Demonstrating the Associative Law

gate that combines three inputs can be selected instead of two gates each with two inputs.

The **distributive law** is stated in two forms. One allows individual terms to be factored from an expression. The other permits parentheses to be removed for further simplification.

Factoring
$$A \cdot B + A \cdot C = A \cdot (B + C)$$

Clearing Parentheses
$$(A + B)(A + C) = A + BC \qquad (3-6)$$

This law also provides the means of building more efficient circuits. The expression to the left of the equal sign of the factoring law requires three gates (two ANDs and one OR), while the expression to the right uses only two (one AND and one OR).

How many gates does the law for removing parentheses allow you to eliminate? The answer is one. Two OR gates are needed in the left expression, while only one is needed for the right-hand expression. Did you notice that there is an *implied* AND between the two groups of terms? That is,

$$(A + B)(A + C) = (A + B) \cdot (A + C)$$

Identities

By examining the truth tables for the three functions covered so far, we can uncover additional facts about AND, OR, and NOT operations. These equations are called **identities** because the condition applies for any value for the variables in the expression. The derivation of some of these identities is provided below. Others are covered in the problems. Remember that the variable can only take on values of 0 or 1.

AND	**Derivation from Truth Table**	
$X \cdot 1 = X$	$0 \cdot 1 = 0$	
	$1 \cdot 1 = 1$	(3-7)
$X \cdot 0 = 0$	$0 \cdot 0 = 0$	
	$1 \cdot 0 = 0$	(3-8)
$X \cdot X = X$	$0 \cdot 0 = 0$	
	$1 \cdot 1 = 1$	(3-9)

OR

$$X + 1 = 1 \qquad (3-10)$$
$$X + 0 = X \qquad (3-11)$$
$$X + X = X \qquad (3-12)$$

Complement

$$\overline{\overline{X}} = X \qquad (3-13)$$
$$X \cdot \overline{X} = 0 \qquad (3-14)$$
$$X + \overline{X} = 1 \qquad (3-15)$$

Simplifying Expressions

With the rules of Boolean algebra, expressions can be simplified to a minimum form. As mentioned above, simplification often results in the elimination of one or more gates in a circuit. But most of the time simplification techniques are used only by design engineers; they are the ones who must find the simplest implementation of a circuit. Furthermore, as functions grow in complexity, only a computer can solve the equations in a reasonable amount of time.

However, technicians must understand enough Boolean algebra to read equipment manuals. Sometimes equipment manuals express the equivalent equation for a circuit element without explaining how the equivalent was obtained. Thus you should have some appreciation for simplification techniques. The next example shows one simplifying procedure.

□ **EXAMPLE 3-4**

The method for obtaining the distributive law for clearing parentheses (Equation 3-6) will demonstrate the use of the Boolean algebra laws, postulates, and identities. For each operation, the Boolean principle used is identified.

Associative Law 3-5
$$(A + B)(A + C) = AA + AC + BA + BC$$

Commutative Law 3-4
$$= AA + AC + AB + BC$$

Identity 3-9
$$= A + AC + AB + BC$$

Factoring Law 3-6
$$= A + A(C + B) + BC$$

Factoring Law 3-6
$$= A(1 + (C + B)) + BC$$

Associative Law 3-5
$$= A(1 + C + B) + BC$$

Identity 3-10
But $1 + C + B = 1$
$$= A \cdot 1 + BC$$

Identity 3-7
$$= A + BC$$

Therefore,
$$(A + B)(A + C) = A + BC$$

TABLE 3-4. Precedence of Boolean Operations

Rank	Operation
1	parentheses
2	NOT
3	AND
4	OR

Precedence of Operations

You may sometimes be uncertain about the order to use for evaluating a Boolean expression. Consider the circuit presented at the beginning of this section (Figure 3-4). The expression for the circuit is

$$(A + B) \cdot C \cdot D$$

How do you know which operation to perform first, then second, and so on in evaluating it, given the values of the variables? That is, if $A = 1$, $B = 0$, $C = 1$, and $D = 1$, how do you determine the output?

To prevent such confusion, a *precedence* (ranking) is assigned to each Boolean operation, as shown in Table 3-4. If expressions are always evaluated in the order shown in the table, the correct output will be found.

Using Table 3-4, we see that the values of the terms in the parentheses are to be combined first. Substituting the values for A and B, we obtain

$$A + B = 1 + 0 = 1$$

Placing this value back into the original expression, we get

$$(1) \cdot C \cdot D$$

All the remaining operations are ANDs, which are of equal rank. So we merely substitute values for C and D:

$$1 \cdot 1 \cdot 1 = 1$$

Thus the output is 1.

☐ EXAMPLE 3-5

Evaluate the following expressions, using the rules of precedence, if $W = 0$, $X = 1$, $Y = 1$, and $Z = 0$.

1. $\overline{X} + Y$
2. $(\overline{W + Z})X$
3. $XY + Z$

Solution

1. $\overline{X} + Y = \overline{1} + Y$
$= 0 + Y$
$= 0 + 1$
$= 1$

2. $(\overline{W + Z})X = (\overline{0 + 0})X$
$= (\overline{0})X$
$= 1 \cdot X$
$= 1 \cdot 1$
$= 1$

3. $XY + Z = 1 \cdot 1 + Z$
$= 1 + Z$
$= 1 + 0$
$= 1$

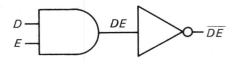

(a) Circuit

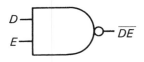

(b) NAND Symbol

FIGURE 3-6. NAND Gate

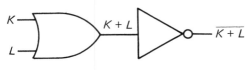

(a) Circuit

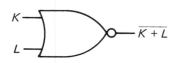

(b) NOR Symbol

FIGURE 3-7. NOR Gate

☐ COMBINING GATES

Now that you know how to read and evaluate Boolean expressions, let's practice that ability by combining simple gates to form other functions. Figure 3-6a shows an AND gate that has its output connected to an inverter. The AND gate has an output equal to DE. Inverting this quantity gives us $\overline{DE}$. If D is 0 and E is 1, the output is

$$\overline{0 \cdot 1} = \overline{0} = 1$$

Be careful to evaluate the complement properly. Because two variables are enclosed by the complement bar, parentheses are implied:

$$\overline{DE} = (\overline{DE})$$

Explicitly writing the parentheses makes the precedence of operations more obvious.

The combination shown in Figure 3-6a is such a common logic circuit that it has been given its own schematic symbol, as shown in Figure 3-6b. The circle from the inverter is shown on the output of the AND gate. The combined symbol is called a **NAND gate** (NOT combined with AND).

OR gates can also be used with inverters, as shown in Figure 3-7a. The output of the entire circuit is $\overline{K + L}$. Evaluating it when $K = 0$ and $L = 1$, we have

$$\overline{K + L} = (\overline{K + L}) = (\overline{0 + 1}) = \overline{1} = 0$$

Here, too, parentheses are implied by the long complement bar.

This circuit is called a **NOR gate**. Its symbol is shown in Figure 3-7b. Just as before, the circle from the inverter is shown on the output of the basic gate.

Inverters can also be placed on the input terminals of a gate. Figure 3-8a gives an example for a three-input gate with two inverters. In this case, the output is $\overline{Q}\overline{R}S$. Only the individual signals Q and R are inverted, so be sure to distinguish between this situation and the NAND gate. In the case of the NAND gate, both inputs were inverted as a combined quantity after the AND operation. Therefore, the complement bar spanned both terms in the expression.

Evaluation of this expression when $Q = 0$, $R = 0$, and $S = 1$ yields

$$\overline{Q}\overline{R}S = \overline{0} \cdot \overline{0} \cdot S$$
$$= 1 \cdot 1 \cdot S$$
$$= 1 \cdot 1 \cdot 1$$
$$= 1$$

These inverters are also frequently drawn in a more simplified form, as shown in Figure 3–8b. The circles on the input lines mean that those signals are inverted *before* they pass through the AND gate. A similar convention is used with OR gates.

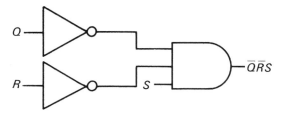

(a) Inverted Input Circuit

☐ DE MORGAN'S THEOREM

The caution in the last section to distinguish complement bars over single terms from bars over multiple terms leads to an important proposition of Boolean algebra called **DeMorgan's theorem**. This theorem specifies exactly how complements involving many terms may be evaluated. The theorem provides for both AND gates and OR gates:

$$\overline{X \cdot Y \cdot Z} = \overline{X} + \overline{Y} + \overline{Z} \qquad (3\text{--}16)$$

$$\overline{X + Y + Z} = \overline{X} \cdot \overline{Y} \cdot \overline{Z} \qquad (3\text{--}17)$$

The left-hand expression in Equation 3–16 corresponds to the output of a NAND gate. DeMorgan's theorem states that this output is equivalent to the complements of the *individual* inputs ORed together. The significance of this theorem might be better grasped by comparing the equivalent circuits in Figure 3–9a. The

(b) Simplified Symbology

FIGURE 3–8. Symbology for Inverted Inputs

NAND gate performs a transformation identical to that of an OR gate with inverted inputs.

The second form of DeMorgan's theorem (Equation 3–17) applies to NOR gates. The output of a NOR is the same as that generated by an AND gate with inverted inputs (see Figure 3–9b).

DeMorgan's theorem is not limited to three variable terms, as shown in Equations 3–16 and

(a) NAND Gate Form

FIGURE 3–9.
DeMorgan's
Theorem

(b) NOR Gate Form

3-17. It can be used with any number of variables, such as

$$\overline{W \cdot X} = \overline{W} + \overline{X}$$
$$\overline{A + B + C + D + E} = \overline{A} \cdot \overline{B} \cdot \overline{C} \cdot \overline{D} \cdot \overline{E}$$

□ EXAMPLE 3-6

Show that $\overline{A \cdot B} \neq \overline{A} \cdot \overline{B}$. (Not keeping this distinction straight is a very easy mistake to fall into.)

Solution DeMorgan's theorem will be used to evaluate the left expression by the theorem, $\overline{A \cdot B} = \overline{A} + \overline{B}$. To demonstrate that the two original terms were unequal, let $A = 0$ and $B = 1$. Then

$$\overline{A \cdot B} = \overline{A} + \overline{B} = \overline{0} + \overline{1} = 1 + 0 = 1$$
$$\overline{A} \cdot \overline{B} = \overline{0} \cdot \overline{1} = 1 \cdot 0 = 0$$

□ EXAMPLE 3-7

Evaluate the expression

$$\overline{\overline{\overline{A} + B} + C}$$

Solution When multiple complement bars are to be cleared by repeated application of DeMorgan's theorem, always start with the shortest bar. Insert any implied parentheses before beginning:

$$\overline{\overline{(\overline{A} + B)} + C} = \overline{(\overline{\overline{A}} \ \overline{B}) + C}$$
$$= \overline{(A \ \overline{B}) + C}$$
$$= \overline{(A \ \overline{B})} \cdot \overline{C}$$
$$= (\overline{A} + \overline{\overline{B}}) \cdot \overline{C}$$
$$= (\overline{A} + B)\overline{C}$$
$$= \overline{A} \ \overline{C} + B\overline{C}$$

□ ANALYZING DIGITAL CIRCUITS

An example showing the analysis of the operation of a digital circuit will illustrate how all the ideas of this chapter can be used together. The circuit we wish to analyze is shown in Figure 3–10a. The first step in the analysis is to write a Boolean expression that represents the circuit.

The outputs of the two AND gates are found first:

output of gate 1 $= A\overline{B}$
output of gate 2 $= \overline{A}B$

These are the inputs to the OR gate, which produces

$$A\overline{B} + \overline{A}B \qquad (3\text{-}18)$$

To show how this circuit, which is called an **exclusive OR circuit**, operates, we develop a truth table (Table 3–5).

For the first row, $A = 0$ and $B = 0$. The AND gate outputs are found as follows:

$$A\overline{B} = A \cdot \overline{0} = A \cdot 1 = 0 \cdot 1 = 0$$
$$\overline{A}B = \overline{0} \cdot B = 1 \cdot B = 1 \cdot 0 = 0$$

The output is these values ORed together, which in this case is

$$0 + 0 = 0$$

In the second row, $A = 0$ and $B = 1$:

$$A\overline{B} + \overline{A}B = 0 \cdot \overline{1} + \overline{0} \cdot 1 = 1$$

For the third row, we have

$$A\overline{B} + \overline{A}B = 1 \cdot \overline{0} + \overline{1} \cdot 0 = 1$$

And, finally, for the last row, we have

$$A\overline{B} + \overline{A}B = 1 \cdot \overline{1} + \overline{1} \cdot 1 = 0$$

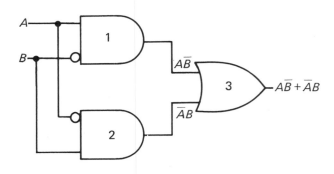

(a) Circuit

FIGURE 3-10. Exclusive OR

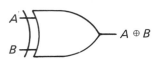

(b) Exclusive OR Symbol

TABLE 3-5. Exclusive OR Truth Table

Input		AND Gate Output		Output,
A	B	$A\overline{B}$	$\overline{A}B$	$A\overline{B} + \overline{A}B$
0	0	0	0	0
0	1	0	1	1
1	0	1	0	1
1	1	0	0	0

Table 3-5 is now examined to determine how the circuit functions. Whenever the values of A and B are equal, the output of the exclusive OR is 0. Only when the states of A and B are opposites does this circuit have an output of 1.

The exclusive OR can be used to find out if two Boolean values are not equal. The condition being tested is true whenever the exclusive OR output is 1. Because this circuit is so useful, it has been given its own circuit symbol, shown in Figure 3-10b. The notation for writing the exclusive OR function is

$$A \oplus B = A\overline{B} + \overline{A}B$$

Another circuit that produces an output of 1 when the two input variables are equal is shown in Figure 3-11a. Here the output equation is

$$AB + \overline{A}\overline{B}$$

found by ORing together the output of the AND gates. The symbol for this **equality circuit** is shown in Figure 3-11b. The notation for writing the equality function is

$$A \odot B = AB + \overline{A}\overline{B}$$

A truth table for the equality circuit can be generated row by row, just as was done for the exclusive OR. It is given in Table 3-6. The table shows that A and B must be equal for the output to be 1.

TABLE 3-6. Equality Truth Table

Input		
A	B	Output
0	0	1
0	1	0
1	0	0
1	1	1

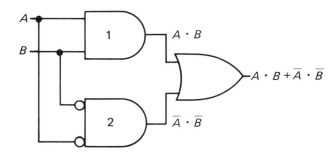

(a) Circuit

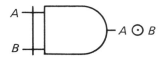

(b) Symbol

FIGURE 3-11. Equality Circuit

☐ BOOLEAN ALGEBRA REVIEW

To show how the laws and identities of Boolean algebra can be used to simplify expressions, we prove two theorems in the next example. (Other theorems are developed in the problems.) Table 3-7 provides a summary of Boolean algebra relationships.

☐ EXAMPLE 3-8

Show that $A(\overline{A} + B) = AB$ and $A(A + B) = A$.

Solution For the first theorem, after clearing the parentheses, we have

$$A\overline{A} + AB$$

But $A\overline{A} = 0$, so

$$A(\overline{A} + B) = AB$$

In the second case, clearing parentheses gives

$$AA + AB$$

But $AA = A$, so

$$A(A + B) = A + AB$$
$$= A(B + 1)$$

However, $B + 1 = 1$, so

$$A(A + B) = A$$

TABLE 3-7. Boolean Algebra Summary

Relationship	Equation
Boolean algebra postulates	$0 \cdot 0 = 0 \quad 0 + 0 = 0 \quad \overline{0} = 1$ $0 \cdot 1 = 0 \quad 0 + 1 = 1 \quad \overline{1} = 0$ $1 \cdot 0 = 0 \quad 1 + 0 = 1$ $1 \cdot 1 = 1 \quad 1 + 1 = 1$
Commutative law	$A \cdot B = B \cdot A \quad A + B = B + A$
Associative law	$A(BC) = (AB)C = ABC$ $A + (B + C) = (A + B) + C$ $ = A + B + C$
Distributive law	$AB + AC = A(B + C)$ $(A + B)(A + C) = A + BC$
Identities of Boolean algebra	$A \cdot 0 = 0 \quad A + 0 = A \quad A = \overline{\overline{A}}$ $A \cdot 1 = A \quad A + 1 = 1$ $A \cdot A = A \quad A + A = A$ $A \cdot \overline{A} = 0 \quad A + \overline{A} = 1$
DeMorgan's theorem	$\overline{ABCD \cdots} = \overline{A} + \overline{B} + \overline{C} + \overline{D} + \cdots$ $\overline{A + B + C + D + \cdots} = \overline{A}\,\overline{B}\,\overline{C}\,\overline{D} \cdots$
Exclusive OR	$A \oplus B = A\overline{B} + \overline{A}B$ $A \odot B = AB + \overline{A}\,\overline{B}$
Theorems	$A(\overline{A} + B) = AB \quad A + AB = A$ $A(A + B) = A \quad A + \overline{A}B = A + B$

Problems

3-1. Draw a switching circuit to implement each of these expressions.

    a. $K \cdot L \cdot M$

    b. $W + X + Y$

3-2. Are the switches in Problem 3-1 open or closed if the variable settings are as shown below?

$$K = 0 \quad W = 1$$
$$L = 1 \quad X = 0$$
$$M = 1 \quad Y = 0$$

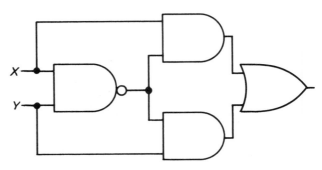

FIGURE 3-12.

3-3. Prepare truth tables for the gates listed below.

   a. gate 1 $= F\overline{G}H$

   b. gate 2 $= \overline{M} + \overline{L} + J$

3-4. Draw the circuit symbols for the two gates given in Problem 3-3.

3-5. Write the expression for the gate network of Figure 3-12.

3-6. Develop the truth table for the circuit shown in Figure 3-12.

3-7. Evaluate the Boolean expressions below for $C = 0$, $F = 1$, $Q = 0$, $R = 1$, $T = 0$, and $V = 1$.

   a. $(Q + 1)RT + \overline{V}$

   b. $\overline{RF} + TV \cdot (Q + C)$

3-8. Use DeMorgan's theorem to evaluate these expressions:

   a. $\overline{(A + B)} \cdot \overline{(C + D)}$

   b. $\overline{FGH} + \overline{QRS}$

3-9. Draw the circuit for the expression $(A + C) + B$. Compare this circuit with that in Figure 3-5b. What do you conclude?

3-10. Prove the identities in Equations 3-10 through 3-12 for the OR gate by means of the truth table.

3-11. Using a truth table, demonstrate the validity of the complement identities (Equations 3-14 and 3-15).

3-12. Prove the expression below, using the Boolean laws and identities.

$$X(X + Y) = X$$

3-13. The beginning steps for a proof of the *absorption theorem*, $X + XY = X$, are given below. Complete the steps required for the proof.

$$X + XY = X(\underline{Y + \overline{Y}}) + XY \qquad \text{(identity 3-15)}$$

$$= XY + \underline{X\overline{Y} + X\overline{Y}} + XY \qquad \text{(identity 3-12)}$$

3-14. What is the output of this combination of exclusive OR operation,

$$(A \oplus B) \cdot (C \oplus D)$$

if $A = 0$, $B = 1$, $C = 1$, and $D = 0$?

3-15. Draw the gate network that performs the operation given below.

$$A + B \cdot C + \overline{D}$$

Chapter Four

Transistor-Transistor Logic

A major segment of the logic circuits available today are implemented by using transistor-transistor logic (TTL or T²L). Because of the widespread applications of this integrated circuit family, a detailed study of its characteristics and capabilities is presented here. This chapter examines the principles of operation of TTL circuits. The following chapter discusses the most popular form of TTL, 5400/7400 logic. A final chapter (Chapter 6) covers the features of TTL output stages.

Chapter Objectives

Upon completion of this chapter, you should be able to:

☐ Define the standard terminology used in reference to TTL circuits.

☐ Draw waveforms that define the pulse width, propagation delay, and hold time for TTL circuits.

☐ Distinguish among nominal, typical, and worst-case parameters.

☐ Describe the mechanical characteristics of TTL circuits.

☐ Discuss the quality assurance measures used to test TTL parts.

☐ Explain how multiple-emitter transistors act as the input stage of a TTL gate.

☐ TTL TERMINOLOGY

The quantities that describe the operation of TTL gates are specified by the Electronics Industries Association (EIA) and the International Electrotechnical Commission (IEC). Both organizations have worked together to define a standard set of parameters for TTL circuits. Thus, to understand the specifications for these devices, you must first have knowledge of these definitions.

Voltages and Currents

Of primary interest are the voltages and currents that appear in the circuits. The power supply voltage is designated V_{CC}. The current flowing *into* the V_{CC} pin of an integrated circuit is identified as I_{CC}. (All currents for TTL circuits are positive if they are flowing into the IC, negative if they are flowing out.)

As you recall from earlier chapters, gate operation depends on two ranges of voltages: high levels and low levels. A high-level input voltage is labeled V_{IH}. This voltage represents a binary value and must be positive. A minimum level for V_{IH} that guarantees proper operation of the TTL gate is always specified for each type of gate. Typically, V_{IH} is in the range of 2.0 to 5.5 V. The corresponding high-level input current is I_{IH}.

The high-level output voltage, V_{OH}, is produced at the output pin when the specified input conditions have been met. When the output voltage is V_{OH}, the current will be I_{OH}.

A similar set of circumstances applies to low levels. A low-level input voltage is indicated as V_{IL}. A level is established for the most positive value that V_{IL} can be for proper operation. These levels might range from 0.8 to -1.5 V, for example. The current at the input when V_{IL} is applied is I_{IL}. The low-level output voltage is the value of V_{OL} when the inputs meet specified conditions. The low-level output current is I_{OL}.

☐ EXAMPLE 4-1

A particular TTL NAND gate produces an output of 3.8 V and a current of 100 µA flowing out of the IC. The two input pins have 0.7 V on them with a current of 2 mA flowing into the circuit. What are the values of V_{OH}, I_{OH}, V_{IL}, and I_{IL}?

Solution

$$V_{OH} = 3.8 \text{ V} \qquad V_{IL} = 0.7 \text{ V}$$
$$I_{OH} = -100 \text{ µA} \qquad I_{IL} = 2 \text{ mA}$$

The high-level output current is negative because I_{OH} flows out of the pin.

As you might expect, the currents and voltages for a TTL gate are not precise values. Instead, they fall into a range that varies with temperature, manufacturer, and even the particular lot that the IC came from. The value of the power supply voltage also influences the operational levels. Frequently used conditions for temperature and supply voltage are 25°C and V_{CC} of 5.0 V. The other values are then measured under these conditions. Data sheets for gates list the parameters under these stated environmental conditions.

Often, you may see gate voltages and currents listed in various ways. The **nominal value** for a voltage or current is the one resulting from calculations based on schematic diagrams and approximations for the characteristics of components used in the gate. Another value frequently listed is the **typical value** for voltage or current. Typical values are those you would expect to obtain by averaging the measured levels of many identical gates based on a statistical sampling procedure. The **worst-case values** are guaranteed limits. Usually, worst-case values are stipulated as maximums, minimums, or both.

In logic designs, only worst-case values can be relied on. The danger of designing a network by using nominal or typical values is that in some lots of ICs you may come across one circuit that does not fall within those ranges yet still meets the worst-case conditions. In such cases, the circuit will fail. The worst-case values are also important considerations when you replace an IC in a circuit with another one from a different lot or manufacturer. Obviously, the worst-case parameters of the new IC should meet or exceed those of the one being replaced.

☐ EXAMPLE 4-2

The values for some of the voltages and currents of a TTL gate are shown below.

Parameter	Nominal Value (V)	Typical Value (V)	Worst-Case Value (V)
V_{IH}	5	3.6	2.0
V_{IL}	0.2	0.2	0.8 max
V_{CC}	5	5	5.5 max
			4.5 min

As you can see, there can be considerable variation in the levels specified in these three ways.

Timing

Another important aspect of TTL operation is the speed with which the devices can operate. Many of these circuits are controlled by a square wave called the **clock** (see Figure 4-1). The clock frequently determines how fast the IC can be driven. Clocks will become more important in later chapters on integrated circuits. For now, we just note that there is an upper limit to the clock frequency. The **maximum clock frequency**, f_{max}, is the highest clock rate that you can use with one of these circuits and still be assured that operation will meet all specified conditions.

A key timing measure of signals is the **pulse width**. The interval between reference points on the leading edge and trailing edge of the waveform is the pulse width, or t_w. Figure 4-2 shows that, for TTL circuits, the pulse width is measured between the 1.5 V level on the leading and trailing edges of the pulse. As the figure shows, it makes no difference whether the pulse is going high (Figure 4-2a) or going low (Figure 4-2b). The measurement is still made between identical points on the leading and trailing edges. For some circuits, a minimum pulse width for proper functioning may be specified.

Because pulses and levels are frequently encountered in logic circuits, we often want to know when a particular level is reached. But the **transition time** for a signal to change levels may not be identical when switching to a high level and when going to a low one. The transition time from the low to the high level, t_{TLH} (where T stands for transition, L for low, and H for high), is the interval between the low-level voltage and a specified high-level voltage on the signal. Of course, t_{TLH} is only measured on a signal that is switching from low to high. The corresponding transition time from a high to a low level is designated t_{THL}. This parameter measures the elapsed time between the high-level and low-level voltage of a falling waveform.

None of the measures discussed so far tell us how fast a gate operates. That information is provided by the **propagation delay** values. The propagation delay is the time, between specified points on the input and output waveforms, needed for the output to change levels. Like the transition time, the propagation delay need not be identical for rising and falling output levels. The low-to-high-level propagation delay, t_{PLH}, applies to outputs that are rising. A high-to-low propagation delay, t_{PHL}, is applicable to the opposite situation.

Figure 4-3 illustrates the propagation delay

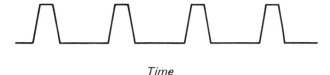

Time

FIGURE 4-1. Clock Waveform

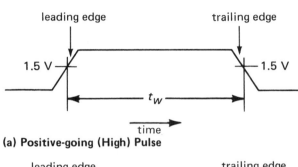

(a) **Positive-going (High) Pulse**

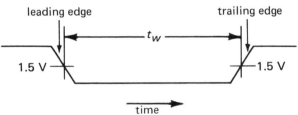

(b) **Negative-going (Low) Pulse**

FIGURE 4-2. Pulse Width

concept. In Figure 4-3a, some finite amount of time must pass after the input signal is applied to the TTL circuit before the output changes level. In this case, an input transition from a low level to a high level will cause the output to drop. The time that elapses between the 1.5-V level on the input signal and the 1.5-V level on the output signal is the propagation delay, t_{PHL}. For a rising output level caused by a falling input, t_{PLH} is found in a similar way on the right-hand side of Figure 4-3a.

If the input situation is reversed—that is, a rising input causes a rising output—Figure 4-3b applies. But regardless of which situation applies, the times t_{PLH} and t_{PHL} are evaluated between the 1.5-V points on the input and output waveforms.

Now let us consider how long the input signal must be held constant before it is allowed

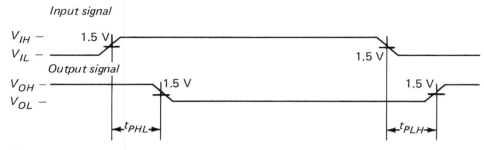

(a) High-to-Low Level

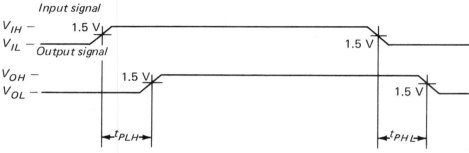

(b) Low-to-High Level

FIGURE 4-3.
Propagation Delay

to change. The **setup time**, t_{su}, is the period between the transition of the input signal and the application of another signal (usually the clock). Figure 4–4 shows an example. The input signal must be above the 1.5-V signal for at least t_{su} prior to the time when the clock reaches 1.5 V.

The **hold time**, t_h, is the minimum interval for which the input must remain steady after some other event (again, usually the clock transition). As Figure 4–4 shows, the input signal must remain above 1.5 V for a period t_h after the clock passes through the 1.5-V level. At that point, the input voltage may be changed without interfering with proper circuit operation.

A final measure of interest in a TTL gate is the **fan-in**. The fan-in is just a count of the number of input terminals on a gate. For example, an AND gate with inputs A and B has a fan-in of two. If an OR gate has inputs A, B, C, and D, its fan-in is four. TTL gates provide a fan-in range of from two to eight. Should this number be insufficient, gate expanders or multiple gates can be used to increase the number of input terminals.

A summary of the parameters used to describe TTL circuits is provided in Table 4–1. These abbreviations will be used throughout this book in referring to these quantities.

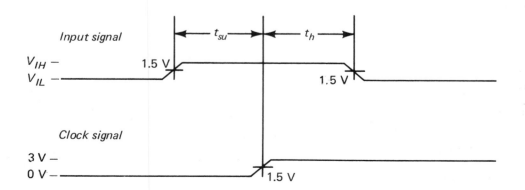

FIGURE 4-4. Setup
and Hold Time

☐ **PACKAGING**

TTL gates are encapsulated in a nonconductive case. Most commonly encountered are the plastic (N) and ceramic (J) packages. The pins used to make contact with the signal and power terminals are arranged in a double row along the sides of the package—hence the designation dual in-line package (DIP). Figure 4-5 shows some of these DIPs. Note that there may be 14, 16, or 24 leads extending from the package. The plastic packages are less expensive, but they cannot guarantee stable performance in a high-humidity environment. In those environments, the hermetically sealed, ceramic DIP should be used instead. Regardless of their packaging material, however, two identical gates provide the same logic functions.

The dual in-line packages are designed for insertion in rows of mounting holes. The leads must be compressed to be inserted. After insertion, tension holds the package secured until it is soldered in place. Alternatively, DIP sockets can be used to hold the packages. With this arrangement, ICs can be replaced without unsoldering them. Because heat can damage the devices, it is desirable to avoid soldering. However, sockets do not retain the ICs as firmly as a soldered connection. Use of sockets also increases the cost of components and assembly.

Another type of package is the flat pack, shown in Figure 4-6. There are two forms: metal-encased (I) flat packs and ceramic-encased (H and W) flat packs. Flat packs lie very close to the cir-

cuit board and thus are used when space is at a premium—in aerospace applications, for example. All flat packs are hermetically sealed. Flat packs come in 14-, 16-, or 24-lead versions, too. The leads of these packages are always soldered in

TABLE 4-1. Standard TTL Terminology

Voltages	
Power supply voltage	V_{CC}
High-level input voltage	V_{IH}
Low-level input voltage	V_{IL}
High-level output voltage	V_{OH}
Low-level output voltage	V_{OL}
Currents[a]	
Power supply current	I_{CC}
High-level input current	I_{IH}
Low-level input current	I_{IL}
High-level output current	I_{OH}
Low-level output current	I_{OL}
Timing	
Maximum clock frequency	f_{max}
Pulse width	t_w
Transition time	
Low to high level	t_{TLH}
High to low level	t_{THL}
Propagation delay	
Low to high level	t_{PLH}
High to low level	t_{PHL}
Setup time	t_{su}
Hold time	t_h

[a]Current flowing into the circuit is positive.

FIGURE 4-5. Dual In-Line Package

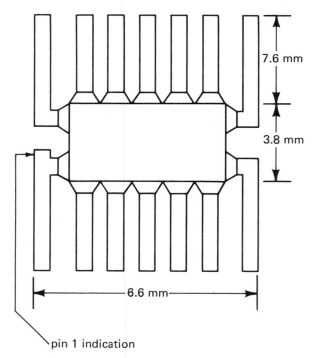

FIGURE 4-6. Flat Package

place. (A less frequently used form of flat pack has a configuration called beam leads, which extend from all sides of the package.)

Because leads extend from both sides of the DIP in a symmetrical arrangement, you can easily insert one of these ICs upside down. To prevent this mistake, carefully note the end of the package that is marked with a notch or dot. With that end pointing to the left, pin 1 is the lower

bottom one, as shown in Figure 4-7. (Some flat packs are not marked with a notch or dot. Instead pin 1 has a tab on it.) Other pins are then numbered sequentially in a counterclockwise direction (when viewed from the top).

Two types of lead construction are used with sockets for DIPs. The first type, the **solder tail**, has already been described. In this construction, the socket leads extend through the mounting hole and are soldered to a pad on the circuit board. Another type of socket lead is the **wire wrap**. In this case, the pins are longer than in the solder tail and are designed to firmly engage wire that is twisted around them. Wire wrap construction is best suited for prototypes or for situations when only a small number of identical circuit cards are to be built.

□ INSPECTION

When ICs arrive at a plant, they often go through an incoming inspection process. While some companies rely on only a simple visual inspection, others run the chips through a series of tests. As a technician, you may become involved in such **quality assurance procedures**.

Rather than submitting all the incoming ICs to quality assurance inspection, an inspector often will use only a sample of the chips. Perhaps 10 to 50 from each lot will be tested. Visual inspection checks for obvious defects in the case and for bent or missing pins.

If the equipment must operate over a range of temperatures, thermal testing of the ICs is done. *Temperature cycling* employs a chamber that can alternately expose ICs to arctic and desert conditions. Remember that the ICs inside the equipment case are at a much higher temperature than the external temperature, so these tests often range in temperature from below freezing to above the boiling point of water. Another thermal test evaluates how well the ICs can stand continuous exposure to heat. For obvious reasons, this inspection is called the *bake test. Thermal shock testing* exposes the ICs to extremes in temperature. The purpose is to ensure that the leads and case, which expand or contract at different rates, remain bonded.

Mechanical shock and *vibration tests* examine how strong the ICs are and ensure that none of the components will shake loose. Vibration testing is also used on finished components

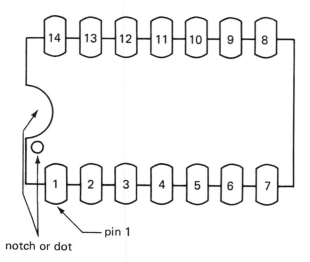

FIGURE 4-7. Locating Pin 1 on a DIP

to eliminate loose pieces of solder, wire, or hardware. If the circuit will experience especially severe acceleration, such as in a satellite, the effects of acceleration can be tested by using a centrifuge.

After construction, circuit boards or the entire piece of equipment may be *burned in*. During burn-in, the equipment is operated at elevated temperatures for many hours. This test eliminates marginal ICs or those subject to early-life failure (sometimes called *infant mortality*).

□ THEORY OF TTL OPERATION

In this section, we will discuss how transistor-transistor logic differs from the logic described in earlier chapters. You may wish to compare the example of a TTL inverter (Figure 4–8) with the one shown in Figure 2–12. As you recall from that circuit, operation is based on a reverse-biased diode on the input and a series of diodes leading to the output transistor.

As Figure 4–8a shows, the TTL inverter uses transistors instead of diodes. However, as you will soon see, operation of the two inverters is quite similar. The input transistor Q_1 replaces the diode of the earlier inverter. As the equivalent circuit for Q_1 shows, the transistor can be considered as two back-to-back diodes. The base-emitter junction of Q_2 also acts like a diode; so we have effectively the same chain of diodes here that we had in the circuit of Figure 2–12.

When the input is 0 V, the base-emitter junction of Q_1 is forward-biased. Current flowing through the 4-kΩ resistor will pull the base of Q_1 down to 0.7 V. (Recall that one diode drop is 0.7 V.) That base voltage is not sufficient to forward-bias the chain of three diode junctions (base-collector of Q_1 and base-emitter of Q_2 and Q_3), so Q_3 must be cut off. Because no current flows in the output leg, there is no drop across the 3-kΩ resistor and the output voltage is 5 V.

Now let the input voltage change to 5 V, reverse-biasing the base-emitter junction of Q_1, as shown in Figure 4–8b. Current in the power supply will flow through the Q_1–Q_2–Q_3 junctions, dropping the voltage to 0.7 V for each. Therefore, Q_3 is saturated. The voltage across the emitter to the collector of Q_3 is consequently 0.2 V. Similarly, the voltage on the base of Q_2 is 1.4 V (0.7 V higher than the 0.7 V at the base of Q_3). Moving

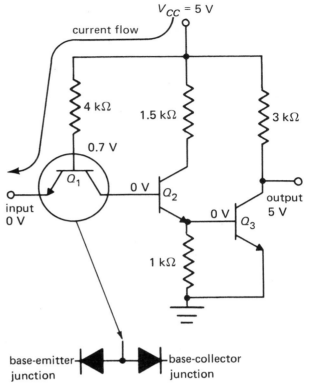

Equivalent circuit for Q_1

(a) Low-Level Input

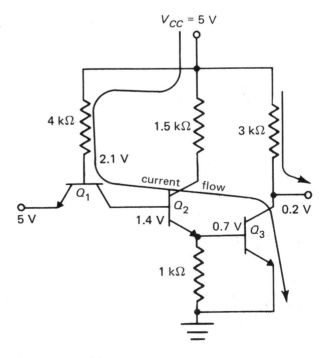

(b) High-Level Input

FIGURE 4–8. TTL Inverter

TABLE 4-2. TTL Inverter Voltages

Input (V)	Base of Q_1 (V)	Base of Q_2 (V)	Base of Q_3 (V)	Output (V)
0	0.7	0	0	5
5	2.1	1.4	0.7	0.2

left to the base of Q_1, we can find its voltage by adding the drop across the base-collector of Q_1 to 1.4 V, giving a result of 2.1 V.

We have now found the voltages throughout the circuit for either a high or a low input and also have demonstrated the inverting action of this circuit. Table 4-2 summarizes the voltages.

□ **EXAMPLE 4-3**

For the TTL inverter, what current flows through the 4-kΩ resistor when the input voltage is 0 V?

Solution The voltage on one side of the resistor is V_{CC} and is 0.7 V on the other. The voltage drop can then be found:

$$5 - 0.7 = 4.3 \text{ V}$$

And by Ohm's law,

$$I = \frac{V}{R} = \frac{4.3}{4 \times 10^3} = 1.1 \text{ mA}$$

Notice that this current flows *out* of the input terminal.

If the actions of this circuit and the one in Chapter 2 are so similar, what is the advantage of the TTL? The answer is based on the reverse current provided by Q_1. Because of this current (not provided by a diode), Q_1 can pull Q_3 out of saturation faster than the diode alone could.

□ **TTL NAND GATE**

Now we will combine the idea of the TTL inverter with the need for a family of logic functions. Figure 4-9 shows how a small modification changes the inverter to a NAND gate. Here a **multiple-emitter transistor** is used on the input terminals. The multiple-emitter transistor expands the number of input ports. Each input ter-

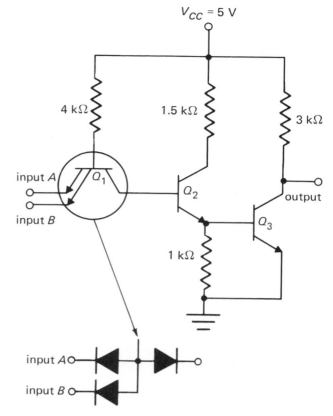

Equivalent circuit for Q_1

FIGURE 4-9. TTL NAND Gate

minal can be considered an independent diode, as the figure shows. The base-collector junction of Q_1 continues to act as a diode biased in the opposite direction, just as in the inverter of Figure 4-8.

To analyze the gate operation, first consider the case when both inputs are low. That voltage causes both base-emitter junctions of Q_1 to become forward-biased, pulling the base to 0.7 V. This low voltage is inadequate to forward-bias the base-collector junction of Q_1 and the series base-emitter junctions of Q_2 and Q_3. The result is that Q_3 must be cut off, and hence the output is 5 V.

Suppose now that input A remains at 0 V while input B becomes 5 V. The base-emitter junction tied to input A is forward-biased (even though the junction for input B is reverse-biased), so the base of Q_1 must remain at 0.7 V. Again, the output will be 5 V. Reversing the input voltage levels (A high and B low) does not change the output, either. That is, if input A is 5 V and input B

is 0 V, one of the base-emitter junctions of Q_1 remains forward-biased, holding Q_3 in the cutoff state.

If both inputs are high, however, the base of Q_1 is not held at the low voltage. Instead, it can rise to a potential that is sufficient to forward-bias the three series junctions. The outcome is that Q_3 switches states and becomes saturated. The output voltage, then, is only that across the collector and emitter of a saturated transistor—about 0.2 V.

We can summarize these results in a voltage table for the gate, as shown in Table 4-3. If we let the higher voltage be represented by a 1 and the lower voltage by a 0, a truth table can be derived. This truth table is shown in Table 4-4. By comparing this table with the function described in the last chapter, we see that this TTL circuit is indeed an implementation of the NAND gate.

Other combinations of components permit us to construct any Boolean function desired using transistor-transistor logic. For example, inverting the output of the NAND circuit converts it to an AND gate. As the next chapter will show, a complete family of such logic functions is available, off the shelf, from any electronics supply house.

TABLE 4-3. NAND Gate Voltage Table

Input (V)		
A	B	Output (V)
0	0	5
0	5	5
5	0	5
5	5	0.2

TABLE 4-4. NAND Truth Table

Input		
A	B	Output
0	0	1
0	1	1
1	0	1
1	1	0

Chapter Summary

☐ Standard definitions have been established for TTL parameters. The voltages, currents, and timing specifications of these circuits are given in terms of these definitions. The voltages and currents associated with high and low levels are among the most important quantities of interest.

☐ In reading a data sheet, you must keep in mind the distinction among nominal, typical, and worst-case values. Only the latter values are guaranteed.

☐ Timing in digital circuits is very important. The maximum clock frequency, pulse widths, transition times, propagation delay, setup time, and hold time must be considered.

☐ TTL circuits are packaged as DIPs or as flat packs. Various types of case materials, including plastic, ceramic, and metal, are used to encapsulate the chip.

☐ Incoming inspection of ICs can reduce the cost of finding faulty components, which is much higher once the device has been built into an assembly. Typical inspections might include visual, thermal, shock and vibration. Burn-in tests after construction can detect and eliminate premature failures.

☐ The theory of TTL gate operation is similar to that of diode-controlled gates. The voltage drop across the base-emitter or base-collector junctions of the transistors are used to control switching of the output transistor. The advantage of TTL is the increased operating speed.

□ An inverter built by using TTL produces a low output for a high input and a high output with a low input.

□ A multiple-emitter transistor allows the inverter to be modified to perform as a NAND gate. Other changes to the TTL circuit provide a complete range of Boolean functions.

Problems

4-1. For the input and output waveform of Figure 4-10, what is the pulse width of the input voltage?

4-2. Find the value of t_{PHL} for a circuit that has the input and output characteristics shown in Figure 4-10. What is t_{PLH} for the circuit?

4-3. The values in Figure 4-10 were the fastest measured for a TTL gate that had a specified maximum hold time of 1.8 ns (nanoseconds) and a minimum setup time of 3.0 ns. Is this particular gate within specifications? If not, how large is the error(s)?

4-4. Draw a diagram of the connections for the 14-pin DIP described below.

Pin Number	Purpose
1	Input A
2	Input B
3	Input C
4	Input D
5	Input E
6	Not used
7	Ground
8	Input F
9	Input G
10	Input H
11	Not used
12	Output
13	Not used
14	V_{CC}

4-5. Find the current in the 1.5-kΩ and 3-kΩ resistors of Figure 4-8 when the input is low.

4-6. The input to the TTL inverter of Figure 4-8 is 4.8 V. What current flows in each of the resistors?

4-7. If both inputs to the TTL NAND gate of Figure 4-9 are −0.1 V, what current flows in the 4-kΩ resistor? Suppose that input A changes to 0 V but that input B remains the same. How is the output voltage affected? What current flows in the 4-kΩ resistor?

4-8. The 3-kΩ resistor in Figure 4-9 is replaced by a 2-kΩ resistor. How much change in the current through that resistor does this substitution produce when both inputs are high?

4-9. What is the power consumption in the output (3-kΩ) resistor in Problem 4-8 before the substitution? After the substitution, how much does it change? Remember that the power P through a resistor can be calculated as

$$P = I^2 R$$

4-10. What is the maximum value of V_{IL} that can be tolerated for proper operation of the inverter in Figure 4-8? What is the minimum V_{IH}?

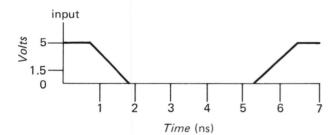

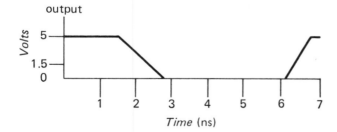

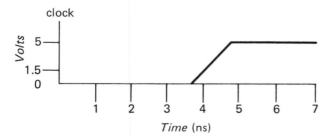

FIGURE 4-10. TTL Waveforms

Chapter Five

5400/7400 Series Logic

Almost all the TTL integrated circuits used by industry are selected from the standard families of gates and functional elements in the 5400 and 7400 lines. Not only are these devices compatible with one another, but they also may be directly connected to other logic series. In this chapter, we will consider the important aspects of this group of ICs and examine how they can be used to build logic networks.

Chapter Objectives

Upon completion of this chapter, you should be able to:

- ☐ Specify the power supply voltage for 5400/7400 ICs.
- ☐ Calculate the noise margin of an integrated circuit.
- ☐ Explain the temperature ratings of TTL circuits.
- ☐ Distinguish among the subseries of the 5400/7400 chips and rank them in terms of speed and power requirements.
- ☐ Decode a typical designator for one of these circuits.
- ☐ Describe the electrical ratings of 5400/7400 TTL gates.
- ☐ Show how connections are to be made to the pins of a TTL package.

☐ THE 5400/7400 FAMILY

A wide spectrum of functions are to be found in the 5400/7400 family of ICs. The Boolean functions of AND, OR, NOT, NAND, and NOR are all provided. These low-cost gates simplify the construction of any logic circuit. If recommended techniques are followed, the circuit can be implemented in a fraction of the time needed to construct an equivalent discrete component version. Furthermore, these ICs also provide many MSI and LSI functional elements that can be connected to the gates without concern about signal levels or logical agreement.

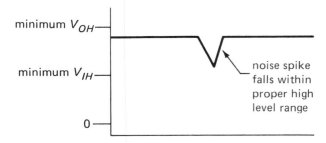

(a) High Level

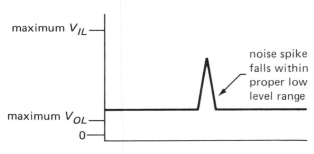

(b) Low Level

FIGURE 5-1. Noise Margin

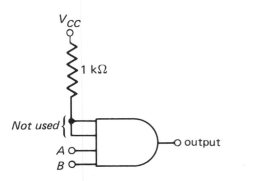

FIGURE 5-2. Unused Inputs of a 5400/7400 Gate

Supply Voltage and Noise Margin

All these devices work from a supply voltage of 5 V, usually with a tolerance of ±10 percent. The **noise margin** is the difference between the input and output voltages at either level. At the low level the noise margin N_L is

$$N_L = V_{IL} - V_{OL} \qquad (5\text{-}1)$$

The high-level noise margin is

$$N_H = V_{OH} - V_{IH} \qquad (5\text{-}2)$$

Typically, both values are greater than half a volt. The larger the noise margin, the less likely it is that the component will generate an erroneous output as a result of a noise spike. See Figure 5-1.

☐ EXAMPLE 5-1

What is the high-level noise margin for a TTL gate with a high-level input voltage of 2 V, which produces a high-level output voltage of 3.4 V?

Solution   From Equation 5-2 we have

$$N_H = 3.4 - 2 = 1.4 \text{ V}$$

Unused Inputs

If any inputs to a 5400/7400 gate are not used, they should be tied to the power supply V_{CC} through a 1-kΩ resistor (if the logic function, such as AND, calls for a high level) or grounded (for a low level, such as an OR gate). Figure 5-2 shows a case where two of the inputs to an AND gate are not needed. Connecting the inputs to the supply voltage does not change the logic function of the gate. In addition, the propagation delay in the gate is decreased if these unused inputs are properly terminated.

Two undesirable effects will be noticed if this termination is not made. First, the switching time will increase if the inputs are left *floating*. Second, noise can enter the circuit through these leads. Both conditions result from the capacitance that is produced by the floating input and lead. As you know from your previous studies, if the capacitance in a circuit increases, so does the *RC* time constant. The latter increase means that the gates cannot switch states as rapidly as desired.

□ EXAMPLE 5–2

The RC time constant of a TTL gate is 2.8 ns. If the distributed capacitance of the gate increases by 40 percent because one input is left floating, how much is the propagation delay increased? (Let the low-to-high-level propagation delay be approximated by 5 times the time constant.)

Solution The original propagation delay is

$$t_{PLH} = 5 \times 2.8 = 14 \text{ ns}$$

The new RC time constant is 140 percent, or 1.4 times, the original. So

$$RC = 1.4 \times 2.8 = 3.9 \text{ ns}$$

The changed propagation delay is

$$t_{PLH} = 5 \times 3.9 = 19.5 \text{ ns}$$

for an increase of 5.5 ns.

Temperature Ratings

TTL circuits in this family can be obtained to operate under different thermal conditions. The *commercial* 7400 series devices offer the most limited range, of 0° to 70°C. These ICs are suitable for ordinary commercial conditions. This spread of temperatures may seem more than adequate at first glance. But remember that even in an air-conditioned room, the interior of the electronics equipment is at a much higher temperature than the room temperature.

If more tolerance to heat is required, the *military* 5400 series can be operated over a range of −55° to 125°C. These ICs find a great deal of use in aerospace and military equipment. Naturally, a 5400 circuit costs more than an equivalent 7400 component. Price differences between the two types of three to four times are common.

□ SUBSERIES OF TTL CIRCUITS

The 5400/7400 family is further divided into subseries of chips that offer especially low costs, fast switching time, or low power dissipation. Because the characteristics of the device are determined by a compromise among these factors, you can buy an IC that improves one factor at the sake of the other two.

The **standard** 5400/7400 series features low cost, but it is neither very fast nor very conservative on power. By changing the value of components in the standard series, emphasis can be placed on the other parameters.

If, for example, the resistor values in the standard TTL are cut in half, a family of **high-speed** TTL circuits is created. Reductions in the propagation delay on the order of one-half can be achieved. The penalty for this speed is a greater power consumption: in a high-speed TTL, the power usage is about double that of a standard TTL.

On the other hand, power can be conserved by increasing the resistor values to some 10 times those of a standard TTL. The resulting **low-power** TTL uses a miserly 10 percent of the standard power—but at a sacrifice of 20 to 30 times the speed.

Another type of TTL that is becoming increasingly popular is the **Schottky-clamped** (sometimes called just Schottky) TTL. This type of gate is similar to the high-speed series, except that the input transistor is not permitted to go into saturation. Therefore, Schottky TTL competes well with the high-speed series in terms of power requirements. Yet Schottky is even faster. Another series, the **Low-power Schottky** TTL, is also being built into more and more equipment.

Table 5–1 provides a comparison of these types of transistor-transistor logic gates. The table also indicates the **speed-power product** of

TABLE 5–1. Typical TTL Characteristics

Series	Propagation Delay (ns)	Power Dissipation (mW)	Speed-Power Product (pJ)	Cost, SSI (cents)
Standard	10	10	100	16
Low-power	30	1	30	59
High-speed	5	22	110	19
Schottky-clamped	3	20	60	35
Low-power Schottky	10	2	20	29

these devices. This rating allows us to compare a combined measure of the propagation delays and power dissipation of two types of gates. The speed-power product (*SP*) is simply

$$SP = t_{PD} \times P \qquad (5\text{-}3)$$

where

t_{PD} = propagation delay
P = power dissipation

The speed-power product is measured in joules (J).

☐ EXAMPLE 5–3

Which has the smaller speed-power product: a standard TTL or a high-speed TTL?

Solution From Table 5–1 and Equation 5–3, we have, for a standard TTL,

$$\begin{aligned} SP &= (10 \times 10^{-9})(10 \times 10^{-3}) \\ &= 100 \times 10^{-12} \\ &= 100 \text{ pJ} \end{aligned}$$

For a high-speed TTL, we have

$$\begin{aligned} SP &= (5 \times 10^{-9})(22 \times 10^{-3}) \\ &= 110 \times 10^{-12} \\ &= 110 \text{ pJ} \end{aligned}$$

So *SP* is smaller for the standard series.

☐ 5400/7400 TTL DESIGNATIONS

The manufacturers of a 5400/7400 integrated circuit print a label for the device on its case. The label completely identifies the type of circuit contained within the package. While this designation is not standardized within the industry, most manufacturers use a similar system. For purposes of illustration, the method used by one company will be described here. However, you may have to check the specific data sheets for a particular make of IC to decode its designator.

The full designation for one gate is shown below.

```
             SN  74  S  02  J
prefix ─────────────┘   │   │   │   └─package
temperature range ──────┘   │   │     └─type
subseries ──────────────────┘   │
```

The prefix identifies any special construction techniques used on the gate. For example, the SN designation indicates standard construction. Special characteristics that may be found include radiation hardening (RSN), high reliability (SNA, SNB, SNH, or SNM), and beam-lead flat packaging (BL). The temperature rating has already been described, with the militarized 54 series covering wider extremes than the commercial 74 series.

The subseries of the device is designated by letters. An IC designator without a letter is a standard device, such as 7400 or 5421. Low-power circuits are identified with an L and high-speed circuits with an H, as in 74L04 and 54H14, respectively. Schottky-clamped devices are identified with an S in the label, as in the example given in this section. A low-power Schottky uses LS, as in 74LS30.

The type of gate or function, and possibly the most useful information in the designation, is identified—with the help of a data book—by the last two or three digits. For example:

☐ The digits 00 indicate a NAND gate.
☐ The digits 02 indicate a NOR gate.
☐ The digits 08 indicate an AND gate.

The range of these numbers is from 00 to over 300, and new numbers are continually being added.

The final letter in the designator specifies the packaging, such as plastic and ceramic DIPs or flat packs. Recall from the last chapter that the package identifier can be H, J, N, T, or W.

Putting all of this information together, we can decode the designation for the gate given at the beginning of this section:

☐ standard device
☐ narrow temperature range (0°–70°C)
☐ Schottky-clamped TTL
☐ NOR gate
☐ ceramic DIP

Often, the prefix and package identifiers are not included in a general discussion of a gate when *a standard* plastic DIP is implied. So the device above might generically be referred to as 74S02. Of course, that label would not be complete enough for use in ordering the device from the manufacturer.

Another important concern is the number of

gates in a package. Usually, there is more than one. If two gates are provided, the device is called a *dual-gate* package, such as a dual AND gate. With three gates, we have a *triple-gate* package; with four, a *quad-gate* package; and with six, a *hex-gate* package. The 5400 contains four 2-input NAND gates and thus is referred to as a quad NAND. The 7405 provides six inverters and hence is called a hex-inverter package.

□ **EXAMPLE 5-4**

Give a full description of an SN74LS00N circuit.

Solution This device is a standard series, commercial temperature range, low-power Schottky, quad 2-input NAND gate in a plastic DIP.

TABLE 5-2. Electrical Characteristics of 5400/7400 TTL

Parameter	Minimum	Typical	Maximum
V_{CC}	4.5 V	5 V	5.5 V
I_{CC}			
Outputs high		4 mA	8 mA
Outputs low		12 mA	22 mA
I_{OH}			$-400\ \mu\text{A}$
I_{OL}			16 mA
V_{IH}	2 V		
V_{IL}			0.8 V
V_{OH}	2.4 V	3.4 V	
V_{OL}		0.2 V	0.4 V
I_{IH}			$40\ \mu\text{A}$
I_{IL}			-1.6 mA
t_{PLH}		11 ns	22 ns
t_{PHL}		7 ns	15 ns

□ ELECTRICAL CHARACTERISTICS

While the 5400/7400 circuits are compatible with one another, a technician must always know a device's specific electrical characteristics. These parameters should be reviewed before attempting to interface TTL devices to other types of logic or discrete components or before interconnecting 5400/7400 TTLs made by different companies. The propagation delays are also important if signals from the various gates must arrive simultaneously at one point in the circuit.

The manufacturer's data sheet will always give the electrical information. Table 5-2 lists values that are characteristic of SSI gates like the 5400.

From the table, we observe that there can be quite a spread between typical and guaranteed values. The power supply voltage must be 5 V ±0.5 V. Current drawn from the supply varies, depending on the state of the gate outputs. If all outputs are high, the power supply provides a maximum current of 8 mA. This value increases to a maximum of 22 mA if all outputs are low.

The high-level output current (I_{OH}) is 400 μA, which is flowing *out* of the output pin, as indicated by the minus sign (-400) in the table. The low-level output current is 16 mA flowing *in*. Similarly, the input currents are a maximum of 40 μA for the high level and 1.6 mA for the low level. The minimum, recognizable, high-level input voltage is 2 V, and the minimum high-level

output 2.4 V. The low-level voltages have maximums of 0.8 V on input and 0.4 V on output.

The propagation delay for a low-to-high transition has a maximum of 22 ns, while an opposite-going output has a maximum delay of 15 ns. A main contributor to the increased rise time of t_{PLH} is the output transistor, which must be pulled out of saturation.

□ PIN DIAGRAMS

The manufacturer's data sheet tells you what each pin on the package does. While some conventions for pin usage exist, there are so many exceptions that one should not rely on the "normal way of doing things." Instead, use the data sheets. One of the conventions (not always followed) is that pin 7 is the ground terminal (GND) and pin 14 the V_{CC} terminal of a 14-pin DIP. On a 16-pin DIP, pin 8 is often ground and pin 16 the V_{CC} connection.

Figure 5-3 shows two examples of IC pin diagrams. The 5400 shown in Figure 5-3a contains four NAND gates, as mentioned previously. The quad two-input NAND gate package allows you to use each of the gates independently. The only common circuitry among the gates is that for the power supply and ground pins.

The pins on each gate are labeled to identify the input or output terminals and the gate they are used with. The function performed by the gates is specified by the equation to the right on the diagram. This equation applies to each gate; that is,

$$1Y = \overline{1A \cdot 1B}$$
$$2Y = \overline{2A \cdot 2B}$$

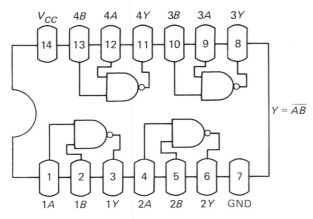

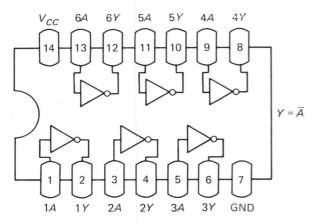

(a) 5400 Quad Two-Input NAND Gate

(b) 7405 Hex Inverter

FIGURE 5-3. IC Pin Diagrams

TABLE 5-3. Gate Connections for Example 5-5

TTL	Pin	Signal
7405	1	A input
	2	Pin 1 of 7400
	7	Ground
	14	V_{CC}
7400	1	Pin 2 of 7405
	2	B input
	3	Output
	7	Ground
	14	V_{CC}

$$3Y = \overline{3A \cdot 3B}$$
$$4Y = \overline{4A \cdot 4B}$$

Inputs are always identified with letters at the beginning of the alphabet (A, B, etc.), outputs by letters near the end (X, Y, etc.). For SSI gates, the logic symbols are shown with their pin connections.

Suppose we want to set up a two-input NAND gate, using the 5400. What connections must be made? One obvious solution is to route the two input signals to pins 1 and 2. The output would be available at pin 3. We must not forget to ground pin 7 and attach pin 14 to the supply voltage. Alternatively, we could use the input pins on any of the other three gates, using the output pin that is appropriate. Each of these four NAND gates can be used at any point in a logic circuit.

Another example is shown in Figure 5-3b. Here, the Y outputs are the inverse of the A inputs. All six inverters are identical. And they may be separately connected, just as with the NAND gates. Often the data sheets will provide only the type designation on the circuit diagrams. (There is no functional difference between a 5400 and 7400, so just the last two digits are sufficient to describe the IC.)

☐ **EXAMPLE 5-5**

When using a 7400 and a 7405, what pin connections are necessary to implement this expression?

$$\text{output} = \overline{\overline{A}B}$$

Solution The connections are listed in Table 5-3. A schematic diagram is provided in Figure 5-4.

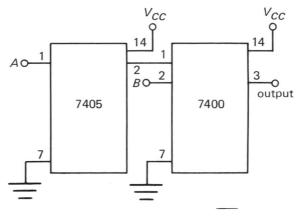

FIGURE 5-4. Implementation of $\overline{\overline{A}B}$

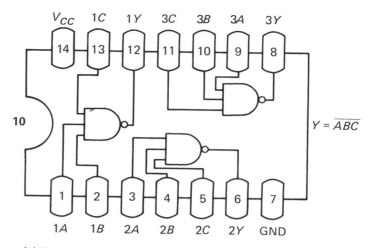

(a) Triple Three-Input NAND Gates

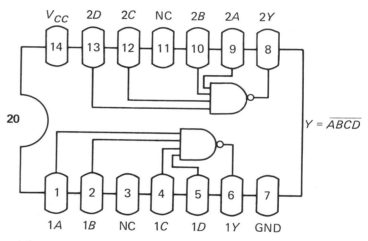

(b) Dual Four-Input NAND Gates

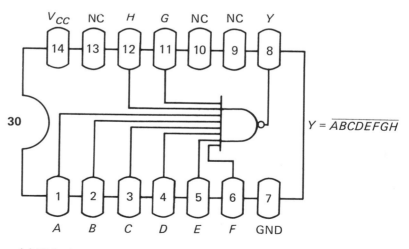

(c) Eight-Input NAND Gate

FIGURE 5–5.
NAND Gates

☐ FAN-IN CONSIDERATIONS

So far, our discussion has covered only a two-input NAND gate. What if the circuit requires a fan-in of three, four, eight, or even more signals? Many of these situations are covered by different TTL gates in the 5400/7400 family. As Figure 5-5a shows, the 5410/7410 is a triple three-input NAND circuit. If even more inputs are needed, the 5420/7420 dual four-input NAND (Figure 5-5b) and the 5430/7430 eight-input NAND (Figure 5-5c) are available. For both of the latter two gates, some pins are unnecessary and hence are not connected (NC).

Not all types of gates are as richly represented as the NAND function. Table 5-4 lists a sampling of gates included in the 5400/7400 series and their fan-in. While there are nine varieties of NAND gates, the OR function is only represented by a single circuit. (This table is not an exhaustive list; only simple gates without special features are included. There are at least as many special-purpose NAND gates as those listed in the table.) If the required number of inputs is not available, two or more gates can be connected in parallel to increase the fan-in. The outputs of those gates are then combined through an AND function (that is, the outputs are ANDed).

TABLE 5-4. Sampling of TTL Gates

Function	Identifier	Number of Gates	Inputs per Gate
NAND	00	4	2
	01	4	2
	03	4	2
	10	3	3
	12	3	3
	20	2	4
	22	2	4
	30	1	8
	133	1	13
NOR	02	4	2
	27	3	3
	25	2	4
	260	2	5
AND	08	4	2
	09	4	2
	11	3	3
	15	3	3
	21	2	4
OR	32	4	2

☐ OTHER BASIC GATE CIRCUITS

Some combinations of gates are also included in the 5400/7400 TTL family. One common combination is the AND-OR-invert gate. As the name implies, the inputs are first ANDed, then ORed, and finally inverted. One example of this type of circuit, the 5454/7454, is shown in Figure 5-6 (NU in the figure means not used). This circuit is

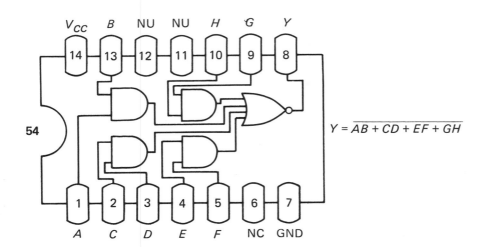

$$Y = \overline{AB + CD + EF + GH}$$

FIGURE 5-6. AND-OR-Invert Gate

described as a four-wide AND-OR-invert gate. The output Y can be written as

$$Y = \overline{AB + CD + EF + GH} \qquad (5\text{-}4)$$

☐ EXAMPLE 5-6

Let the inputs to the various pins of a 7454 be as shown below. A high input represents a value of 1. What is the output level?

Pin	Level
1	H
2	L
3	L
4	L
5	H
9	L
10	H
13	H

Solution From Equation 5-5, we have

$$\overline{Y} = \overline{1 \cdot 1 + 0 \cdot 0 + 0 \cdot 1 + 0 \cdot 1}$$
$$= \overline{1 + 0 + 0 + 0}$$
$$= \overline{1}$$

or $\quad Y = 0$

The output level is low.

Other AND-OR-invert gates provide various combinations of fan-in. Another example is the 5464/7464 with an output of

$$Y = \overline{ABCD + EF + GHI + JK} \qquad (5\text{-}5)$$

Here the AND gates have, respectively, four, two, three, and two inputs.

Another function that we have discussed previously, the exclusive OR, is also provided in the 5400/7400 series. That function is available as a quad two-input exclusive OR gate. The pin assignments for this circuit, the 5486/7486, are shown in Figure 5-7. The output can be described as

$$Y = A \oplus B$$

or $\quad Y = \overline{A}B + A\overline{B}$

There is a new feature on the exclusive OR diagram not seen on the earlier ones. A function table is provided. It summarizes the operations

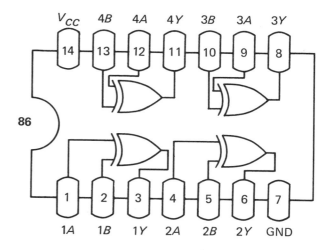

Function Table		
Input		Output
A	B	Y
0	0	0
0	1	1
1	0	1
1	1	0

FIGURE 5-7. Exclusive OR Gate

performed by the 5486/7486. For the more complicated circuits, you must understand the function table in order to follow their operations.

☐ OTHER FAMILIES OF TTL

Though not as widely used as 5400/7400, other families of TTL products are available. These devices may be encountered in special applications or in replacing ICs in older equipment. In some cases, there are direct 5400/7400 replacements for these series, but in others, the devices are unique.

As a technician, you will undoubtedly encounter some of these other TTL series in your work. And just as with the 5400/7400 series, referring to the data sheets will provide you with all the information you will need to work on circuits containing these devices. Table 5-5 lists several examples of other TTL series. The recommended procedure is to use 5400/7400 ICs in all new designs.

TABLE 5-5. Other TTL Families

Series	Manufacturer	Typical Designators	Series	Manufacturer	Typical Designators
2500	Advanced Micro Devices	AM2505	3600	Intel (continued)	P3604
2600		AM26123	8200		C8224
2700		AM27LS00	8300		P8338
3100		AM3101	5500	Intersil	IM55S18
9300		AM9309	5000	Monolithic Memories	MM5330
9600		AM9601	6300		MM6309
9000	Fairchild	9H107	3000	Motorola	MC3024
M7600	Harris	M7611	7000	National Semiconductor	DM7091
3101	Intel	P3102	7500		DM7544
3200		P3212	8000		DM8551
3300		C3304A	800	Signetics	8H16
3400		C3404A	8000		82S66

Chapter Summary

☐ The 5400/7400 series is a standard, compatible set of gates and functional elements.

☐ Noise margin is the difference between input and output voltage levels. The typical noise margin for a 5400/7400 TTL exceeds half a volt.

☐ Unused inputs of gates should be terminated either by grounding them or by tying them to the power supply.

☐ There are two temperature ratings for these TTL devices. The commercial 7400 line operates under more restrictive conditions than the militarized 5400 line.

☐ Trade-offs between power and speed are possible by selecting a TTL device from among the standard, high-speed, low-power, Schottky-clamped, and low-power Schottky series. Most new designs emphasize Schottky TTLs.

☐ The speed-power product is sometimes used to compare the effectiveness of different types of TTL devices.

☐ The label or designator on a TTL package provides a complete description of the construction technique, temperature range, subseries, package, and type of device. To decode the designation, you must use a data sheet. The type identifier is the information used most often.

☐ Electrical characteristics for the 5400/7400 TTLs are listed in tables on the data sheet. These specifications can be especially important in interfacing TTLs to other types of devices.

☐ Pin diagrams show you how to connect the appropriate input, output, ground, and voltage terminals of the gates.

☐ For many types of gates, you can obtain a variable fan-in simply by choosing one of several chips. The NAND gate is especially well represented, with from 2 to 8 inputs provided.

☐ Combination gates, such as AND-OR-invert and exclusive OR, can also be found in the 5400/7400 family.

☐ Not all TTL devices are in the 5400/7400 series; many other families are available. But newer equipment is fabricated exclusively from the standard line of TTL devices.

Problems

5-1. What are the high- and low-level noise margins for the 5400 gate described in Table 5-2?

5-2. Assume that V_{IL} is 0.8 V and V_{OL} is 0.3 V for a gate. How large a noise spike can the device tolerate without causing an error?

5-3. The 5430 gate is used in a logic circuit with only five inputs. Draw a schematic showing the proper termination of the F, G, and H inputs.

5-4. How much does t_{PHL} increase if the capacitance of a 5406 gate is increased to 60 pF. The original capacitance was 45 pF and t_{PHL} was 15 ns.

5-5. If the propagation delay for the gate in Example 5-2 were to increase to 26.5 ns, by what percentage would the capacitance increase?

5-6. Find the speed-power product of a gate with these characteristics:

$$t_{PHL} = 9 \text{ ns} \qquad V_{CC} = 5 \text{ V}$$
$$P = 11 \text{ mW} \qquad I_{CC} = 4 \text{ mA (outputs low)}$$

5-7. What would be the propagation delay of a gate with a speed-power product of 57 pJ and a power dissipation of 21 mW? What subseries of 5400/7400 would this gate belong to?

5-8. Decode the following TTL labels:

a. SN74LS10N

b. RSN5408J

5-9. Draw a schematic of the 7400 series TTL gates that would implement the logic expression

$$Y = \overline{AB} + \overline{C}$$

Be sure to show all necessary connections.

5-10. Write the Boolean expression for the circuit shown in Figure 5-8.

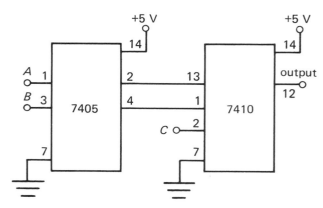

FIGURE 5-8.

Chapter Six

TTL Output Stages

In previous chapters, we covered the essentials of TTL operation and characteristics of the 5400/7400 line. We will next turn our attention to the way in which these devices are interconnected. As you will see, the interfacing between ICs is quite straightforward. However, you must be aware of the types of IC output stages involved. The output stage determines the drive capabilities of the logic circuits, which can be a key factor in building circuits.

Chapter Objectives

Upon completion of this chapter, you should be able to:

- ☐ Distinguish between open-collector and totem pole output stages.
- ☐ Calculate minimum and maximum values of pull-up resistors for open-collector integrated circuits.
- ☐ Describe the switching characteristics of totem pole output stages.
- ☐ Compute the loading effects of various series of TTL devices.
- ☐ Explain the use of three-state outputs.
- ☐ Analyze voltage levels in wired logic circuits.
- ☐ Explain how to interface TTL devices to other logic families.

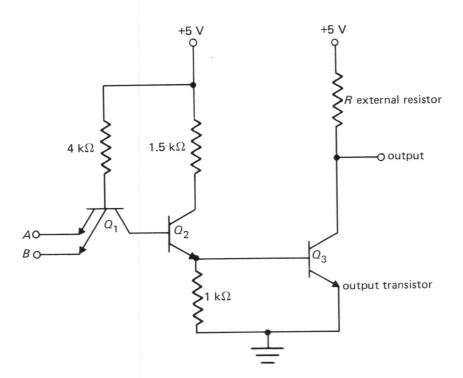

FIGURE 6-1.
Open-Collector
Output

☐ OPEN-COLLECTOR OUTPUT STAGES

The gate shown in Figure 6-1 uses an **open-collector output stage**. The output terminal of the IC is the collector of Q_3—hence the name. As you recall from previous chapters, this circuit is a NAND gate, as shown in Table 6-1. The output is 5 V, except when both inputs are high.

Pull-up Resistors

The output level of an open-collector circuit depends on the external resistor. Therefore, a *pull-up resistor* must always be used with open-collector ICs. The purpose of the resistor is to provide a *passive* pull-up to the supply voltage when transistor Q_3 is cut off.

Consider the result if that resistor is not provided and Q_3 is off. The output is isolated from the rest of the circuit. If it is connected to the input of another gate, the output may be pulled low by that gate, even when Q_3 is off.

With the resistor in place, the output does not switch from low to high levels instantaneously. Instead, a time period—determined by the value of the resistor, the capacitance of the circuit elements, and the switching time of Q_3—elapses. Figure 6-2 shows this effect. Note that time is ex-

TABLE 6-1. NAND Gate

Input (V)		Output (V)
A	B	
0	0	5
0	5	5
5	0	5
5	5	0

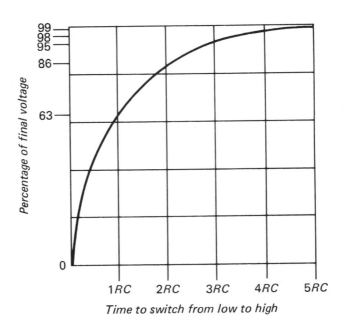

FIGURE 6-2. Switching Time Constant

pressed in multiples of the product of the resistor and circuit capacitance. This product is called the *RC* **time constant** of the circuit. The time constant is measured in seconds.

□ **EXAMPLE 6-1**

Find the *RC* time constant for a 10-kΩ resistor and a 2-μF circuit capacitance.

Solution

$$
\begin{aligned}
\text{time constant} &= (10 \times 10^3)(2 \times 10^{-6}) \\
&= 20 \times 10^{-3} \\
&= 20 \text{ ms}
\end{aligned}
$$

□ **EXAMPLE 6-2**

What is the change in the time constant if a resistor value ten times larger than the resistor value of Example 6-1 is used?

Solution

$$
\begin{aligned}
\text{time constant} &= (100 \times 10^3)(2 \times 10^{-6}) \\
&= 200 \text{ ms}
\end{aligned}
$$

The time constant increases by a factor of ten also.

Obviously, decreasing the size of the resistor will make the switching time faster. Why not use a very small resistor then, perhaps just 1 Ω? The reason for not using such a small resistor is that as the resistor value decreases, power consumption rises.

□ **EXAMPLE 6-3**

To best see the effect described above, consider the current flowing through the external resistor in Figure 6-1 when Q_3 is saturated. For a drop across Q_3 of 0.3 V, we will find the current through three values of resistors. Compare the power used in the open-collector circuit for pull-up resistor values of 100 Ω, 1 kΩ, and 10 kΩ.

Solution The equation for the current is

$$
I = \frac{V_{CC} - V_{CE}}{R}
$$

where
$$
\begin{aligned}
V_{CC} &= \text{supply voltage} \\
V_{CE} &= \text{collector-to-emitter drop across } Q_3 \\
R &= \text{external resistance}
\end{aligned}
$$

For $R = 100$ Ω, we have

$$
I = \frac{5 - 0.3}{100} = 47 \text{ mA}
$$

For $R = 1$ kΩ, we have

$$
I = \frac{5 - 0.3}{10^3} = 4.7 \text{ mA}
$$

For $R = 10$ kΩ, we have

$$
I = \frac{5 - 0.3}{10^4} = 0.47 \text{ mA}
$$

Now we find the power consumption for each case, using the equation

$$
P = I^2 R
$$

The power consumptions are shown below.

R	P
100 Ω	221 mW
1 kΩ	22 mW
10 kΩ	2 mW

The time constant and power consumption for these three situations are compared in Figure 6-3.

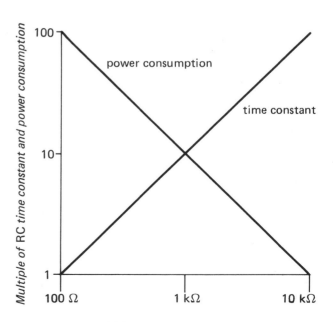

FIGURE 6-3. Comparison of Time Constant with Power Consumption

A factor that was not taken into account in Example 6-3 is the amount of current the transistor Q_3 can sink to ground. Too much current will burn out the transistor. In fact, a current of more than 25 mA would probably destroy Q_3. This is another reason for limiting the current by using a large resistor.

Selecting Pull-up Resistors

Manufacturers provide guidelines for choosing the size of the pull-up resistor. However, the circuit builder is still given a range of values to pick from, depending on whether maximum speed or minimum power consumption is more important. Of course, an intermediate value between the extremes would provide a compromise of moderate switching time and power consumption.

The minimum resistance (and fastest switching time) is calculated by the manufacturer-supplied formula

$$R_{\text{MIN}} = \frac{V_{CCMAX} - V_{OL}}{I_{OL} - 1.6 \times 10^{-3}} \qquad (6\text{-}1)$$

where

$$\begin{aligned} V_{OL} &= \text{low-level output voltage} \\ I_{OL} &= \text{low-level output current} \\ V_{CCMAX} &= \text{maximum supply voltage} \end{aligned}$$

The largest resistor value is found by the formula

$$R_{\text{MAX}} = \frac{V_{CCMIN} - V_{OH}}{I_{OH} + 40 \times 10^{-6}} \qquad (6\text{-}2)$$

where

$$\begin{aligned} V_{OH} &= \text{high-level output voltage} \\ I_{OH} &= \text{high-level output current} \\ V_{CCMIN} &= \text{minimum supply voltage} \end{aligned}$$

□ EXAMPLE 6-4

Find the resistor that provides the fastest switching time for an open-collector 74LS01 gate with the following characteristics:

$$\begin{aligned} I_{OH} &= 100\ \mu\text{A} & V_{CCMIN} &= 4.75\ \text{V} \\ I_{OL} &= 8\ \text{mA} & V_{OL} &= 0.5\ \text{V} \\ V_{CCMAX} &= 5.25\ \text{V} & V_{OH} &= 2.4\ \text{V} \end{aligned}$$

Solution Using Equation 6-1, we obtain

$$R_{\text{MIN}} = \frac{5.25 - 0.5}{8 \times 10^{-3} - 1.6 \times 10^{-3}}$$

$$= \frac{4.75}{6.4 \times 10^{-3}}$$

$$= 742\ \Omega$$

□ EXAMPLE 6-5

The power consumption of the 74LS01 must be minimized in another application. What resistor value would you recommend?

Solution From Equation 6-2, we have

$$R_{\text{MAX}} = \frac{4.75 - 2.4}{100 \times 10^{-6} + 40 \times 10^{-6}}$$

$$= \frac{2.35}{140 \times 10^{-6}}$$

$$= 16,786$$

$$\approx 16.8\ \text{k}\Omega$$

□ TOTEM POLE OUTPUT STAGES

The output stage used on the gate in Figure 6-4 is referred to as a **totem pole output**. Other names sometimes encountered for this configuration are power-driver or power-buffer output stages. In contrast to the open collector, the totem pole uses Q_4 to provide *active* pull-up of the output line when Q_3 is cut off. In that case, Q_4 is saturated through the 1.5-kΩ resistor (because Q_1 and Q_2 are also cut off).

Note that only a small internal resistor is needed in this case, because Q_4 and D_1 limit the current when Q_3 is saturated and the output is low. In that state, Q_4 and D_1 are switched off, because the voltage on the base of Q_4 is insufficient to forward-bias the base-emitter diode as well as D_1. In effect, then, Q_3 is a current sink when the output is low. On the other hand, when the level is high, Q_4 acts as a current source.

Let us briefly review the purpose of the other transistors. Recall that Q_2 acts as a level shifter, and its collector voltage is in the opposite state from that of the emitter. (Because the collector is 180° out of phase with the emitter, Q_2 is sometimes called a **phase splitter**.) The input transistor Q_1 is switched on or off by the input level combination.

The 120-Ω resistor limits the current through Q_3 and Q_4. Assume that initially Q_3 is saturated and Q_4 is cut off. When the output level

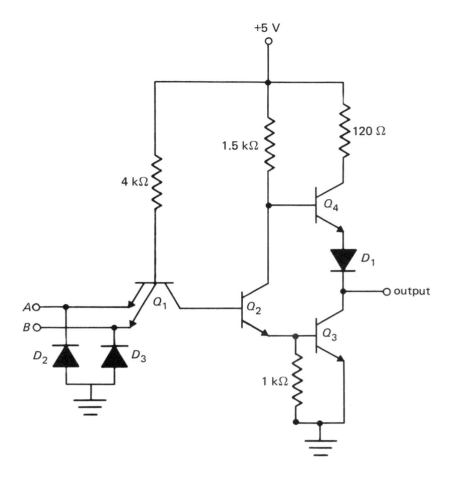

FIGURE 6–4. Totem
Pole Output

changes, these transistors must change to the opposite states. If Q_3 is slow in coming out of
saturation, both transistors may be on for a brief
period of time. In such cases, the current will be
no more than

$$\frac{V_{CC}}{120} = \frac{5}{120} = 42 \text{ mA}$$

which is within the current-sinking capacity of Q_3.

A possible shortcoming of the fast time constant of the gate output through a totem pole
state is **ringing**. In ringing, the signal lines connected to downstream gates may oscillate, as
shown in Figure 6–5a. If clamping diodes (D_2 and
D_3) are used on the inputs, however, the negative
excursions of the inputs are limited, as shown in
Figure 6–5b.

The low output resistance of the totem pole
stage offers a high noise margin in both states.
Typically, the resistance is no more than 10 Ω for
the low level and less than 100 Ω for the high
level.

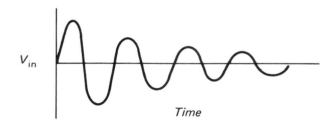

(a) Ringing Without Diode Clamps

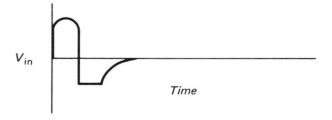

(b) Ringing with Diode Clamps

FIGURE 6–5. Diode Clamping

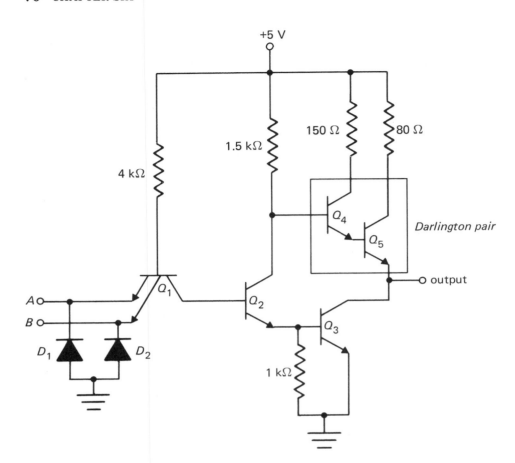

FIGURE 6-6.
Darlington Pair Used
in a Totem Pole
Output

An alternative circuit configuration sometimes used as a totem pole output involves a **Darlington pair** of transistors, as shown in Figure 6-6. The advantages gained with a Darlington pair in place of the transistor-diode combination include higher current gain, lower output resistance, and higher speed.

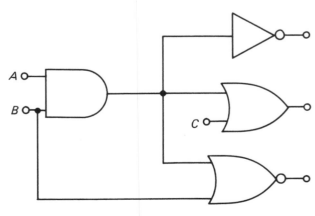

FIGURE 6-7. Fan-out

☐ FAN-OUT AND LOADING

Regardless of the type of output a gate has, the number of downstream gates that can be connected to it is limited by maximum **fan-out**. The fan-out of the AND gate circuit in Figure 6-7, for example, is three. Every gate is rated on its data sheet by the maximum number of loads it can drive.

Table 6-2 provides an example of the loading characteristics for one type of TTL gate.

TABLE 6-2. Loading and Fan-out

TTL Series	Input Loading Coefficient	Fan-out
Standard	1	10
High-speed	1.25	12.5
Low-power	0.5	15
Schottky	1.25	12.5
Low-power Schottky	0.5	15

It lists the loading coefficient for input to the gate as well as the fan-out from the gate. When using this table, you need not be concerned with whether the load is being driven from a high or low output level.

□ EXAMPLE 6-6

Assume that Table 6-2 lists the characteristics of all the gates shown in Figure 6-7. Compute the input loading coefficient if the gates are in the following series:

□ inverter: standard
□ OR: high-speed
□ NOR: low-power Schottky
□ AND: standard

Solution

$$\text{input loading} = \text{inverter} + \text{OR} + \text{NOR}$$
$$= 1 + 1.25 + 0.5 = 2.75$$

□ EXAMPLE 6-7

How many more standard gates can the AND gate of Figure 6-7 fan out to, if the gates are the same as those used in Example 6-6?

Solution

fan-out from standard AND gates = 10

Computing the spare capacity, we obtain

$$\begin{array}{r} 10 \\ - \quad 2.75 \text{ (input load in Figure 6-7)} \\ \hline 7.25 \text{ (spare fan-out capacity)} \end{array}$$

which means that seven more standard gates (each with a load factor of 1) can be driven.

Increasing fan-out beyond these limits can be accomplished by paralleling the inputs and outputs of gates within the *same* package. Connecting gates in separate packages in parallel may produce large power supply current transients because of different switching speeds for the gates. Therefore, this approach is not recommended. The transient current will not damage the gates, but it is likely to disrupt the logic action.

□ THREE-STATE OUTPUT STAGES

Three-state output stages facilitate the connection of several gates to a common line, or **data bus**. On three-state gates, a control input is provided, which disables both the high and low output levels. This condition is called the **high-impedance** (high-Z) state. Figure 6-8 illustrates a circuit constructed from three-state inverters.

Assume that the inputs to inverters 1 and 2 are low, and the input to inverter 3 is high. If the output-enabling control lines (labeled $\overline{C}$) were not present, inverter 3 with a low output would have to sink the current from the other two inverters. As pointed out in the totem pole output discussion, each inverter may have a current source of 40 mA or more. The combined current flowing into the single low output could damage that inverter.

With the use of the control inputs, however, this problem can be eliminated. For example, in the situation just described, let the control inputs to inverters 1 and 2 be set to disable their outputs. The control of inverter 3 is set to enable. The result of this circuit is shown below.

Inverter	Control	Output Level	Current (Source/Sink)
1	Disable	High Z	None
2	Disable	High Z	None
3	Enable	Low	Normal sink

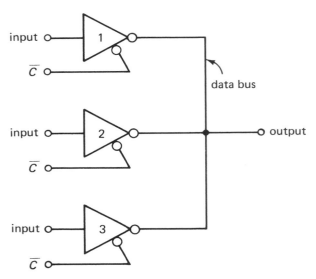

FIGURE 6-8. Three-State Inverters

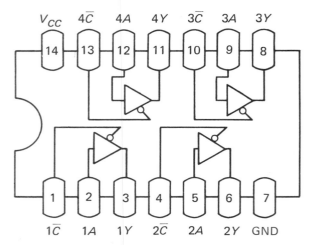

FIGURE 6-9. 74125 Quad Bus Buffer with Three-State Output

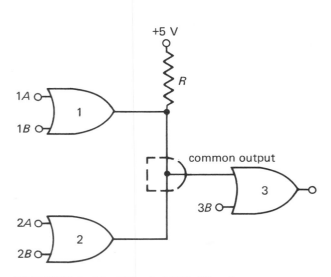

FIGURE 6-10. Wired AND Circuit

TABLE 6-3. Wired Logic

Output Level		Common Output
Gate 1	Gate 2	
H	H	H
H	L	L
L	H	L
L	L	L

Another effect of the control usage is that only one of the three outputs is routed onto the bus. In this way, signals from many sources can be selectively sent over a single bus. Consequently, interconnection is simplified and construction costs are reduced.

Figure 6-9 shows the 74125 quad buffer, which has three-state outputs. This buffer is often used as a driver for signals to a data bus. The $\overline{C}$ input must be low in order for the buffer to function normally. In that case, the output is

$$Y = A$$

for each of the four buffers. When $\overline{C}$ is high, the high-impedance output level is produced. (The small circle shown on the $\overline{C}$ inputs indicates that that signal is true when low.)

☐ **EXAMPLE 6-8**

Describe the output levels for the 74125 gate if the inputs are as follows:

$1A = L$	$1\overline{C} = L$
$2A = L$	$2\overline{C} = H$
$3A = H$	$3\overline{C} = L$
$4A = L$	$4\overline{C} = H$

Solution From the information given in Figure 6-9, the outputs would be as follows:

$1Y = L$
$2Y = \text{high } Z$
$3Y = H$
$4Y = \text{high } Z$

☐ **WIRED LOGIC**

A common, though not recommended, practice in circuit construction is to create the effect of a gate by simply joining the outputs of other gates. Figure 6-10 shows how two OR gate outputs can be connected in this manner. If both gates have the same level of output, obviously the common point is at that level. When the outputs are in the opposite states, the low output will pull the high output to ground. Table 6-3 summarizes the various possibilities.

With positive logic, this voltage table is equivalent to an AND gate—hence the name "wired AND" for this circuit. The figure indicates the logic function with the small AND symbol in dashed lines. (If negative logic is used, the circuit is a "wired OR." In negative logic, the low-level signal represents a binary 1 and the high level represents a 0.)

Wired logic can only be used with open-collector output devices. Totem pole outputs must *never* be used in this configuration, because the excessive current that the gate with the low-output level must sink will damage it.

If wired logic is used, the open-collector, pull-up resistor value is not the same as that for single gates (Equations 6–1 and 6–2). Instead, the range of resistor values is found from the equations below.

$$R_{\text{MIN}} = \frac{V_{CCMAX} - V_{OL}}{I_{OL} - 1.6 \times 10^{-3}M} \tag{6-3}$$

$$R_{\text{MAX}} = \frac{V_{CCMIN} - V_{OH}}{NI_{OH} + 40 \times 10^{-6}M} \tag{6-4}$$

where

M = number of input loads driven
N = number of wired logic outputs connected together

☐ EXAMPLE 6–9

Show that Equations 6–3 and 6–4 are equivalent to Equations 6–1 and 6–2, respectively, when the gates are connected in a single manner.

Solution In this situation, M and N are both 1. Substituting that value into Equations 6–3 and 6–4 gives

$$R_{\text{MIN}} = \frac{V_{CCMAX} - V_{OL}}{I_{OL} - 1.6 \times 10^{-3}}$$

$$R_{\text{MAX}} = \frac{V_{CCMIN} - V_{OH}}{I_{OH} + 40 \times 10^{-6}}$$

These equations are the same as Equations 6–1 and 6–2, respectively.

☐ EXAMPLE 6–10

Find the resistor value that would produce the fastest switching speed if the gate from Example 6–4 were used in a wired-logic configuration.

Solution The gates are wired so that four wired AND outputs are driving three other gate inputs. Thus,

$$R_{\text{MIN}} = \frac{5.25 - 0.5}{8 \times 10^{-3} - (3)(1.6 \times 10^{-3})}$$
$$= \frac{4.75}{3.2 \times 10^{-3}}$$
$$= 1484 \ \Omega$$
$$\approx 1.5 \ \text{k}\Omega$$

☐ EXAMPLE 6–11

Find the resistor value that would conserve the most power if the gate of Example 6–4 were used in a wired AND circuit.

Solution In this example, there are two inputs being driven by three gate outputs joined in a wired AND. Thus

$$R_{\text{MAX}} = \frac{4.74 - 2.4}{(3)(100 \times 10^{-6}) + (2)(40 \times 10^{-6})}$$
$$= \frac{2.35}{380 \times 10^{-6}}$$
$$= 6184 \ \Omega$$
$$\approx 6.2 \ \text{k}\Omega$$

Before leaving the subject, we should mention several disadvantages of wired logic. First, this type of circuit is quite difficult to service. As Figure 6–10 shows, a malfunction in the output of gate 3 may be caused by failure of any of the three gates. Only by unsoldering the common point can the defective component be isolated. Second, the purpose of TTL is to increase switching speed, but wired logic causes delays, arising from the slow level changing of passive elements. Finally, wired AND and wired OR introduce additional noise into the circuit.

☐ TRANSMISSION LINE EFFECTS

The length of the printed circuit board connections (*traces*) or of the interconnecting wires that provide acceptable service with TTL is limited by transmission line effects. When the round trip delay in a line exceeds the rise or fall time of the TTL circuit, these effects disrupt circuit action. Since the rise and fall times are known, and since the signals propagate at about the speed of light, the maximum interconnection length, without transmission line effects, can be calculated. Table 6–4 lists these lengths for the various TTL families.

TABLE 6–4. Maximum Printed Circuit Board Interconnections

Family	Length (in.)	(cm)
Standard	18	45
High-speed	9	22.5
Low-power	18	45
Schottky	7.5	19
Low-power Schottky	9	22.5

☐ INTERFACING

Interconnection of the various circuits within the 5400/7400 series of TTL devices is straightforward. Only minimal problems will arise even when different families are mixed. (When standard, low-power, and Schottky TTL are used together, worst-case noise immunity is slightly degraded.) Of course, open-collector outputs must be provided with a pull-up resistor, as described previously.

A frequently encountered interfacing situation is that of discrete transistors. Figure 6–11 shows how TTL can be used with transistors. Here, pull-up resistors are used with an open-collector TTL to drive a transistor (Figure 6–11a). Transistor inputs to the TTL gate require diode clamping and pull-up resistors as well (Figure 6–11b).

☐ APPLICATIONS OF GATE OUTPUTS

With the large number of Boolean functions available, an almost unlimited number of output-signal control circuits can be implemented with TTL gates. A frequently encountered requirement is that of disabling the output of a circuit until the appropriate time—perhaps waiting until

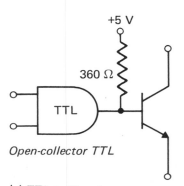

(a) TTL to Transistor

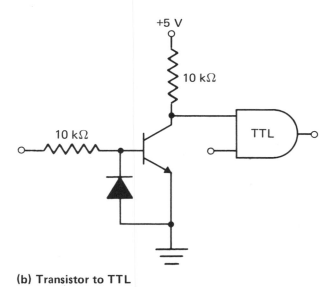

(b) Transistor to TTL

FIGURE 6–11. TTL and Transistor Interfacing

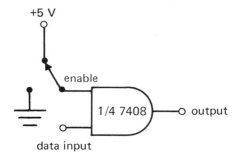

Function Table		
Enable	Data input	Data output
0	0	0
0	1	0
1	0	0
1	1	1

FIGURE 6–12. Digital Transmission Gate

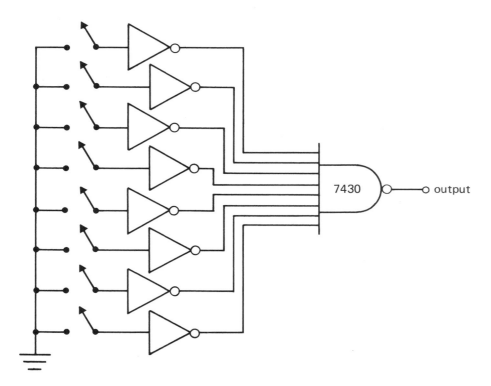

FIGURE 6-13.
Unanimous-Vote
Detector

a switch is thrown. The circuit in Figure 6–12 shows a digital transmission gate comprised of an AND gate and a switch. As long as the switch is grounded, the output of the circuit is low. When the switch is placed in the +5-V position, the AND gate output is equal to the data input. The switch signal acts as an enabling or disabling control for the gate.

As another example of output control, suppose you would like to build a vote-tallying machine that would indicate when all the voters were unanimously agreed on an issue. A circuit like the one in Figure 6–13 would do the job. When the switches are open, the floating leads on the inverters act as a high input. This signal is inverted prior to entering the NAND gate. So if any switch is open, the NAND gate receives an input of zero.

As you recall, any 0 input to a NAND produces a 1 output. Consequently, if one or more of the switches are open, the output of this circuit is a 1. Now consider the case when all switches are closed. Every inverter has an input of 0, which is complemented. All eight inputs to the NAND gate are therefore equal to 1. Then, and only then, does the NAND gate have an output of 0, which indicates that all the voters agreed on the matter and each had closed the switch.

Chapter Summary

☐ Open-collector output stages require the use of external pull-up resistors. This passive pull-up influences the switching speed of the logic.

☐ The size of the pull-up resistor can be chosen to reduce switching time, at the price of increased power consumption, or vice versa. Manufacturers provide equations for finding the appropriate value of the pull-up resistor.

☐ Totem pole outputs offer faster switching than an open collector because active pull-up with a transistor-diode pair is incorporated within the chip.

☐ The fast time constant of totem pole outputs may produce ringing in the circuit. Clamping diodes on gate inputs damp out these oscillations.

□ Darlington pairs of transistors are also used in totem pole output stages.
□ The fan-out of a gate is limited by loading effects. Manufacturers' data sheets specify fan-out constraints for each type of gate.
□ Three-state outputs can assume low, high, and high-impedance states. This type of logic is often used on data buses.
□ With wired logic, the equivalent of an AND or an OR gate is formed by a common junction of the output leads. A major disadvantage of wired logic is the difficulty in servicing it. Speed and noise immunity also suffer in circuits with wired logic.
□ Transmission line effects limit the length of printed circuit card traces that should be used with each series of logic.
□ By introducing level-shifting components, one can interface TTL devices to other logic families and to discrete devices.

Problems

6-1. Find the time constant for an open-collector TTL circuit that has an equivalent capacitance of 1.8 μF. A 1.8-kΩ pull-up resistor is used.

6-2. How much change in power drain would be observed if the resistor in Problem 6-1 were changed to 2.4 kΩ? Assume that a standard TTL power supply is provided and the collector-to-emitter drop across Q_3 is 0.3 V.

6-3. Find the pull-up resistor value for maximum switching speed of a 74LS01 gate with these parameters:

$$V_{OL} = 0.5 \text{ V} \qquad I_{OL} = 7.5 \text{ mA}$$
$$V_{OH} = 2.4 \text{ V} \qquad I_{OH} = 90 \text{ } \mu\text{A}$$
$$V_{CCMAX} = 5.2 \text{ V} \qquad V_{CCMIN} = 4.8 \text{ V}$$

6-4. What resistor value would conserve the most power for the gate in Problem 6-3?

6-5. Compute the minimum recommended resistor value for the circuit in Figure 6-14. All

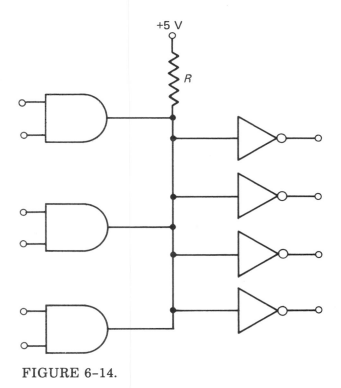

FIGURE 6-14.

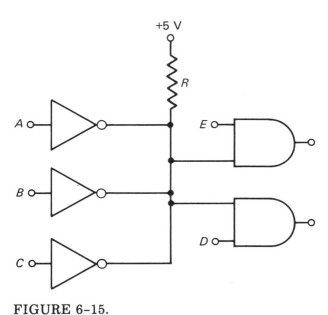

FIGURE 6-15.

the gates and inverters have the characteristics given in Problem 6–3.

6–6. What fan-out would produce acceptable operation for a 74LS123 gate? How many 74S08 gates could the 74LS123 drive?

6–7. Draw a three-state data bus that receives data from three OR gates and one AND gate. What would the control input be if only the AND gate output appears on the bus?

6–8. Find the maximum value for the pull-up resistor to be used in the circuit of Figure 6–15. The gates have parameters identical to those in Example 6–4.

6–9. Find the power consumed in the resistor of Problem 6–8.

6–10. How much would the RC time constant of the circuit in Figure 6–15 be reduced if the minimum resistor value were selected?

Chapter Seven
MOS Logic

Metal-oxide-semiconductor (MOS) logic circuits differ from the TTL families studied earlier principally in the form of transistors used. Instead of the bipolar transistors of TTL, unipolar field effect transistors (FETs) form the switching components for MOS circuits. Consequently, the electrical characteristics of MOS devices differ considerably from those of TTL devices.

In this chapter, we introduce the standard 4000 MOS series of logic functions, which offer many of the same capabilities as TTL. We will also discuss how to interface these devices, how to provide power and grounding, and how to handle them.

Chapter Objectives

Upon completion of this chapter, you should be able to:

☐ Distinguish between PMOS and NMOS transistors.

☐ Explain the difference between enhancement and depletion MOS.

☐ Identify the symbols used for various MOS transistors.

☐ Describe how two transistors are combined to form basic complementary MOS gates.

☐ Analyze functional diagrams of the 4000 series MOS devices.

☐ Compute the power requirements for MOS gates.

☐ Explain why a protective-diode network is required on MOS gates.

☐ Describe the noise margins and electrical characteristics of 4000 series circuits.

☐ List precautions necessary for the proper handling of MOS integrated circuits.

☐ Define other series of metal-oxide-semiconductor logic, including VMOS, HMOS, and SOS.

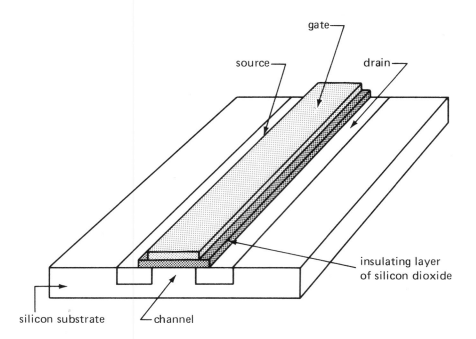

FIGURE 7-1. MOS Transistor

☐ MOS INTEGRATED CIRCUITS

A complete understanding of the solid-state physics involved in the construction of MOS circuits is unnecessary in order to employ them successfully. You must, however, be aware of the terminology used to describe the circuits. The metal-oxide-semiconductor transistor consists of layers of aluminum, silicon dioxide, and silicon. The aluminum forms the terminals, or electrodes, for the transistor. The oxide layer is a form of glass that insulates the components, which are composed of silicon semiconductors (see Figure 7-1). The silicon is often called the **substrate**.

Unlike bipolar transistors, FETs use only one (unipolar) type of **charge carrier** within the semiconductor. These charge carriers can be either *electrons* or *holes*. (A **hole** is the absence of a bound electron in an atom of the crystalline semiconductor.) The charge carrier is designated by the name for a particular type of MOS circuit. Electrons (negative charge) are the carriers for *n* **channel MOS (NMOS)**, while holes (positive charge) are the carriers for *p* **channel MOS (PMOS)**.

The FET has three terminals, like the bipolar transistor. In this case, though, the terminals are named the **source** (*S*), the **drain** (*D*), and the **gate** (*G*). The source is the origin for the current that flows through the transistor to the drain terminal. The current flows in an area of the semiconductor called the **channel**. The amount of current that can flow is determined by the gate voltage. Because the gate is insulated from the transistor by the silicon dioxide layer, the transistor is at times referred to as an **insulated gate FET (IGFET)**.

The type of transistor depends not only on the charge carriers but also on the channel config-

TABLE 7-1. MOS Transistors

Type	Charge Carriers	Conditions Turning Transistor Off	
		Enhancement	Depletion
PMOS	Holes	Gate and source at same potential	Gate positive with respect to source
NMOS	Electrons	Gate and source at same potential	Gate negative with respect to source

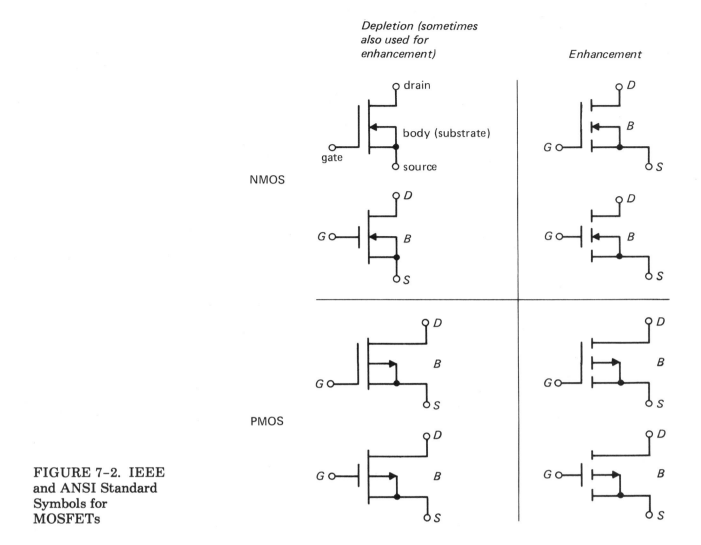

FIGURE 7-2. IEEE and ANSI Standard Symbols for MOSFETs

uration. Again, the atomic structure of the transistor will be ignored; we will concentrate on the electrical characteristics.

The **enhancement MOSFET** has no current flow in the channel, and hence is off, when the gate and source are at the same potential. The other common variety of MOS, the **depletion MOSFET**, has no current flow when the gate is (a) negative with respect to the source for NMOS or (b) positive with respect to the source for PMOS. Table 7-1 lists the various arrangements of channel configuration and charge carriers. Be sure to note the conditions that turn each type of transistor off.

The symbology that indicates the type of MOS transistor in schematic diagrams is not always consistent throughout the industry. The symbols specified by the Institute of Electrical and Electronics Engineers (IEEE) and the American National Standards Institute (ANSI), which are used in this book, are shown in Figure 7-2. To prevent confusion in reading other books, you must be aware that the depletion MOS symbols are sometimes also used to indicate enhancement transistors. However, the substrate is always internally connected to the source.

The MOSFET symbology is sometimes also simplified to that shown in Figure 7-3. This symbology is used when showing the substrate contact explicitly is not important. When there is no likelihood of confusing the type of transistor, the arrows are omitted as well (see Figure 7-3c). This latter symbol is frequently used in schematics for memory circuits. Though the symbology may be confusing at first, you will find that reading schematics drawn with any of these symbols is quickly learned.

Another point worth noting about the sym-

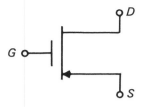

(a) PMOS (Enhancement or Depletion)

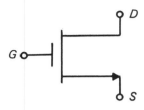

(b) NMOS (Enhancement or Depletion)

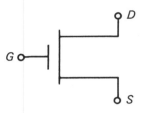

(c) General MOSFET

FIGURE 7-3. Alternative MOSFET Symbology

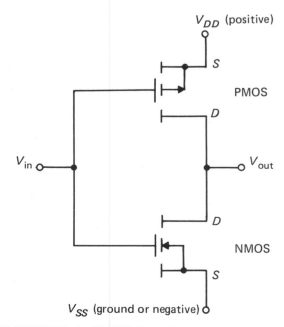

FIGURE 7-4. CMOS Inverter

bols of Figure 7-3 is that the arrows point in a direction opposite to that of the arrows of Figure 7-2. The reason for this change is that the substrate is not shown. So the arrows in Figure 7-3 point in the direction of conventional current flow: source to drain for PMOS (Figure 7-3a) and drain to source for NMOS (Figure 7-3b).

☐ COMPLEMENTARY MOS

The combination of a PMOS and an NMOS transistor forms a **complementary MOS (CMOS) inverter**. Figure 7-4 illustrates this simple circuit. The transistor pairs working together give CMOS gates certain advantages when compared with gates built with only one type of transistor. For example, the power consumption of CMOS is quite low, while the speed is quite high. From an economic standpoint, the requirement for only a single power supply makes CMOS very attractive.

Only enhancement transistors are used in CMOS. Recall that the gates must be biased in order to attract charge carriers of the opposite polarity into the channel to switch the transistor on. The PMOS transistor is on when the gate is negative relative to the source, attracting holes into the channel. A gate more positive than the source of the NMOS transistor switches that transistor on, as electrons are attracted into the channel.

Understanding the operation of the CMOS inverter is simple if you remember those rules. Suppose the V_{SS} terminal of the inverter is grounded and V_{DD} is +5 V. An input of +5 V will cause the NMOS transistor to turn on. (The gate is 5 V more positive than the grounded source.) On the other hand, the PMOS transistor is off because the gate is at the same potential as the source. The NMOS transistor will create a low-resistance path to the ground—hence the designation *pull-down transistor*.

Figure 7-5 provides a model of this situation, replacing the transistors with equivalent resistance. The pull-down transistor has a resistance of only 1 kΩ, while the PMOS transistor is practically an open circuit with a resistance of 10^{10} Ω.

What happens if the input is now grounded? The gate and source of the NMOS transistor are at the same voltage, so it switches off. The gate of the PMOS transistor is 5 V less than the source, though. The gate is therefore negative relative to

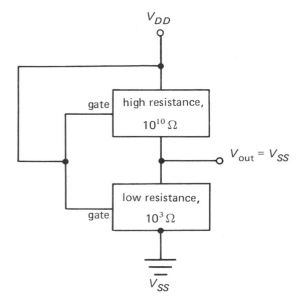

FIGURE 7-5. Model of CMOS Inverter with $V_{in} = V_{DD}$

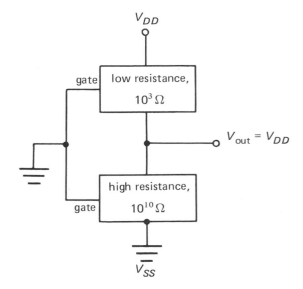

FIGURE 7-6. Model of CMOS Inverter with $V_{in} = $ Ground

the source terminal, so the transistor switches on. Figure 7-6 shows the resistance model for this input value. The PMOS transistor acts to pull up the output voltage to V_{DD}.

In summary, the inverter effect can be outlined as in Table 7-2. A low input produces a high output, and vice versa. This is the inverter function that you saw earlier in the TTL circuits. The NMOS transistor acts to pull down the output voltage, while the PMOS transistor pulls up the output.

Just like TTL circuits, combinations of transistors can provide all the Boolean functions. But instead of concerning ourselves with the transistor networks that form the gates, we will investigate a standard series of CMOS logic.

□ 4000 SERIES LOGIC

Though not as extensive as the 54/74 series of TTL, the 4000 logic series does provide a large number of CMOS gates and other more sophisticated functions. This series is manufactured by several companies with compatible logic chips. A few of these devices will be investigated in detail. Others are readily found in manufacturers' data sheets.

The first chip we will look at is the 4049 shown in Figure 7-7. This IC is a hex inverter, of-

TABLE 7-2. CMOS Inverter

Input Voltage	PMOS Transistor	NMOS Transistor	Output Voltage
V_{DD} (high)	Off	On	V_{SS} (low)
V_{SS} (low)	On	Off	V_{DD} (high)

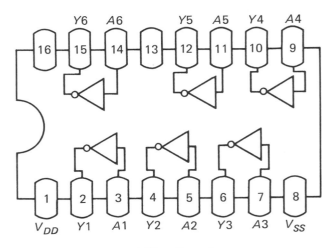

FIGURE 7-7. 4049 Hex Inverter

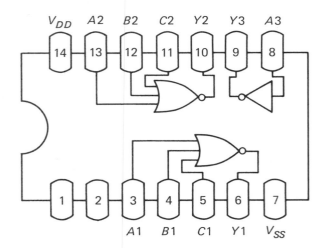

FIGURE 7-8. 4000 Dual Three-Input NOR Gate Plus Inverter

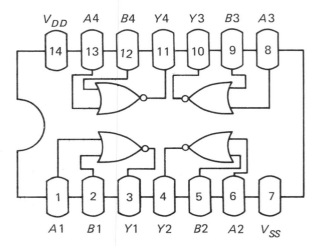

FIGURE 7-9. 4001 Quad Two-Input NOR Gate

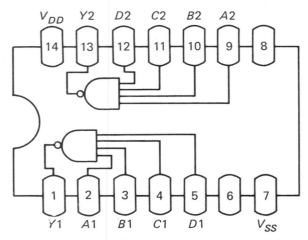

FIGURE 7-10. 4012 Dual Four-Input NAND Gate

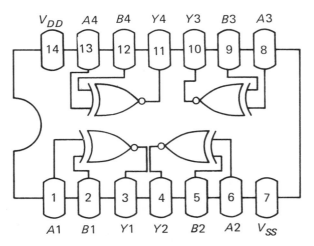

FIGURE 7-11. 4077 Quad Exclusive NOR Gate

fering six independent inverting functions. The outputs are the complement of the inputs. Symbolically, we have

$$Y1 = \overline{A1} \qquad Y4 = \overline{A4}$$
$$Y2 = \overline{A2} \qquad Y5 = \overline{A5}$$
$$Y3 = \overline{A3} \qquad Y6 = \overline{A6}$$

Pin 1 of the circuit is connected to the power supply and pin 8 to ground.

The 4000 chip of Figure 7-8 offers a dual three-input NOR gate and a separate inverter. For any NOR gate, the output is

$$Y = \overline{A + B + C}$$

and for the inverter, it is

$$Y3 = \overline{A3}$$

A quad two-input NOR gate is available as the 4001 circuit. This IC is shown in Figure 7-9. Here, the output is

$$Y = \overline{A + B}$$

Other functions from this series include the 4012 dual four-input NAND gate and the 4077 quad exclusive NOR (see Figures 7-10 and 7-11). The output function for NAND is

$$Y = \overline{ABCD}$$

and for the exclusive NOR, it is

$$Y = \overline{A \oplus B}$$

Wired Logic

CMOS gates cannot be used in wired-logic configurations for the same reason that precluded TTL with totem pole outputs. With the outputs wired together, the pull-down transistor would be, practically speaking, a short to ground. Without any current limitation, that transistor would be damaged.

However, a three-state output stage for CMOS that avoids this problem is available. Figure 7–12 shows a schematic representation of this circuit. The high-impedance output stage is formed by a **transmission gate**, also called a *bilateral switch*. The transmission gate acts like a closed switch when the ENABLE/$\overline{\text{DISABLE}}$ is high. It acts like an open circuit when that signal is low. In the open-circuit condition, the output presents a high-impedance state.

Power Requirements

There are two series of devices within the 4000 CMOS family. The A series can accept a supply voltage (V_{DD}) in the range of 3 to 12 V. The more rugged B series extends these limits to 3 to 18 V. Although the circuits will work with the lower voltage, a minimum of 4 V for the power supply is recommended.

From the supply voltage, worst-case power dissipation for any circuit can be computed. The equation used is

$$P_D = P_{dc} + P_{ac} \qquad (7\text{-}1)$$

where

P_D = power dissipation
P_{dc} = dc component of power dissipation
P_{ac} = dynamic component of power dissipation

The dc component, also called the **quiescent component**, is consumed regardless of whether or not the inputs are changing. The dc component is computed as

$$P_{dc} = i_Q V_{DD} \qquad (7\text{-}2)$$

where

i_Q = quiescent current

The value of i_Q is found on the data sheets for the device. A typical value, for a power supply voltage of 5 V, is 1 μA.

The ac component is a result of the changing inputs and the loading. Its equation is

$$P_{ac} = CV_{DD}{}^2 f \qquad (7\text{-}3)$$

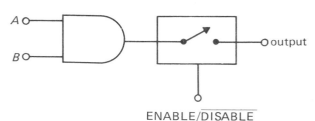

Transmission gate

FIGURE 7–12. CMOS Gate with Three-State Output Stage

where

C = the capacitance of the load being charged or discharged
f = switching frequency

□ **EXAMPLE 7–1**

Find the power used in a CMOS gate with the following characteristics:

$$i_Q = 1 \ \mu\text{A} \qquad C = 7500 \ \text{pF}$$
$$V_{DD} = 5 \ \text{V} \qquad f = 1 \ \text{kHz}$$

Solution Using the equations above, we obtain

$$P_{dc} = (1 \times 10^{-6})(5) = 5 \ \mu\text{W}$$
$$P_{ac} = (7.5 \times 10^{-9})(5^2)(1 \times 10^3)$$
$$= 187.5 \ \mu\text{W}$$
$$P_D = 5 + 187.5$$
$$= 192.5 \ \mu\text{W}$$

As you can see, this gate is consuming a very small amount of power. Most of the power is drawn during the switching time.

Electrical Characteristics

Two supply voltages are used with CMOS devices. The more positive supply is labeled V_{DD} and the other one is labeled V_{SS}. Frequently, V_{SS} is at ground potential. The input voltages must always be within the range between V_{DD} and V_{SS}.

If the input signals run from a card connector, a shunt resistor should be connected between V_{DD} and V_{SS} on the card. This shunt protects the input terminals should the card be unplugged while the power is on.

The gate output terminals must never be shorted to ground, especially when the supply voltage exceeds 5 V. Shorts will damage the devices. (This event is most likely to occur during testing or assembly, so be careful.) Similarly, capacitive loads of more than 5 nF should be avoided, because they act like a transient short circuit on the outputs. Also, do not connect large resistors in series with V_{DD} or V_{SS}. Inputs and outputs can be connected in parallel to increase

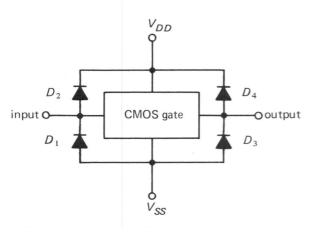

FIGURE 7-13. Simplified Protective-Diode Network

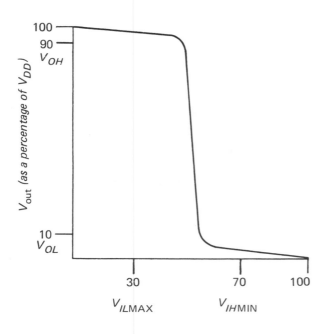

FIGURE 7-14. CMOS Switching Characteristics

fan-in or fan-out, but only for gates within the same package.

The electrical characteristics of CMOS gates depend a great deal on the field effect transistors used in their construction. Because of the extremely high input resistance, the insulating oxide layer must be protected against breakdown. As part of the manufacturing process, *protective diodes* are built into the gate. Figure 7-13 shows an example of the protective-diode network.

When a voltage higher than the normal range appears at either the input or output terminals, the diodes conduct. Because of the nature of these diodes, V_{DD} should never become more than 0.5 V, negative with respect to V_{SS}. Otherwise a short will develop between the two power supplies through the protective diodes. Remember, therefore, that a necessary condition for satisfactory operation is that *at all times*

$$V_{DD} - V_{SS} \geq -0.5 \text{ V} \qquad (7-4)$$

□ **EXAMPLE 7-2**

The supply voltages for a CMOS gate are

$$V_{DD} = 5.0 \text{ V} \qquad \text{and} \qquad V_{SS} = 0 \text{ V}$$

Explain the circuit action caused by an input of 15,000 V. This excessive voltage is a result of static electricity. (Although the voltage is high, current is negligible.)

Solution This voltage causes D_2 to conduct, channeling the excessive voltage away from the gate through the power supply V_{DD}. This diode action protects the oxide layer of the input transistor.

Knowing the sensitivity of CMOS circuits to excessive voltages, you should develop good working habits in servicing them. If a separate supply is used for the power and the inputs, always turn on the CMOS power first before applying the inputs. When turning off the circuit, turn off the inputs first. Limit the range of input voltages between V_{DD} and ground (or V_{SS}).

Noise

CMOS gates are less sensitive to noise on the power and ground lines than are TTL devices. Figure 7-14 shows the switching characteristics for a CMOS inverter. The noise margin can be computed from

$$\text{noise margin} = |V_{OL} - V_{IL}|$$
$$\text{or} \quad \text{noise margin} = |V_{OH} - V_{IH}|$$

☐ **EXAMPLE 7-3**

If V_{DD} is 5 V for a CMOS device, what is the noise margin?

Solution Using the graph in Figure 7-14, we have

$$V_{OH} = 4.5 \text{ V} \qquad V_{IH\text{MIN}} = 3.5 \text{ V}$$
$$V_{OL} = 0.5 \text{ V} \qquad V_{IL\text{MAX}} = 1.5 \text{ V}$$

Thus

$$\text{noise margin} = |0.5 - 1.5| = 1.0 \text{ V}$$
$$\text{or} \quad \text{noise margin} = |4.5 - 3.5| = 1.0 \text{ V}$$

☐ **EXAMPLE 7-4**

The power supply voltage of Example 7-3 is increased to 10 V. How does the noise margin of the IC change?

Solution Again from Figure 7-14, we have

$$V_{OH} = 9.0 \text{ V} \qquad V_{IL\text{MAX}} = 3.0 \text{ V}$$
$$V_{OL} = 1.0 \text{ V} \qquad V_{IH\text{MIN}} = 7.0 \text{ V}$$

Thus

$$\text{noise margin} = |1.0 - 3.0| = 2.0 \text{ V}$$
$$\text{or} \quad \text{noise margin} = |9.0 - 7.0| = 2.0 \text{ V}$$

The noise margin has doubled.

Handling

In comparison with other electronic components, MOS circuits require extra care in handling. To prevent damage from static electricity, the technician must ground tabletops, tools, and soldering irons. The technician must also be grounded, usually with a wrist strap in series with a 1-MΩ resistor to ground.

The ICs must always be stored on conductive carriers. This technique maintains all the pins at the same potential. In wiring the DIP into the circuit, connect the V_{DD} pin first to the external connections. The remaining pins may then be connected in any order.

Series 4000A Electrical Characteristics

The 4000A series has a specified supply voltage range of 3 to 12 V. (A supply of -0.5 to 15 V can be used without damaging these devices; however, these extremes are not recommended.) The typical parameters of a 4000A series gate are listed in Table 7-3. Low and high output levels about equal to V_{SS} and V_{DD}, respectively, characterize the 4000A series devices. A 1-V noise margin is usual for any gate in this series.

Series 4000B Electrical Characteristics

The 4000B series gates are available in both a commercial and militarized line. This discussion will concentrate on the commercial devices. Because the recommended supply voltage is 3 to 18 V (-0.5 to 20 V can be applied without

TABLE 7-3. 4000A Series Parameters

Parameter	V_{in} (V)	V_{out} (V) Minimum	Maximum	V_{DD} (V)	Parameter Minimum (V)	Parameter Maximum (V)
V_{OL}	5			5		0.05
	10			10		0.05
V_{OH}	0			5	4.95	
	0			10	9.95	
Noise margin		4.5		5	1	
Low		9.0		10	1	
Noise margin			6.5	5	1	
High			1.0	10	1	

damage), the 4000B CMOS series is sometimes referred to as the *high-voltage series*. Table 7–4 lists the key parameters. Note the tight specifications on logic levels. Noise margins are also quite good.

The CMOS industry has further classified these devices by establishing a standard for output stages. Referred to as **buffered** or **unbuffered outputs**, the type is indicated by a suffix:

☐ UB: Logical outputs are not buffered. The requirements for V_{IL} and V_{IH} are relaxed.

☐ B: Logical outputs are buffered. The output impedance for a high logic level is constant regardless of the state of the inputs.

A comparison of the buffered and unbuffered output stages is provided in Table 7–5.

☐ INTERFACING

If a +5-V power supply is used with a 4000 series CMOS, interfacing to TTL circuits is quite simple. As Figure 7–15a shows, open-collector TTL gates can be connected directly to CMOS inputs. The pull-up resistor should be small to achieve rapid switching. Power consumption increases as the resistor value decreases, however. In no case should the resistor be less than 720 Ω, which

TABLE 7–4. 4000B Series Parameters

Parameter	V_{DD} (V)	Parameter Minimum	Parameter Maximum
V_{OL} (V)	5		0.05
	10		0.05
	15		0.05
V_{OH} (V)	5	4.95	
	10	9.95	
	15	14.95	
V_{IL} (V)	5		1.5
	10		3.0
	15		4.0
V_{IH} (V)	5	3.5	
	10	7.0	
	15	11.0	
I_{OL} (mA)	5		0.44
	10		1.1
	15		3.0
I_{OH} (mA)	5	−0.16	
	10	−0.4	
	15	−1.2	
Noise margin (V)	5	1.0	
	10	2.0	
	15	2.5	

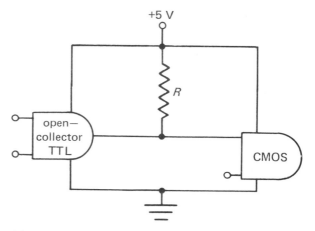

(a) TTL to CMOS

TABLE 7–5. Comparison of Buffered and Unbuffered CMOS Outputs

Characteristic	Unbuffered	Buffered
Propagation delay	Low	Medium
Noise margin	Good	Excellent
Output impedance	Variable	Constant
Output transition time	Variable	Constant
Output oscillation (caused by slowly changing inputs)	No	Yes

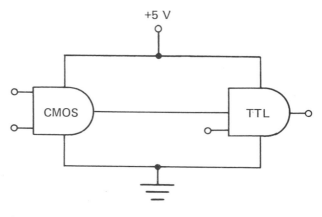

(b) CMOS to TTL

FIGURE 7–15. Interfacing CMOS to TTL

limits the current in the TTL output stage to a safe value. A 10-kΩ resistor will almost always work.

The CMOS-to-TTL interface shown in Figure 7-15b is even simpler. The only concern is the low-input drive current necessary. The 4000B series gates are all capable of driving one Schottky TTL or two low-power TTL inputs. Buffers, such as the 4049 inverter described earlier, can drive a maximum of two standard TTL loads.

□ OTHER MOS FAMILIES

There are several other MOS series of logic. The 74C series are pin-for-pin compatible with 74/54 TTL devices, and this CMOS series requires only a single +5-V power supply. The 74C family uses less power but is slower than the TTL family.

Vertical MOS (VMOS) is a form of NMOS used in driving high-power loads. It offers a high output current and is relatively immune to noise. These transistors differ from traditional NMOS in that a vertical V-shaped structure is fabricated in the silicon. This structure increases the amount of current that can be safely handled, because current flows perpendicular to the chip plane rather than parallel to it, as in standard NMOS. For example, a 43 × 71-mil VMOS chip can conduct a steady 2-A current. The shorter channel length of the VMOS also reduces the chip capacitance (typically 45 pF rather than the 300 pF of NMOS). Less capacitance results in a switching speed that is four time faster.

High-performance NMOS (HMOS) also offers faster switching times. HMOS differs from NMOS mainly in that the transistors on the chip are smaller.

If CMOS is put on a sapphire substrate, a **silicon-on-sapphire (SOS) transistor** is formed. Because sapphire is a better insulator than silicon, parasitic capacitance between the substrate and aluminum conductors is reduced. Switching speed is thereby increased by a factor of three in SOS. Another advantage of SOS is better packing density, resulting from smaller transistors. Since the transistors are packed more densely, the SOS chip can offer more functions than a CMOS chip of the same size. A comparison of the speed and power consumption for various MOS circuits, as well as TTL, is provided in Figure 7-16. In general, the MOS devices offer lower power consumption at the cost of reduced speed.

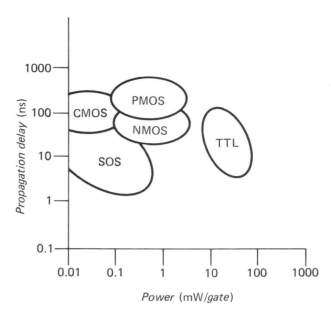

FIGURE 7-16. Speed-Power Comparison of Logic Families

□ CMOS APPLICATIONS

Because of their low power consumption, CMOS gates are popular components in battery-powered equipment. Digital watches are major users of these circuits. As an example of a timing circuit (though not the one used in a watch), refer to the phase detector in Figure 7-17. The exclusive OR gate has two independent clock waveforms with the same frequency as the inputs. The problem to be solved is that the clock pulses drift. We must detect when the two series of square waves are in phase. Also, during the time they are in phase, a low output signal must be produced.

The exclusive OR will continually compare

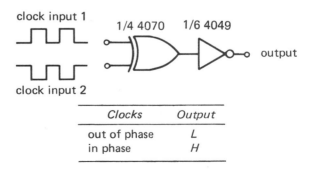

Clocks	Output
out of phase	L
in phase	H

FIGURE 7-17. Phase Detector

the two signals. If the signals are out of phase, one of the inputs to the gate will be low while the other is high. As a result, the exclusive OR will have a high output, which is inverted to a final low output. As the phase between the two inputs changes, they will eventually reach an in-phase condition. With the inputs equal (either both high or both low), the exclusive OR output becomes low. The inverter complements the signal, and the final output is the specified high level.

The low power consumption in a CMOS gate means that the output has limited ability to supply current to a downstream gate. Often, we want to have a fan-out of one CMOS gate into several TTL gates. An output expander is suitable for providing the needed current drive in such circuits (see Figure 7–18).

With the output expander, one CMOS gate drives four TTL loads. The fan-out can be even greater with more buffers, because the 4050 noninverting buffers supply the current needed in interfacing to each of the TTL gates. The buffers do not change the levels of the logic signals. Buf-

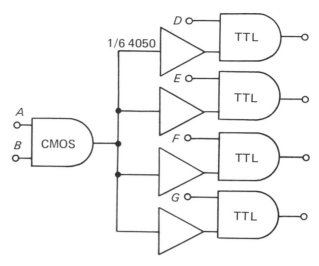

FIGURE 7–18. CMOS Output Expander

fering just provides the "boost" required for the CMOS gate to meet the current requirements of the substantial TTL load.

Chapter Summary

☐ Aluminum, insulator, and semiconductor layers comprise the MOS transistor. The semiconductor forms the substrate for the chip. Field effect transistors are used exclusively in MOS circuits.

☐ Only a single charge carrier (electrons or holes) is required in a FET. An n channel MOS has electrons as charge carriers; a p channel MOS uses holes.

☐ The terminals of a field effect transistor are called the source, the drain, and the gate. Current flows from the source to the drain in the channel. The gate voltage controls the amount of current.

☐ No current flows in enhancement MOS transistors when the gate and source are at the same potential. The current flow in depletion MOS depends on the charge carriers. A negative gate relative to the source stops the flow in NMOS. A positive gate with respect to the source stops the current in PMOS.

☐ While IEEE and ANSI standards exist for MOS transistor symbology, they are not applied uniformly throughout the industry. Often, simplified symbology appears in manufacturers' literature.

☐ A CMOS gate is built from complementary pairs of PMOS and NMOS transistors. Only enhancement FETs are used in CMOS gates.

☐ The 4000 series of CMOS logic offers a standardized set of functions that can be readily interconnected.

☐ Standard CMOS cannot be used in wired-logic configurations. But the three-state versions can be, because they offer a high-impedance output state. Even so, the three-state devices must be used correctly to prevent a low output stage from sinking excessive current. A transmission gate forms the output stage in three-state CMOS.

☐ The 4000 series provides two subfamilies. The 4000A devices run on a voltage of 3 to 12 V, and the 4000B devices run on 3 to 18 V.

☐ Because of the high input resistance of the oxide layer, a MOS device must be protected against high voltage from static electricity. Protective diodes are built into the gates for this reason.

☐ The noise margin of CMOS is better than that of TTL.

☐ Because of susceptibility to damage from static electricity, MOS circuits require special handling in order to protect them from damage.

☐ Interfacing the 4000 series CMOS and TTL is quite simple. Pull-up resistors are used with open-collector TTL. However, in driving TTL from CMOS, one must consider the loading effects.

☐ Other MOS families include 74C, VMOS, HMOS, and SOS.

Problems

7-1. Draw a schematic diagram for implementing the following Boolean expression by using 4000 series logic:

$$Y = \overline{A}\,\overline{B}\,\overline{C}$$

Only one IC is required.

7-2. The following voltages are applied to a MOS transistor:

$$\text{gate} = +5 \text{ V}$$
$$\text{source} = +5 \text{ V}$$
$$\text{drain} = 0 \text{ V}$$

For each of the FETs below, decide if the transistor is on or off.

    a. PMOS enhancement
    b. NMOS enhancement
    c. PMOS depletion
    d. NMOS depletion

7-3. What would be the output of the CMOS inverter in Figure 7-4 if $V_{DD} = +10$ V, V_{SS} is grounded, and the input is $+10$ V? How much equivalent resistance will the PMOS transistor offer?

7-4. Find the dc component of power dissipation for a series 4000B gate with the following parameters:

$$V_{SS} = \text{ground}$$
$$V_{DD} = +7 \text{ V}$$
$$\text{quiescent current} = 0.9 \text{ }\mu\text{A}$$

7-5. Find the total power dissipation for the gate in Problem 7-4 if it is operated at a switching frequency of 4.5 MHz into a load capacitance of 10 pF.

7-6. Find the quiescent current for a 4000A gate with a supply voltage of $+4$ V if the load is 5 pF and the switching rate is 2.5 MHz. Total power dissipation is 208 μW.

7-7. How would a voltage of $-10,000$ V caused by static electricity applied at the input affect the CMOS gate shown in Figure 7-13?

7-8. What are the ranges for the output levels (high and low) for a 4001A IC? (Use Figure 7-14.)

7-9. What is the noise margin for a 4000A hex inverter with power inputs of

$$V_{DD} = 8 \text{ V}$$
$$V_{SS} = \text{ground}$$

7-10. You are asked to design the interface between a 7400 gate and a 4012B gate. Draw the schematic diagram, showing all voltages and values for all circuit elements (minimize switching time). The 4012B had previously been used in a circuit with a $+12$-V power supply, but it is converted to $+5$-V operation in order to be compatible with the TTL interface. How does this change affect the noise margin of the CMOS gate?

Chapter Eight
Number Systems

The numbers used in digital electronics are not those of the familiar decimal system. Instead, the binary numbers, which can easily be represented by a two-state signal, are preferred. Learning the binary number system is a fundamental requirement in understanding the functions of these circuits.

In this chapter, we introduce number system concepts. The following chapter will then extend the study to the arithmetic of nondecimal systems. With this background, you will be able to analyze a variety of circuits that can add, subtract, multiply, and divide.

Chapter Objectives

Upon completion of this chapter, you should be able to:

☐ Explain the requirements for positional number systems.

☐ Count in the binary number system.

☐ Convert between number systems of any base.

□ NUMBER SYSTEMS BASICS

The decimal number system is the one most commonly used today, but it has not always been so. Early mathematicians in the Middle East preferred the sexagesimal number system, which is based on the number 60. Even now you come across the sexagesimal system daily. This system is the basis for telling time; that is, there are 60 seconds to the minute and 60 minutes to the hour.

Just as the ancient technologist had to know base 60 numbers, the modern electronics technician is required to know the **base 2**, or **binary, system**. Both number systems have their own rules for counting and arithmetic. The fundamentals are exactly the same as those for the familiar decimal system, but the results look different, as you will see.

Terminology

The distinguishing factor of all **positionally weighted number systems**, such as the decimal, sexagesimal, or binary systems, is the **base**, or **radix**. In this chapter, we will concentrate on number systems with bases of 10, 2, 8, and 16. The latter two systems are referred to as the **octal** and **hexadecimal systems**, respectively. Each number system has a symbol set called **digits**, and the number of digits in the system is equal to the base. The special term **bits** is often used in referring to the binary digits.

□ EXAMPLE 8–1

List the digits in the decimal, binary, octal, and hexadecimal number systems.

Solution

Decimal	Binary	Octal	Hexadecimal
0	0	0	0
1	1	1	1
2		2	2
3		3	3
4		4	4
5		5	5
6		6	6
7		7	7
8			8
9			9
			A
			B
			C
			D
			E
			F

In each case, note that the largest digit is equal to the base minus 1. (The largest decimal digit is $10 - 1 = 9$, the largest binary is $2 - 1 = 1$, and so on.)

Note also that the hexadecimal system (sometimes called simply "hex") requires symbols for the digits above 9 to be devised. The first six capital letters serve to represent the decimal numbers 10 through 15.

The base of a number is indicated by a subscript. Otherwise, there would be no way to differentiate numbers in different bases, because they all use common digits. Some examples of writing numbers this way are as follows:

$$1011_{10}$$
$$1011_2$$
$$17625_8$$
$$2EA7_{16}$$

The fractional portion of a number is separated from the integer portion in the decimal system by a decimal point. In general, the symbol is called a *radix point* and can be written for any number system. Thus, we have

$$21.182_{10}$$
$$101.11_2$$
$$63.40_8$$
$$789A.2F7_{16}$$

In summary, then, any number system that we are interested in must have a base, symbols for digits, and a special symbol for "nothing." We call that symbol *zero*, 0.

Counting

The special consideration of zero comes about because all the number systems discussed above are positionally weighted. That is, we begin counting with 0 and continue until all the digits have been used (to 9 in the decimal system). Then we *carry* a 1 into the next position (the tens position in the decimal system) and continue counting from 0 again. The digit transferred to the next position is called the **carry**. This process is repeated in the succeeding positions (hundreds, thousands, and so on in the decimal system). Table 8–1 shows how counting proceeds in the decimal, binary, octal, and hexadecimal systems.

In any of the bases, once the largest digit is reached, a digit is carried into the next position. In the binary system, for example, after we count to 1, a carry is propagated to the next position, and the digit in the right column becomes 0 again. So we have the sequence

0, 1, 10, 11, 100, . . .

In the decimal system, each position is designated by a power of ten. For example, the position weights in the number 5149_{10} are as follows:

Thousands	Hundreds	Tens	Ones
5	1	4	9
10^3	10^2	10^1	10^0

In any other radix, the weightings are also the base raised to increasing power. Thus, for the binary number 1101_2, we have

Eights	Fours	Twos	Ones
1	1	0	1
2^3	2^2	2^1	2^0

With that concept in mind, reexamine the counting procedure in the binary system, as listed in Table 8-2.

Exactly the same process is followed in the octal and hexadecimal systems, except that the weights are powers of 8 or 16. For example, for 1423_8, we have

Five Hundred Twelves	Sixty-Fours	Eights	Ones
1	4	2	3
8^3	8^2	8^1	8^0

And for $35B9_{16}$, we have

Four Thousand Ninety-Sixes	Two Hundred Fifty-Sixes	Sixteens	Ones
3	5	B	9
16^3	16^2	16^1	16^0

The value of a number, then, is determined by the digits in the number, the base of the number system, and the positions of the digits.

So far, only integers have been considered. But the fractional portion of a number is also written in terms of the base raised to a power. Here, though, the exponents are negative. Thus, for 247.25_{10}, we have

2	4	7.	2	5
10^2	10^1	10^0	10^{-1}	10^{-2}

TABLE 8-1. Counting in Various Bases

Decimal	Binary	Octal	Hexadecimal
0	0	0	0
1	1	1	1
2	10	2	2
3	11	3	3
4	100	4	4
5	101	5	5
6	110	6	6
7	111	7	7
8	1000	10	8
9	1001	11	9
10	1010	12	A
11	1011	13	B
12	1100	14	C
13	1101	15	D
14	1110	16	E
15	1111	17	F
16	1 0000	20	10
17	1 0001	21	11
18	1 0010	22	12
19	1 0011	23	13
20	1 0100	24	14
21	1 0101	25	15
22	1 0110	26	16
23	1 0111	27	17
24	1 1000	30	18
25	1 1001	31	19
26	1 1010	32	1A
27	1 1011	33	1B
28	1 1100	34	1C
29	1 1101	35	1D
30	1 1110	36	1E
31	1 1111	37	1F
32	10 0000	40	20

TABLE 8-2. Binary Counting

Positional Weighting				
2^3	2^2	2^1	2^0	Comments
			0	Start
			1	
		1	0	Zero in the ones position, and carry 1
		1	1	
	1	0	0	Zero in the ones and twos positions, and carry 1
	1	0	1	
	1	1	0	
	1	1	1	
1	0	0	0	Zero in the ones, twos, and fours positions, and carry 1

For 10.111_2, we have

1	0.	1	1	1
2^1	2^0	2^{-1}	2^{-2}	2^{-3}

For 633.42_8, we have

6	3	3.	4	2
8^2	8^1	8^0	8^{-1}	8^{-2}

And for $923.BF_{16}$, we have

9	2	3.	B	F
16^2	16^1	16^0	16^{-1}	16^{-2}

Observations of these facts leads to a method (though not a very efficient one) of converting numbers between bases. We will look at this method next.

FIGURE 8-1. Texas Instruments Programmer Calculator

Polynomial Expansion

A number in any base can be converted to a number in the decimal system by multiplying each digit by its weight and summing the resulting products. This process is called **polynomial expansion**.

☐ EXAMPLE 8-2

Express the following numbers as their decimal equivalents by use of polynomial expansion.

1. $1\,0111.1_2$
2. 213.47_8
3. $2B.9_{16}$

Solution

1. $1\,0111.1_2 = 1 \times 2^4 + 0 \times 2^3 + 1 \times 2^2$
$+ 1 \times 2^1 + 1 \times 2^0$
$+ 1 \times 2^{-1}$
$= 1 \times 16 + 0 \times 8 + 1 \times 4$
$+ 1 \times 2 + 1 \times 1$
$+ 1 \times 1/2$
$= 23.5_{10}$

2. $213.47_8 = 2 \times 8^2 + 1 \times 8^1 + 3 \times 8^0$
$+ 4 \times 8^{-1} + 7 \times 8^{-2}$
$= 2 \times 64 + 1 \times 8 + 3 \times 1$
$+ 4 \times 1/8 + 7 \times 1/64$
$= 139.609375_{10}$

3. $32B.9_{16} = 3 \times 16^2 + 2 \times 16^1$
$+ 11 \times 16^0 + 9 \times 16^{-1}$

Note that B_{16} has to be changed to 11_{10} to carry out the arithmetic. So

$$32B.9_{16} = 811.5625_{10}$$

☐ BASE CONVERSION BY GROUPING

While polynomial expansion can always be used to convert from any base to the decimal system, the number of steps increases rapidly with the number of digits. In this section, we will show you more efficient ways of doing these conversions. Because such conversions are often needed, specialized calculators are manufactured to carry them out. Figure 8-1 shows a typical pocket calculator that performs these operations.

In this section, you will learn how to do conversions by using just a standard four-function calculator or a pencil and paper. The simplest conversion process is that used to change a binary number to an octal or a hexadecimal number.

Perhaps you noticed in Table 8-1 that the number of digits needed for binary numbers increased much more rapidly than those of the octal or hexadecimal systems. The compactness of the hexadecimal and octal systems is the reason for our interest in these bases. For example, the number $1110\ 0110_2$ can be written

$$1110\ 0110_2 = 346_8 = E6_{16}$$

Here, two hexadecimal and three octal digits take the place of eight binary digits. The convenience of the octal and hexadecimal systems also lessens the possibility of making a mistake by omitting a digit, as often happens when dealing with a long binary string.

To convert a binary number to one of these bases, you just group the binary number in sets of digits on either side of the radix point. To convert to the octal system, use groups of three digits. For example,

$$1110\ 0110_2 = 11|100|110$$

The first group must have a zero appended in order to have a full set of three digits. Thus,

$$1110\ 0110_2 = 011|100|110$$

Then, simply change each group to the equivalent octal digit.

$$
\begin{aligned}
011_2 &= 3_8 \\
100_2 &= 4_8 \\
110_2 &= 6_8 \\
1110\ 0110_2 &= 346_8
\end{aligned}
$$

For hexadecimal conversion, the groups are four digits long. Thus, we have

$$
\begin{aligned}
1110\ 0110_2 &= 1110|0110 \\
1110_2 &= E_{16} \\
0110_2 &= 6_{16} \\
1110\ 0110_2 &= E6_{16}
\end{aligned}
$$

□ **EXAMPLE 8-3**

Convert the following numbers to their octal and hexadecimal equivalents.

1. $1\ 1010_2$
2. 1111.111_2

Solution

1. In the octal system, we have

$$1\ 1010_2 = 11|010$$

Appending a leading zero to form a group of three digits, we obtain

$$1\ 1010_2 = 011|010 = 32_8$$

In the hexadecimal system, we have

$$1\ 1010_2 = 1|1010$$

Appending three leading zeros, we obtain

$$1\ 1010_2 = 0001|1010 = 1A_{16}$$

2. In the octal system, grouping by three digits on either side of the radix point, we obtain

$$
\begin{aligned}
1111.111_2 &= 1|111.\ 111 \\
&= 001|111.\ 111 \\
&= 17.7_8
\end{aligned}
$$

In the hexadecimal system, we group by four digits, to obtain

$$1111.111_2 = 1111.|111$$

A trailing zero must be appended to the rightmost set of digits to complete the group of four. So

$$1111.111_2 = 1111.|1110 = F.E_{16}$$

Changing from the octal or hexadecimal systems back to the binary system is just as easy. You simply write each octal or hexadecimal digit as the equivalent binary number, in groups of three or four digits, respectively. Thus, converting 371.4_8 to a binary digit, we have

$$
\begin{aligned}
3_8 &= 011_2 \\
7_8 &= 111_2 \\
1_8 &= 001_2 \\
4_8 &= 100_2
\end{aligned}
$$

So

$$371.4_8 = 011\ 111\ 001.100_2$$

The leading and trailing zeros may be omitted, giving

$$371.4_8 = 11\ 111\ 001.1_2$$

With the same method, the binary equivalent of $7C2.4_{16}$ can be found as follows:

$$
\begin{aligned}
7_{16} &= 0111_2 \\
C_{16} &= 1100_2
\end{aligned}
$$

$$2_{16} = 0010_2$$
$$4_{16} = 0100_2$$

Thus

$$7C2.4_{16} = 0111\ 1100\ 0010.0100_2$$
$$= 111\ 1100\ 0010.01_2$$

☐ EXAMPLE 8-4

Convert these numbers to binary numbers.

1. 3741.56_8
2. $29AE.D7_{16}$

Solution

1. $3741.56_8 = 011\ 111\ 100\ 001.101\ 110_2$
2. $29AE.D7_{16} = 0010\ 1001\ 1010\ 1110.1101\ 0111_2$
                  $= 10\ 1001\ 1010\ 1110.1101\ 0111_2$

TABLE 8-3. Calculator Notation

Key	Meaning
0 1 2 3 4 5 6 7 8 9	Decimal digits
+	Addition
−	Subtraction
×	Multiplication
÷	Division
STO	Store the number currently displayed into memory
RCL	Recall the number from memory
=	Equal (to evaluate the operation)
·	Decimal point

☐ CONVERTING OTHER BASES TO THE DECIMAL SYSTEM

An improved method for finding the decimal equivalent of numbers in other bases will be described here. To reduce the effort and improve the accuracy of these operations, we will discuss the conversions in terms of solution by calculator. The most inexpensive calculator can be used, since only addition, multiplication, and one memory storage are needed. The notation in Table 8-3 is used in the discussion that follows.

The process begins by separating the number into integer and fractional portions. Each portion is converted to the decimal system separately. Then, the partial results are added. For the integer conversion, the base of the number is stored in memory. Then, the most significant digit (MSD)—that is, the leftmost digit—is entered. It is then multiplied by the base. That product is added to the next digit to the right, and the sum is again multiplied by the base. These operations are repeated until the least significant digit (LSD) is reached. The number $1\ 1001_2$ is converted to the decimal system as an example in Table 8-4, which lists the steps of the conversion.

With a little practice, you should be able to perform the steps shown in the table in just a few seconds. Another time saver is to first convert the binary number to a hexadecimal or octal number. The only change in the process is in the first step, when the base stored will be 16 or 8 instead of 2. The next example shows the procedure.

☐ EXAMPLE 8-5

Convert $1\ 1001_2$ to a decimal number by first changing the original number to the octal or hexadecimal system.

Solution The steps for the octal conversion are as follows (see Table 8-5):

$$1\ 1001_2 = 011|001_8 = 31_8$$

In the hexadecimal system, we have these steps (see Table 8-6):

$$1\ 1001_2 = 0001|1001 = 19_{16}$$

TABLE 8-4. Converting 1 1001$_2$ to the Decimal System with a Calculator

Step	Entry	Display	Comment
1	[2] [STO]	2	Store base in memory
2	[1] [×] [RCL]	1	Most significant digit multiplied by the base
	[=]	2	First product
3	[+] [1] [=]	3	Added to next digit to the right
4	[×] [RCL] [=]	6	Multiplied by the base
5	[+] [0] [=]	6	Added to the next digit to the right
6	[×] [RCL] [=]	12	Multiplied by the base
7	[+] [0] [=]	12	Added to the next digit to the right
8	[×] [RCL] [=]	24	Multiplied by the base
9	[+] [1] [=]	25	Added to least significant digit
10	None	25	Stop; answer is displayed

TABLE 8-5. Octal Conversion

Step	Entry	Display	Comment
1	[8] [STO]	8	Store base in memory
2	[3] [×] [RCL] [=]	24	MSD multiplied by base
3	[+] [1] [=]	25	Add next digit
4	None	25	Stop after LSD is added

TABLE 8-6. Hexadecimal Conversion

Step	Entry	Display	Comment
1	[1] [6] [STO]	16	Store base in memory
2	[1] [×] [RCL] [=]	16	MSD multiplied by base
3	[+] [9] [=]	25	Add to next digit
4	None	25	Stop after LSD is added

TABLE 8-7. Converting 0.1011_2 to a Decimal Number with a Calculator

Step	Entry	Display	Comment
1	\[2\] \[STO\]	2	Store base in memory
2	\[1\] \[÷\] \[RCL\] \[=\]	0.5	Least significant digit is divided by base
3	\[+\] \[1\] \[=\]	1.5	Added to next digit to left
4	\[÷\] \[RCL\] \[=\]	0.75	Divided by base
5	\[+\] \[0\] \[=\]	0.75	Added to next digit to left
6	\[÷\] \[RCL\] \[=\]	0.375	Divided by base
7	\[+\] \[1\] \[=\]	1.375	Added to most significant digit
8	\[÷\] \[RCL\] \[=\]	0.6875	Divided by base
9	None	0.6875	Stop; the answer is displayed

Comparing the effort, you can see that only four steps are needed in both cases above, instead of the ten needed for conversion directly from binary.

Now we will look at the conversion method for the fractional portion of a number. Again, the base is stored in memory. The LSD is then entered and divided by the base. That product is added to the next digit to the left, and the division by the base is repeated. This process continues until the MSD is divided by the base, and that quotient is the desired result. Table 8-7 shows how the number 0.1011_2 is converted to a decimal number. Again, the number of steps is reduced if you do octal or hexadecimal conversion first.

□ **EXAMPLE 8-6**

Convert 0.1011_2 to a decimal number by first converting to the octal or hexadecimal system.

Solution The steps for the octal conversion are as follows (see Table 8-8):

$$0.1011_2 = 0.101|100_2 = 0.54_8$$

The steps for the hexadecimal conversion are as follows (see Table 8-9):

$$0.1011_2 = 0.B_{16}$$

The process for conversion to the decimal system, by use of a calculator, is summarized schematically in Figure 8-2. Remember that hexadecimal digits greater than nine must be changed to the decimal equivalent to enter them on the calculator keyboard. The comprehensive example that follows illustrates the complete conversion process.

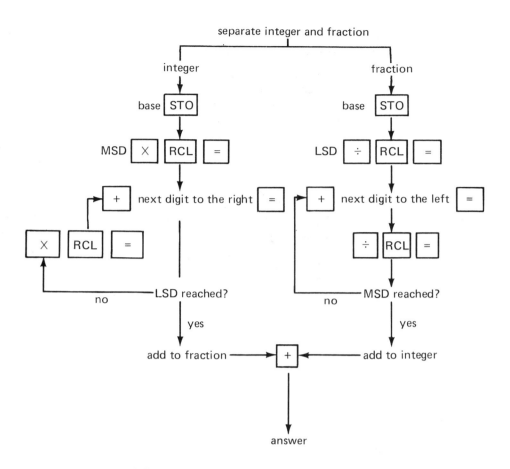

FIGURE 8-2.
Conversion of Any
Base to Decimal
System on a
Calculator

TABLE 8-8. Octal Conversion

Step	Entry	Display	Comment
1	8 STO	8	Store base
2	4 ÷ RCL =	0.5	Divide LSD by base
3	+ 5 =	5.5	Add next digit to left
4	÷ RCL =	0.6875	Divide by base
5	None	0.6875	Stop

TABLE 8-9. Hexadecimal Conversion

Step	Entry	Display	Comment
1	1 6 STO	16	Store base
2	1 1 ÷ RCL =	0.6875	Divide LSD by base (B_{16} must be converted to 11_{10} to enter it)
3	None	0.6875	Stop

□ EXAMPLE 8-7

Find the decimal equivalent of 111 1101.1011 01$_2$.

Solution Conversion first to a hexadecimal number will be used, and the integer and fractional components will be found separately. The hexadecimal conversion is as follows:

$$111\,1101.1011\,01_2 = 0111|1101|.1011|0100_2$$
$$= 7D.B4_{16}$$

The steps for the integer portion are as shown in Table 8-10. The steps for the fractional portion are as shown in Table 8-11.

Now we add component parts:

$$125 + 0.703125 = 125.703125$$
$$111\,1101.1011\,01_2 = 125.703125_{10}$$

□ CONVERTING DECIMAL NUMBERS TO OTHER BASES

Now we will consider how a decimal number can be changed to its equivalent in the binary, octal, or hexadecimal systems. Again, a calculator solution will be presented, but this time you will have to write down partial results. Just as before, integers and fractions must be treated separately.

Integers are converted by storing the base in memory and then dividing by the base. Find the remainder as a whole number and write it down. The quotient from the first step is divided again, and the process continues until the quotient is zero. The remainders give the desired number, with the first remainder generated representing the least significant digit.

TABLE 8-10. Steps for Integer Components

Step	Entry	Display	Comment
1	1 6 STO	16	Base
2	7 × RCL =	112	MSD
3	+ 1 3 =	125	Add next digit (convert to 13$_{10}$)
4	None	125	Integer answer

TABLE 8-11. Steps for Fractional Components

Step	Entry	Display	Comment
1	1 6 STO	16	Base
2	4 ÷ RCL =	0.25	LSD
3	+ 1 1 =	11.25	Add next digit
4	÷ RCL =	0.703125	Divide
5	None	0.703125	Stop

TABLE 8-12. Converting 29_{10} to a Binary Number

Step	Entry	Display	Comment
1	[2] [STO]	2	Store base
2	[2] [9] [÷] [RCL] [=]	(14)(.5)	Divide number by base Record new integer quotient, 14
3	[.] [5] [×] [RCL] [=]	1	Compute and record integer remainder (1)
4	[1] [4] [÷] [RCL] [=]	(7)(.0)	Previous integer quotient is divided by base; record new integer of quotient (7)
5	[0] [×] [RCL] [=]	0	Compute and record integer remainder (0)
6	[7] [÷] [RCL] [=]	(3)(.5)	Previous integer quotient is divided by base; record new integer of quotient (3)
7	[.] [5] [×] [RCL] [=]	1	Compute and record integer remainder (1)
8	[3] [÷] [RCL] [=]	(1)(.5)	Previous integer quotient is divided by base; record new integer of quotient (1)
9	[.] [5] [×] [RCL] [=]	1	Compute and record integer remainder (1)
10	[1] [÷] [RCL] [=]	(0)(.5)	Previous integer quotient is divided by base; record new integer quotient
11	[.] [5] [×] [RCL] [=]	1	Compute and record integer remainder
12	None		Last integer quotient was zero, so form answer from the integer remainders (first remainder is the LSD)

	MSD				LSD
	↓				↓
Integer remainders	1	1	1	0	1
	Step 11	Step 9	Step 7	Step 5	Step 3

$$29_{10} = 1\,1101_2$$

TABLE 8-13. Conversion of 0.75_{10} to a Binary Number

Step	Entry	Display	Comment
1	[2] [STO]	2	Store base
2	[.] [7] [5] [×] [RCL] [=]	(1).5	Multiply by base; record integer generated (1)
3	[−] [1] [=]	0 .5	Subtract integer
4	[×] [RCL] [=]	(1).0	Multiply by base; record integer generated (1)
5	[−] [1] [=]	0	Subtract integer
6	[×] [RCL] [=]	0	Multiply by base; record integer generated (0)
7	None	0	Three digits obtained; stop

Form the answer. The first digit is the MSD.	MSD		LSD
	1	1	0
	Step 2	Step 4	Step 6

$$0.75_{10} = 0.110_2$$

Table 8-12 shows the conversion of 29_{10} to a binary number. (Because the calculator can only find fractional remainders, steps such as 3 and 5 in the table just compute the equivalent integer remainder.) Fewer steps are needed to convert from a decimal number to the larger bases of octal or hexadecimal.

The procedure for generating the equivalent of a decimal fraction begins by storing the base. The fraction to be converted is multiplied by the base, and the integer produced is recorded. That integer is also subtracted from the product, and the result is multiplied by the base again. These steps are repeated until the number of significant digits obtained meets the precision needed. Table 8-13 shows the conversion of 0.75_{10} to a binary number, three digits past the radix point. In this case, the binary fraction is exactly equal to the decimal fraction, because the final digit is zero. Often an exact answer does not result, but the answer can be as accurate as desired by computing a sufficient number of digits.

A comprehensive example illustrating the conversion of a decimal (number) to a hexadecimal number is presented in Example 8-8. The overall procedure is summarized in Figure 8-3.

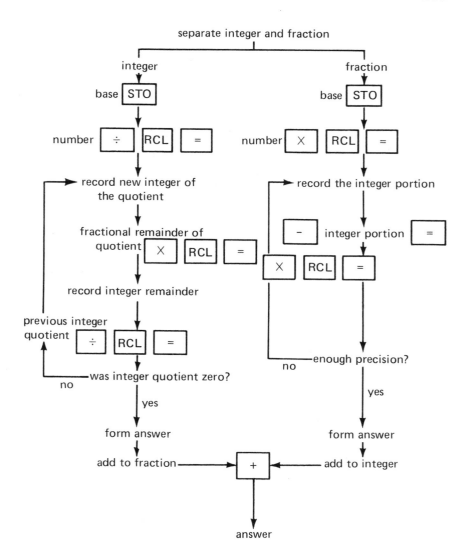

FIGURE 8-3.
Conversion of a
Decimal Number to
Any Base on a
Calculator

□ **EXAMPLE 8-8**

Convert 249.68_{10} to a hexadecimal number. Provide an accuracy of two places past the radix point.

Solution The steps for finding the integer portion are as given in Table 8-14.

Now we find the fractional portion. Three

digits must be generated to allow rounding to two places, as shown in Table 8-15.

Round to two places:

$$0.AE1_{16} = 0.AE_{16}$$

Add to integer result:

$$249.68_{10} = F9.AE_{16}$$

TABLE 8-14. Converting 249_{10} to a Hexadecimal Number

Step	Entry	Display	Comment
1	[1] [6] [STO]	16	Base
2	[2] [4] [9] [÷] [RCL] [=]	(15).5625	Record integer quotient (15)
3	[.] [5] [6] [2] [5] [×] [RCL] [=]	9	Compute integer fraction (9)
4	[1] [5] [÷] [RCL] [=]	0.9375	Generate next digit; record integer quotient (0)
5	[.] [9] [3] [7] [5] [×] [RCL] [=]	15	Compute integer fraction (15_{10} = F_{16})
6	None		Integer quotient was 0 in step 5

TABLE 8-15. Rounding to Two Places

Step	Entry	Display	Comment
1	[1] [6] [STO]	16	Base
2	[.] [6] [8] [×] [RCL] [=]	(10).88	Record integer (10_{10} = A_{16})
3	[−] [1] [0] [=]	0 .88	Subtract integer
4	[×] [RCL] [=]	(14).08	Record next integer (14_{10} = E_{16})
5	[−] [1] [4] [=]	0 .88	Subtract integer
6	[×] [RCL] [=]	(1).28	Record next integer (1); enough digits generated, so stop

Chapter Summary

☐ A positionally weighted number system is characterized by the base or radix. The set of digits in a number system is equal in quantity to the value of the base.

☐ The digits in the binary number system are often called bits.

☐ The fractional portion of a number is separated from the integer by a radix point.

☐ In a positional number system, each column of a number represents the base raised to an appropriate power. The value of the number depends on the digits, the base, and the positions.

☐ Base conversion uses different processes for integers and fractions. Converting from a binary number to an octal or hexadecimal number is most easily accomplished with the grouping method.

☐ Converting back and forth to the decimal system can be readily accomplished with a pocket calculator.

Problems

8-1. Convert the following binary numbers to hexadecimal numbers by grouping.

   a. $10\ 001\ 011\ 100_2$

   b. $111.101\ 01_2$

   c. $-001\ 010\ 110.1111_2$

   d. $101\ 001.010\ 11_2$

8-2. Convert these binary numbers to octal numbers.

   a. $101\ 101\ 100\ 011_2$

   b. $-101\ 010.001\ 01_2$

   c. $110\ 111.000_2$

   d. $-11.111\ 111\ 000\ 1_2$

8-3. Find the binary values of the following numbers.

   a. $D2.8E_{16}$

   b. $-7C45.123_{16}$

   c. $10.A5_{16}$

   d. $64.789C_{16}$

8-4. What binary numbers are equivalent to these octal numbers?

   a. 36.47_8

   b. -121.52_8

   c. 20.156_8

   d. -6.23512704_8

8-5. Convert these numbers to binary numbers. Use four-place precision for all fractions.

   a. 144_{10}

   b. 92.8_{10}

   c. -357.62_{10}

   d. 83.25_{10}

8-6. What are the decimal equivalents for these binary numbers? Use two-place precision in finding fractional values.

   a. 0.110_2

   b. $-111\ 100\ 110.01_2$

   c. $10\ 110\ 101.101\ 111_2$

   d. $-1\ 101\ 111.111_2$

8-7. Convert these numbers to binary numbers.

   a. $F2.D1_{16}$

   b. 70.36_8

   c. 99.82_{10}

8-8. Find the decimal equivalent of $1\ 001\ 010\ 100.11_2$ by first converting it to an octal number.

8-9. Convert 178.9_{10} to a binary number by first converting it to a hexadecimal number.

8-10. Which is larger, 0.52_{10} or 0.61_8?

Chapter Nine
Digital Arithmetic

Inherent in all digital equipment is a need to process numbers. As we will see in this chapter, electronic circuits do not use the familiar decimal system in counting and performing functions. Instead, the binary number system is the basis for these operations. For that reason, an understanding of arithmetic circuits cannot be gained without knowledge of the binary number system.

This chapter continues the discussion of the binary system begun in Chapter 8. Binary arithmetic and common arithmetic circuits will be explained and analyzed.

Chapter Objectives

Upon completion of this chapter, you should be able to:

☐ Perform binary arithmetic.
☐ Subtract by using complement arithmetic.
☐ Analyze the operation of complementing integrated circuits.
☐ Show how adders and multipliers perform arithmetic.

□ BINARY ARITHMETIC

The rules for binary arithmetic resemble those of decimal arithmetic. All operations depend on positional weighting. The first operation we will consider is addition. Table 9-1 completely specifies addition of binary numbers. As shown in the table, there are only four possible combinations. The most likely mistake you can make in binary addition is losing track of the carries. Carefully indicating each carry as it is propagated will lessen the possibility of such an error.

TABLE 9-1. Binary Addition

		Addend	
	Augend	0	1
	0	0	1
	1	1	0 (carry = 1)

□ EXAMPLE 9-1

Add $111\ 0011_2$ to $100\ 1010_2$.

Solution   The addition is shown below.

carries
$$
\begin{array}{r}
111\ 0011_2 \\
+\ 100\ 1010_2 \\
\hline
1011\ 1101_2
\end{array}
$$

In the *least significant bit (LSB)* column, 1 is added to 0 for a sum of 1. In the next column, 1 plus 1 equals 0, with a carry of 1. This carry means that there are three numbers to be added in the third column. The remaining additions are straightforward until the *most significant bit (MSB)* position is reached, where again a carry results.

Binary subtraction is characterized by borrowing a 2 from the next higher column when the minuend digit is larger than the subtrahend digit. Table 9-2 shows the binary subtraction process.

TABLE 9-2. Binary Subtraction

		Subtrahend	
	Minuend	0	1
	0	0	1 (borrow = 1)
	1	1	0

□ EXAMPLE 9-2

Subtract $11\ 0111_2$ from $100\ 1011_2$.

Solution

borrows
$$
\begin{array}{r}
1 \to 10 \\
10 \qquad 10 \\
\not{1}\ \not{0}\ 0\ \not{1}\ 0\ 1\ 1_2 \\
-\ \ \ 1\ 1\ 0\ 1\ 1\ 1_2 \\
\hline
0\ 0\ 1\ 0\ 1\ 0\ 0_2
\end{array}
$$

In column 3 (from the right), the first borrow is required. Borrowing is also necessary in column 5, but the digit in column 6 is 0. Therefore, a borrow is made in column 7, moving a value of 10_2 to column 6. Now the borrow can be made for column 5, leaving a value of 1 in column 6.

One other situation to be aware of in binary subtraction is the consequence of subtracting a larger number from a smaller one. Just as in the decimal system, the rule is to invert the order of the subtraction and place a minus sign in front of the difference. The next example illustrates the process.

□ EXAMPLE 9-3

Subtract 1011_2 from 11_2.

Solution

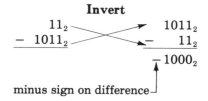

minus sign on difference┘

After the inversion, normal subtraction rules apply.

Binary multiplication is the last arithmetic operation we will study. In only one situation, as shown in Table 9-3, is the product other than 0. Multiplication problems actually become exercises in addition, since the partial products must be summed.

TABLE 9-3. Binary Multiplication

Multiplicand	Multiplier	
	0	1
0	0	0
1	0	1

$$10.100_2 \quad \text{3 bits to right of radix point in multiplicand}$$
$$\times \quad 1.01_2 \quad \text{2 bits to right of radix point in multiplier}$$
$$11.0010\ 0_2 \quad \text{5 bits to right of radix point in product}$$

□ COMPLEMENT BINARY NUMBER SYSTEMS

When you do arithmetic, you can distinguish positive from negative numbers by their signs. Digital circuits, however, must use other means of identifying positive or negative quantities. Most frequently, a complement number convention is adopted for such purposes. An additional benefit of complement number systems is that the same circuit can be used for both adding and subtracting.

There is no unique way to form a complement, and two similar techniques are often encountered. Most manufacturers use the 2's complement system in their equipment, but you may come across the 1's complement as well (especially in older equipment). Because both conventions are in service, you should be familiar with both.

Complements are formed by using the most significant bit of the number to represent the sign. If the MSB is 0, the number is positive. Obviously, a negative number then has a sign bit of 1.

Another requirement of complement numbers is that they must be of fixed length. If the quantity of bits in the number is not specified, you cannot tell which is the sign bit. For example, the binary numbers 0011_2, 011_2, and 11_2 are all equal. But if we are considering complement numbers, they are not, because they are not of the same sign. The size is the number of a specified quantity of bits, called the **word length**. Using the above examples, we have the following word lengths and signs:

□ EXAMPLE 9-4

Multiply 101_2 by 1010_2.

Solution In multiplication, remember to move each row of partial products one column further left than the preceding one, as shown below:

$$
\begin{array}{r}
101_2 \\
\times\ 1010_2 \\
\hline
000 \\
101 \\
000 \\
101 \\
\hline
110010_2
\end{array}
$$

each row of the partial product moves left one column

The radix point in binary arithmetic is handled in the same way as it is in decimal arithmetic. Addition and subtraction require that the radix points be aligned. The number of bits to the right of the radix point in the product is the sum of the bits to the right of the radix points of the multiplicand and multiplier. The problems below illustrate the proper way to use the binary radix point.

$$
\begin{array}{r}
1.011_2 \\
+\ 10.101_2 \\
\hline
100.000_2
\end{array}
$$

radix points aligned in addition

$$
\begin{array}{r}
10.1101\ 1111_2 \\
-\ 1.0111\ 0000_2 \\
\hline
1.0110\ 1111_2
\end{array}
$$

radix points aligned in subtraction

Word Length	Number	Sign
	┌sign bit	
4 bits	0011_2	+
3 bits	011_2	+
2 bits	11_2	−

The last number is negative, so it cannot be equal to the other two.

How do you find the complement of a number? Suppose you want to express -110_2. (A word length of eight bits will be used in this case and throughout the chapter for convenience. However, an eight-bit word length is not a universal standard. The technical manual for the equipment you are working on must be consulted to find this information.) In the succeeding sections, we will discuss how to find the complement of 110_2 in both the 1's complement and the 2's complement systems.

Finding 1's Complement

The **1's complement** of a number is formed by inverting each bit of the word. Every 1 becomes a 0, and each 0 is changed to 1. Thus, for a word length of eight bits, we have

$$-110_2 = 0000\ 0110_2$$
$$= 1111\ 1001_2 \quad \text{complemented}$$

sign bit negative

To review, there are two steps needed to form a 1's complement. First, express the number with the proper word length; then invert each bit. The process is symmetrical. That is, a double negation returns the original number. This property can readily be demonstrated by taking the 1's complement of $1111\ 1001_2$:

complement $1111\ 1001_2$
              $0000\ 0110_2$

Finding 2's Complement

The more common **2's complement** is formed by adding 1 to the 1's complement. The 2's complement of -110_2 is found by expressing the number in the appropriate word length (eight bits):

$$0000\ 0110_2$$

Forming the 1's complement, we have

$$1111\ 1001_2$$

Now adding 1, we obtain

$$
\begin{array}{r}
1111\ 1001_2 \\
+\qquad\quad 1_2 \\
\hline
1111\ 1010_2
\end{array}
$$

The 2's complement exhibits the same type of symmetry as the 1's complement. Using the number above, we have

$$
\begin{array}{rl}
1111\ 1010_2 & \\
0000\ 0101_2 & \text{1's complement} \\
+\qquad\quad 1_2 & \text{adding 1} \\
\hline
0000\ 0110_2 & \text{original number}
\end{array}
$$

You probably observed that forming the 2's complement requires an extra step. So you may be wondering why the more complicated convention is so widely used. The reason is that a 2's complement system has better properties than the 1's complement for doing arithmetic. This advantage can be readily seen by forming the complement of 0 in both systems.

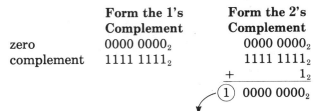

	Form the 1's Complement	Form the 2's Complement
zero	$0000\ 0000_2$	$0000\ 0000_2$
complement	$1111\ 1111_2$	$1111\ 1111_2$
		$+\qquad 1_2$
		① $0000\ 0000_2$

In the 1's complement, the representation for negative zero is not the same as that for positive zero, even though in ordinary arithmetic $+0 = -0$. The 2's complement, on the other hand, has only a single value for zero, regardless of sign. This value results because the carry from the MSB cannot be contained in the eight-bit word. Only the zeros remain. (A **carry-out** from the MSB is called an *overflow condition*.)

The application of complement numbers will be shown with a subtraction example. Both complement systems will be used to demonstrate their characteristics.

☐ **EXAMPLE 9–5**

Repeat Example 9–2 by using complement arithmetic.

Solution The subtrahend will be converted to its complement and *added* to accomplish the operation.

In the 1's complement system, complementing $0011\ 0111_2$ gives $1100\ 1000_2$. Now we add that number to the minuend:

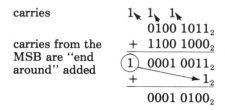

This operation gives the same answer as was obtained in Example 9-2.

In the 2's complement system, we add 1 to the 1's complement obtained above:

$$
\begin{array}{r}
1100\ 1000_2 \\
+\ \ \ \ \ \ \ \ \ \ 1_2 \\
\hline
1100\ 1001_2
\end{array}
$$

Now we add that number to the minuend:

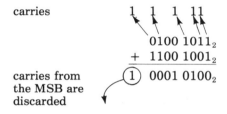

The results are identical. A major distinction between the two systems is the "end around" carry addition in the 1's complement that does not occur in the 2's complement.

A Practical Note

Although digital circuits must use complements in arithmetic, you should avoid them whenever possible. You will find it much easier to do binary arithmetic by using ordinary subtraction rather than forming the complement and adding. Even when troubleshooting a circuit, computing the expected answer by subtraction is usually easier than attempting to "simulate" a machine and doing the arithmetic with complements.

□ ARITHMETIC CIRCUITS

A survey of some typical arithmetic circuits is provided in this section to reinforce the concepts

of digital arithmetic presented in this chapter. A complete understanding of the mathematical principles involved must be acquired before attempting to analyze or diagnose problems in these circuits.

5487/7487
True/Complement Element

The true/complement circuit, shown in Figure 9-1, produces the true (uncomplemented) or the 1's complement of the four-bit input, the resultant condition depending on the settings of the two control bits. Table 9-4 summarizes the operations.

When the two control bits are low, the outputs are the complements of the inputs. If input B is low and C is high, the outputs are equal to the inputs. A high B signal and a low C signal forces all outputs to be high—representing all 1s with positive logic. High levels on both control

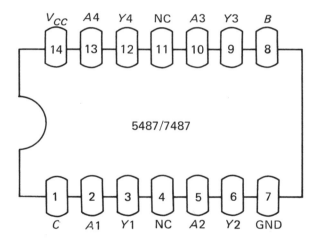

FIGURE 9-1. 5487/7487 True/Complement Element

TABLE 9-4. 5487/7487 True/Complement Element Control

Control Pin		Output			
B	C	$Y4$	$Y3$	$Y2$	$Y1$
L	L	$\overline{A4}$	$\overline{A3}$	$\overline{A2}$	$\overline{A1}$
L	H	$A4$	$A3$	$A2$	$A1$
H	L	H	H	H	H
H	H	L	L	L	L

lines produce lows on all outputs—a 0 with positive logic. With two of these circuits connected in parallel, an eight-bit word can be converted to the 1's complement.

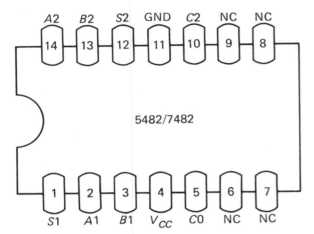

FIGURE 9-2. 5482/7482 Full Adder

TABLE 9-5. Adder Function Table

Input				Carry-in = 0			Carry-in = 1		
B2	B1	A2	A1	C2	S2	S1	C2	S2	S1
0	0	0	0	0	0	0	0	0	1
0	0	0	1	0	0	1	0	1	0
0	0	1	0	0	1	0	0	1	1
0	0	1	1	0	1	1	1	0	0
0	1	0	0	0	0	1	0	1	0
0	1	0	1	0	1	0	0	1	1
0	1	1	0	0	1	1	1	0	0
0	1	1	1	1	0	0	1	0	1
1	0	0	0	0	1	0	0	1	1
1	0	0	1	0	1	1	1	0	0
1	0	1	0	1	0	0	1	0	1
1	0	1	1	1	0	1	1	1	0
1	1	0	0	0	1	1	1	0	0
1	1	0	1	1	0	0	1	0	1
1	1	1	0	1	0	1	1	1	0
1	1	1	1	1	1	0	1	1	1

5482/7482 Two-Bit Adder

The two-bit adder, shown in Figure 9-2, computes the sum of the two-bit inputs. A carry to the next higher position is also provided at the pin identified as $C2$. A carry-in bit from the next lower position is accepted on the $C0$ pin. The function table (see Table 9-5) lists the results for either setting of the carry-in bit.

Looking at the column when the carry-in is 0, we see that the adder performs precisely as expected. (The bits are numbered 1 for the LSB and 2 for the MSB.) For example, in line 8 we have $B2 = 0$, $B1 = 1$, $A2 = 1$, and $A1 = 1$. The bit labels then mean

$$
\begin{array}{ccc}
B = & 0 & 1_2 \\
A = & 1 & 1_2 \\
\hline
S = & 1 \ 0 & 0_2 \\
& \uparrow \ \uparrow & \uparrow \\
& C2 \ S2 & S1
\end{array}
$$

If the carry-in bit is a 1, the resulting sum is increased by one (see the table).

A diagram showing how four of these adders could be combined for eight-bit addition is shown in Figure 9-3. (Power and ground connections are not shown in the figure.) The carry-out from a lower stage becomes the carry-in to the next higher stage.

By combining the 7487 complementer just studied with these adders, one can construct an eight-bit adder/subtracter using 2's complement arithmetic. Figure 9-4 shows the circuit. When addition is to be performed, the SUBTRACT CONTROL line is set high. From the chart in Table 9-4, we see that because pin B is low (grounded) and pin C is high, the inputs to the true/complement element pass through unchanged. Therefore, this circuit performs just like the adder of Figure 9-3.

In subtraction, the SUBTRACT CONTROL signal goes low. Now the control bits to the 7487 cause the B input to be complemented. With the complement of B as an input to the adder, subtraction will occur.

This circuit is a 2's complement adder, but the 7487 produces a 1's complement. How does that happen? The answer lies in the setting of the carry-in pin to the lowest-stage adder. Note that it is grounded in Figure 9-3 for normal addition. Because of the inverter, it is also held low when addition is to be performed in the circuit of Figure 9-4 (SUBTRACT CONTROL high). For subtraction, however, it becomes a 1. Remember that the carry-in is simply added to the four-bit input. By adding 1 to a 1's complement, we convert it to the 2's complement.

Another noteworthy feature of this adder is that the carry-out from the first stage must be held until the addition is completed in that stage. Only then does the correct value appear. The addition takes time, so the final sum is not ready until each adder in the series takes in the carry from a lower stage, adds it, and produces the correct carry-out. Thus, this circuit is an example of an adder with **ripple carry**. It is suitable for applications that do not require the fastest adding speed possible. An adder with look-ahead carry is appropriate when more rapid response is needed. We will examine this device next.

4008 Four-Bit Adder with Look-ahead Carry

An example of an adder with a **look-ahead carry** is shown in Figure 9–5. Each component adder computes the sum of the two input bits and the carry-in. The carry-out from the most significant bit addition is generated in auxiliary circuitry, however. The high-speed parallel carry has a nine-bit input: both of the four-bit numbers and the carry-in from the previous stage. The computation of the carry-out is independent of the process in each adder.

Notice that the carry into each of the adders is still a ripple carry, though. The purpose of such an adder is to save time in generating the carry from each 4-bit word segment. For instance, a 16-bit adder built from four 4008 ICs would have a propagation time of

$$4 \times \text{high-speed parallel carry unit delay}$$

A ripple carry adder would have a propagation time of

$$16 \times \text{single adder delay}$$

54284/74284 Four-by-Four Multiplier

When two numbers are multiplied, the largest product can have a length equal to the sum of the number of bits in the multiplier and the multiplicand. For example,

$$\begin{array}{r} 1011_2 \\ \times\ 1110_2 \\ \hline 1001\ 1010_2 \end{array}$$

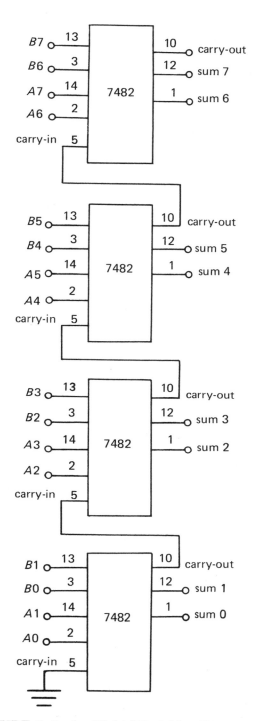

FIGURE 9–3. An Eight-Bit Adder Constructed from 7482 Circuits

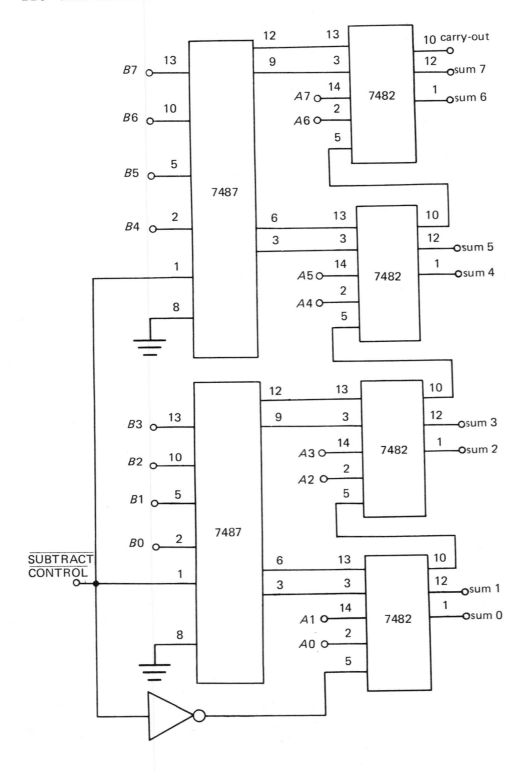

FIGURE 9-4.
Eight-Bit 2's
Complement
Adder/Subtracter

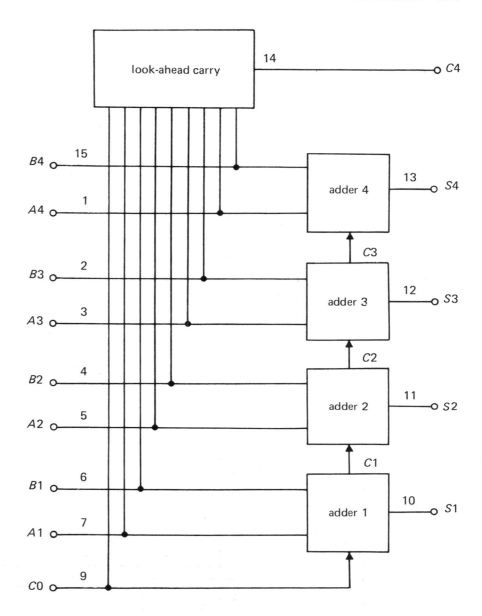

FIGURE 9-5. 4008
Four-Bit Adder with
Look-ahead Carry

The multiplier and multiplicand are each four bits long, resulting in an eight-bit product. Consequently, a multiplier circuit must account for this effect.

A typical multiplier is shown in Figure 9-6. Although the chip has two four-bit inputs, there are only four output pins. Figure 9-7 shows how two of these ICs must be used together to generate an eight-bit product. Another important factor shown on that diagram is the grounding of the two ENABLE pins to set up the operation.

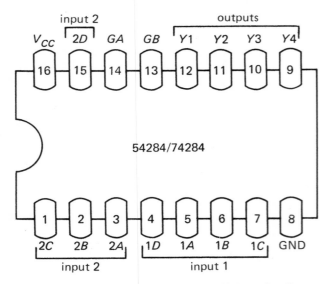

FIGURE 9-6. 54284/74284 Parallel Multiplier

☐ ADDER COMPONENTS

In all the arithmetic circuits in this chapter, the entire function has been performed with one IC. This approach is typical of what you will see in modern digital equipment, but you may come across older equipment with arithmetic circuits implemented from a network of gates. The **half adder** shown in Figure 9-8 is the fundamental element of those networks.

The half adder produces the sum and carry bits of the two-bit addition shown in Table 9-1. The truth table for these two operations is given in Table 9-6. The Boolean equations for these outputs are

$$\text{sum} = \overline{A}B + A\overline{B} \qquad (9\text{-}1)$$
$$\text{carry} = AB \qquad (9\text{-}2)$$

We can relate these equations to the half-adder circuit by finding the inputs and output of the gates, as listed in Table 9-7. The outputs have been reduced to simplest form by use of Boolean algebra laws, especially DeMorgan's theorem.

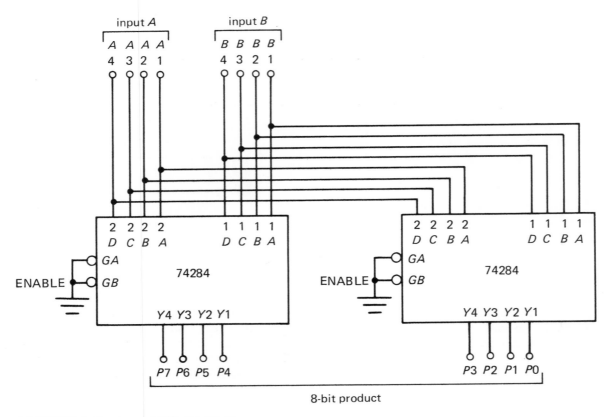

FIGURE 9-7. 4 × 4 Bit Multiplier

TABLE 9-6. Binary Addition Truth Table

A	B	Sum	Carry
0	0	0	0
0	1	1	0
1	0	1	0
1	1	0	1

TABLE 9-7. Gate Inputs and Outputs

Gate Number	Input	Output
1	A	$\overline{A} + \overline{B}$
	B	
2	A	$\overline{A} + B$
	$\overline{A} + \overline{B}$	
3	B	$A + \overline{B}$
	$\overline{A} + \overline{B}$	
4	$\overline{A} + B$	$\overline{A}B + A\overline{B}$
	$A + \overline{B}$	
5	$\overline{A} + \overline{B}$	AB

Note that the output of gate 4 is the same as the sum in Equation 9-1, and the output of gate 5 is the carry of Equation 9-2.

The half adder cannot complete the addition of numbers consisting of several bits because there is no provision for a carry-in from a lower-order bit to the adder. For example, the half adder cannot complete this addition:

```
carries        11
               11
         +      1
              100
```

A **full adder**, shown in Figure 9-9, is used to complete the addition, including the carry input.

The full adder is made from two half adders. The first half adder computes the sum and carry from the two inputs. The second adder provides a corrected sum. Relating this circuit to the 5482/7482 full adder (Figure 9-2), we see that the integrated circuit contains two of these full adders, one for each pair of input bits. The carry-out of the $A1$-$B1$ adder must be internally connected to the carry-in of the $A2$-$B2$ adder. Pin 5 is the carry-in to the $A1$-$B1$ adder, and pin 10 is the carry-out of the $A2$-$B2$ adder.

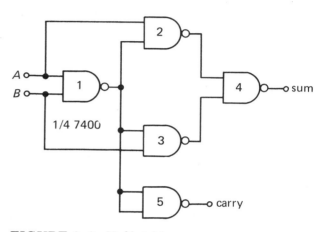

FIGURE 9-8. Half Adder

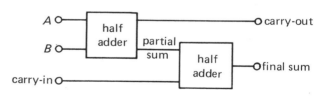

FIGURE 9-9. Full Adder

Chapter Summary

☐ Binary arithmetic follows normal arithmetic rules but uses unique addition, subtraction, and multiplication tables.

☐ Complement number systems distinguish positive and negative numbers. Both 1's and 2's complements are in use.

☐ Arithmetic circuits that add and multiply are listed in manufacturers' data books.

☐ In multiplication, the length of the product can equal the sum of the multiplier and multiplicand word lengths.

☐ Half adders cannot compute a complete sum because they lack a carry-in. A full adder comprised of two half adders is needed for the complete addition.

☐ Adders can use either ripple carry or look-ahead carry circuitry.

Problems

9-1. Perform the additions below.

a. $\quad 1\ 0111_2$
$+ \quad 1011_2$

b. $\quad 11\ 0100.000_2$
$+ \quad 10\ 0010.011_2$

c. $\quad 11\ 1101\ 1010_2$
$+ \qquad 1000\ 1111_2$

d. $\quad 1101\ 1110.101_2$
$+ \quad 1001\ 0110.001_2$

9-2. Find the answer to these binary subtraction problems.

a. $\quad 1110\ 0100\ 0011_2$
$- \qquad 11\ 1010\ 0010_2$

b. $\quad 100\ 0101\ 0001_2$
$- \quad 101\ 0000\ 0000_2$

c. $\quad 110\ 0110\ 0101_2$
$- \quad\ 10\ 1011\ 0111_2$

d. $\quad 110.1000\ 11_2$
$- \qquad 0.0101\ 11_2$

9-3. Carry out the multiplications given below.

a. $\quad 1010\ 1111_2$
$\times \qquad 101_2$

b. $\quad 10\ 0001_2$
$\times \qquad 1011_2$

c. $\quad 1101\ 1110.1111_2$
$\times \qquad 1.0111_2$

d. $\quad 01.0000\ 1_2$
$\times \qquad 1.\ 011_2$

9-4. Form the 1's complement of these numbers. (If the given number is not binary, convert it to a binary number first.) The word length is eight bits.

a. $1110\ 1010_2$
b. 356_8
c. $F2_{16}$
d. 14_{10}

9-5. What are the 2's complements of the numbers below? (Convert to the binary system, if necessary, before finding the complement.) The word length is eight bits.

a. $1010\ 1110_2$
b. 257_8
c. $C5_{16}$
d. 63_{10}

9-6. Use eight-bit words to subtract $2B_{16}$ from $3D_{16}$. The arithmetic is to be performed with a 2's complement. Check your answer by direct subtraction.

9-7. The following number is applied to the inputs of Figure 9-3. What are the sum and the carry-out generated?

$$A = 0010\ 1110_2$$
$$B = 4D_{16}$$

9-8. If the inputs to the subtracter of Figure 9-4 are $A = 375_8$ and $B = 126_8$, what values appear at the sum output pins? The $\overline{\text{SUBTRACT}}$ $\overline{\text{CONTROL}}$ is low.

9-9. With inputs of $A = C_{16}$ and $B = 7_{16}$, what is the output of the circuit in Figure 9-7? Assume that the ENABLE pins are both grounded.

9-10. What is the 2's complement of 8000_{16} in a 16-bit word? Explain why there is no corresponding positive number of equal magnitude.

Chapter Ten

Data Selection and Comparison

Considering the number of different signals that flow through a unit of digital equipment, one quickly realizes the need for proper routing of the signals. Two important circuit elements frequently used to control the source or destination for signals are multiplexers and demultiplexers. A **multiplexer (MUX)** acts as a data selector, switching the desired signal from numerous inputs to the output. On the other hand, a **demultiplexer (DEMUX)** in effect decodes a set of input signals. This decoding may take the form of selecting which path the output signal will take or may result in conversion from one number system to another. General **code converters** take this number system conversion one step further, allowing us to readily change between such bases as decimal and binary.

Another often needed function is a comparison between two numbers to decide their relative sizes. For example, a circuit may turn a heater off if the temperature exceeds 20°C. **Comparators** are used in these applications. Most flexible of all devices is the **arithmetic logic unit (ALU)**, which can do arithmetic, Boolean operations, and comparison all in one chip. In this chapter, we will examine the operation of all these devices.

Chapter Objectives

Upon completion of this chapter, you should be able to:

- ☐ Describe the operation of a typical multiplexer.
- ☐ Show how demultiplexers can route signals over the proper output line.
- ☐ Explain how numbers can be converted from one base to another by using code converters.
- ☐ Draw a block diagram of a digital comparator and analyze the results of any combination of input signals.
- ☐ Use a function table to predict the outputs of an arithmetic logic unit.

☐ MULTIPLEXERS

The principle of multiplexing is based on the ability of Boolean circuits to select one input out of many. A simple multiplexer is shown in Figure 10-1. In this example, there are two input signals, labeled A and B. The signal that is passed to the output through the OR gate depends on whether the Y or $\overline{Y}$ signal is a 1. If Y is 1, the upper AND gate will be enabled. Its output will be the value of the A input. The lower AND gate must have a 0 output because the $\overline{Y}$ input is 0. Reversing the situation and letting $\overline{Y}$ be 1 causes only the lower gate to be enabled, so the output is B. Table 10-1 describes the functions of this circuit. The Y and $\overline{Y}$ signals are called the *select inputs*.

The 74150 multiplexer is a scaled-up version of the simple multiplexer just described. Figure 10-2 shows the signal assignments for the 24-pin DIP. There are 16 input signals, identified as $E0$ through $E15$. The output appears at pin 10. But which of the many input signals is selected?

As Table 10-2 shows, the number of the input line is determined by the select lines A, B, C, and D. Another signal also enters into the multiplexer operation, and that is the strobe on pin 9. This signal must be 0 (low) to enable the chip. Otherwise, the output always has a value of 1.

Once the multiplexer is enabled by the strobe, the output is the *complement* of the input signal designated by the select lines. If more than 16 inputs are to be multiplexed, several 54150s can be cascaded, as shown in Figure 10-3. In this manner, data selection for any number of inputs can be accomplished. For example, for the configuration shown in Figure 10-3, additional intermediate stages can be added if more than 16 signals are present at the second stage. (The selection signals applied at the D, C, B, and A inputs to the second stage are not from the same source as those used on the first stage.)

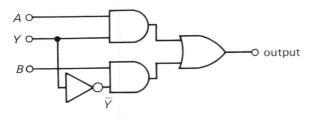

FIGURE 10-1. Simple Multiplexer

TABLE 10-1. Multiplexer Functions

Input				
Select				
Y	$\overline{Y}$	A	B	Output
1	0	0	X^a	0
1	0	1	X	1
0	1	X	0	0
0	1	X	1	1

^{a}X = don't care.

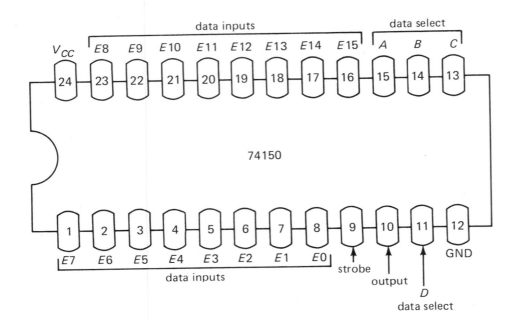

FIGURE 10-2.
74150 Multiplexer

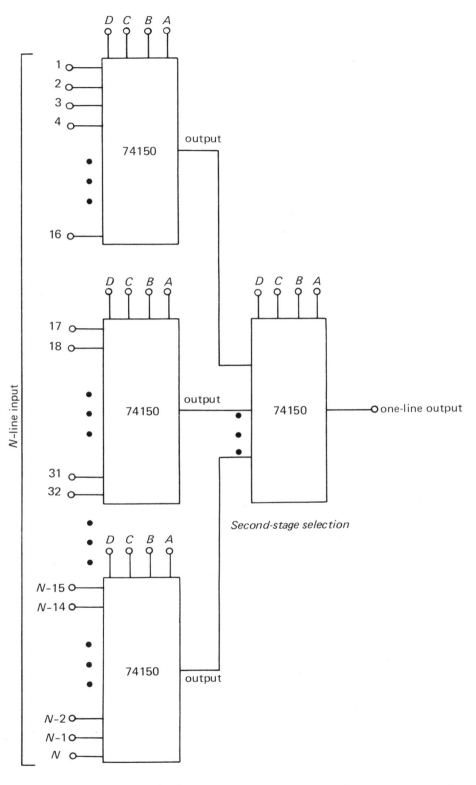

FIGURE 10–3.
N-Line to One-Line
Data Selection

□ EXAMPLE 10-1

The inputs to a 74150 circuit are as follows:

strobe = 0	$A = 0$
$E2 = 1$	$B = 1$
$E3 = 0$	$C = 0$
$E4 = 0$	$D = 0$

What is the output?

Solution Table 10-2 shows that the IC is enabled and the selected output is $\overline{E2}$, which will be 0.

TABLE 10-2. 74150 Multiplexer Functions

	Input				
	Select				
D	C	B	A	Strobe	Output
X^a	X	X	X	1	1
0	0	0	0	0	$\overline{E0}$
0	0	0	1	0	$\overline{E1}$
0	0	1	0	0	$\overline{E2}$
0	0	1	1	0	$\overline{E3}$
0	1	0	0	0	$\overline{E4}$
0	1	0	1	0	$\overline{E5}$
0	1	1	0	0	$\overline{E6}$
0	1	1	1	0	$\overline{E7}$
1	0	0	0	0	$\overline{E8}$
1	0	0	1	0	$\overline{E9}$
1	0	1	0	0	$\overline{E10}$
1	0	1	1	0	$\overline{E11}$
1	1	0	0	0	$\overline{E12}$
1	1	0	1	0	$\overline{E13}$
1	1	1	0	0	$\overline{E14}$
1	1	1	1	0	$\overline{E15}$

^{a}X = don't care.

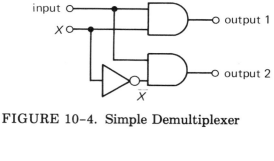

FIGURE 10-4. Simple Demultiplexer

□ DEMULTIPLEXERS

The concept of demultiplexing signals is easily visualized in a diagram like that of Figure 10-4. The demultiplexer has a single input that goes to the proper output, as specified by the X and $\overline{X}$ signals. If X is 1, the upper AND gate is enabled and the signal passes through. A 0 on the X input activates the lower gate, allowing the input to appear at output 2. Table 10-3 summarizes these outcomes.

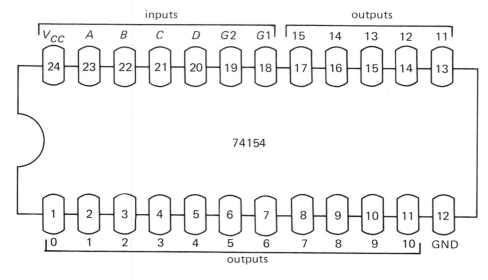

FIGURE 10-5. 74154 Demultiplexer

TABLE 10–3. Simple Demultiplexer Functions

Input			Output	
Select				
X	$\overline{X}$	Input	1	2
1	0	0	0	0
1	0	1	1	0
0	1	0	0	0
0	1	1	0	1

The 74154 demultiplexer circuit, shown in Figure 10–5, causes the output line identified by the select inputs to become 0 (low). All other output lines remain at the 1 level. For proper operation, the $G1$ and $G2$ strobe signals must both be 0. Table 10–4 lists the functions for the demultiplexer.

While perhaps not immediately obvious, the 74154 converts binary numbers to their hexadecimal equivalents. Note from the table that the output line that is 0 corresponds to the hexadecimal digit equal to that binary input.

☐ EXAMPLE 10–2

The discussion above described how 4 bits can be converted to a hexadecimal digit by using the 74154. How can this technique be extended to binary numbers 12 bits long?

Solution Recall, from the number conversion methods, that a binary number can be converted to a hexadecimal number by simply forming groups of 4 bits. The desired 12-bit conversion is achieved by dividing the number into three sets of 4 bits each and applying them to the input terminals of three 74154 demultiplexers. Figure 10–6 shows the circuit configuration.

☐ EXAMPLE 10–3

How can conversion from a binary number to an octal number be performed?

Solution Use only three select inputs to the 74154. The D select input is always grounded. Any binary number can be changed to an octal number by use of multiple 74154s, as in Example 10–2. The only change needed for this example is to group the binary input in units of three bits instead of four bits.

TABLE 10–4. 74154 Demultiplexer Functions

Strobe		Select				Output															
$G1$	$G2$	D	C	B	A	0	1	2	3	4	5	6	7	8	9	10	11	12	13	14	15
0	0	0	0	0	0	0	1	1	1	1	1	1	1	1	1	1	1	1	1	1	1
0	0	0	0	0	1	1	0	1	1	1	1	1	1	1	1	1	1	1	1	1	1
0	0	0	0	1	0	1	1	0	1	1	1	1	1	1	1	1	1	1	1	1	1
0	0	0	0	1	1	1	1	1	0	1	1	1	1	1	1	1	1	1	1	1	1
0	0	0	1	0	0	1	1	1	1	0	1	1	1	1	1	1	1	1	1	1	1
0	0	0	1	0	1	1	1	1	1	1	0	1	1	1	1	1	1	1	1	1	1
0	0	0	1	1	0	1	1	1	1	1	1	0	1	1	1	1	1	1	1	1	1
0	0	0	1	1	1	1	1	1	1	1	1	1	0	1	1	1	1	1	1	1	1
0	0	1	0	0	0	1	1	1	1	1	1	1	1	0	1	1	1	1	1	1	1
0	0	1	0	0	1	1	1	1	1	1	1	1	1	1	0	1	1	1	1	1	1
0	0	1	0	1	0	1	1	1	1	1	1	1	1	1	1	0	1	1	1	1	1
0	0	1	0	1	1	1	1	1	1	1	1	1	1	1	1	1	0	1	1	1	1
0	0	1	1	0	0	1	1	1	1	1	1	1	1	1	1	1	1	0	1	1	1
0	0	1	1	0	1	1	1	1	1	1	1	1	1	1	1	1	1	1	0	1	1
0	0	1	1	1	0	1	1	1	1	1	1	1	1	1	1	1	1	1	1	0	1
0	0	1	1	1	1	1	1	1	1	1	1	1	1	1	1	1	1	1	1	1	0
0	1	X[a]	X	X	X	1	1	1	1	1	1	1	1	1	1	1	1	1	1	1	1
1	0	X	X	X	X	1	1	1	1	1	1	1	1	1	1	1	1	1	1	1	1
1	1	X	X	X	X	1	1	1	1	1	1	1	1	1	1	1	1	1	1	1	1

[a]X = don't care.

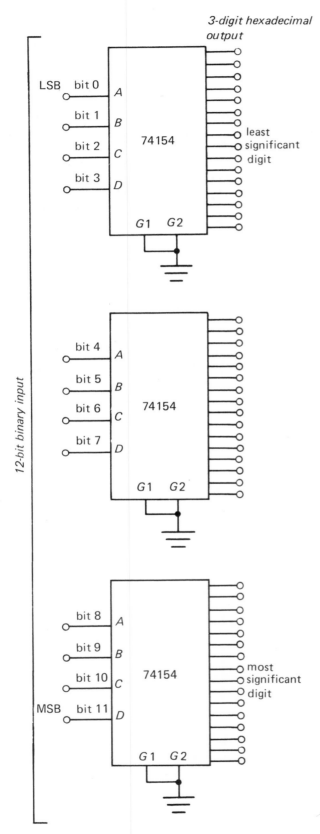

FIGURE 10-6. Binary to Hexadecimal
Conversion

☐ BINARY-CODED DECIMAL CONVERSION

A very simple procedure allows us to change binary-coded decimal (BCD) numbers to true decimal numbers. A binary-coded decimal number represents each decimal digit as a four-bit binary unit. Calculator keyboards often use BCD. In BCD, each decimal digit is written as a separate group. Some examples are shown below.

Decimal	BCD
0	0000
1	0001
5	0101
50	0101 0000
99	1001 1001
3768	0011 0111 0110 1000

BCD is a useful representation of decimal digits, but it should not be used in ordinary arithmetic circuits. The error that can occur is readily seen by adding 1 to the BCD equivalent of 9.

Decimal	BCD
9_{10}	1001
$+\ 1_{10}$	$+\ 1$
10_{10}	1010

This answer is wrong because the BCD form of 10_{10} is 0001 0000.

The 7442 integrated circuit is a demultiplexer that converts BCD inputs to decimal out-

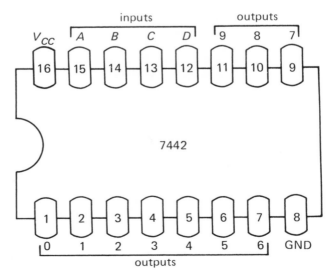

FIGURE 10-7. 7442 BCD-to-Decimal Converter

TABLE 10–5. 7442 BCD-to-Decimal Converter Functions

Input				Output									
D	C	B	A	0	1	2	3	4	5	6	7	8	9
0	0	0	0	0	1	1	1	1	1	1	1	1	1
0	0	0	1	1	0	1	1	1	1	1	1	1	1
0	0	1	0	1	1	0	1	1	1	1	1	1	1
0	0	1	1	1	1	1	0	1	1	1	1	1	1
0	1	0	0	1	1	1	1	0	1	1	1	1	1
0	1	0	1	1	1	1	1	1	0	1	1	1	1
0	1	1	0	1	1	1	1	1	1	0	1	1	1
0	1	1	1	1	1	1	1	1	1	1	0	1	1
1	0	0	0	1	1	1	1	1	1	1	1	0	1
1	0	0	1	1	1	1	1	1	1	1	1	1	0
			Invalid Inputs										
1	0	1	0	1	1	1	1	1	1	1	1	1	1
1	0	1	1	1	1	1	1	1	1	1	1	1	1
1	1	0	0	1	1	1	1	1	1	1	1	1	1
1	1	0	1	1	1	1	1	1	1	1	1	1	1
1	1	1	0	1	1	1	1	1	1	1	1	1	1
1	1	1	1	1	1	1	1	1	1	1	1	1	1

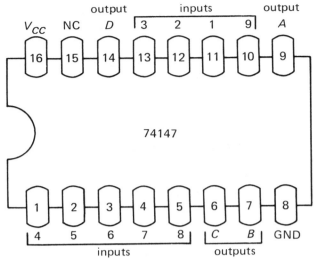

NC = not connected

FIGURE 10–8. 74147 Decimal-to-BCD Converter

puts. Its operation is much like that of the 74154 described above. As Figure 10–7 shows, the BCD-to-decimal converter has four input and ten output pins. Operation is shown in Table 10–5.

There are no strobe inputs for this converter. The output line corresponding to the BCD input code becomes 0. If the input code is more than 1001, all output lines go to 1, because there is no decimal digit greater than 9.

□ CODE CONVERTERS

Continuing the discussion of BCD conversion, we next investigate changing from a decimal input to a BCD number. The 74147 integrated circuit will be used. This device is shown in Figure 10–8 (where NC means not connected). Its functions are described in Table 10–6.

As an example of how the converter is used, a keyboard input will be examined. From Table 10–6, we see that the highest-numbered input controls the operation. If both the 9 and 7 inputs are low, the 9 input dictates the output. This scheme is a **priority encoding scheme**, which means that the inputs are ranked in some order. The highest-ranked input overrides a lower-ranked one.

TABLE 10–6. 74147 Decimal-to-BCD Converter Functions

Input									Output[a]			
1	2	3	4	5	6	7	8	9	D	C	B	A
H	H	H	H	H	H	H	H	H	1	1	1	1
X[b]	X	X	X	X	X	X	X	L	0	1	1	0
X	X	X	X	X	X	H	L	H	0	1	1	1
X	X	X	X	X	X	L	H	H	1	0	0	0
X	X	X	X	X	L	H	H	H	1	0	0	1
X	X	X	X	L	H	H	H	H	1	0	1	0
X	X	X	L	H	H	H	H	H	1	0	1	1
X	X	L	H	H	H	H	H	H	1	1	0	0
X	L	H	H	H	H	H	H	H	1	1	0	1
L	H	H	H	H	H	H	H	H	1	1	1	0

[a]The output corresponds to a complemented BCD code.
[b]X = don't care.

Another feature shown in the table is that the BCD outputs are inverted. Each bit must be complemented to see the actual BCD code. Taking the second row as an example, we have

0110, which when inverted is 1001 = 9_{10}

This IC is designed to be used with a keyboard that produces a ground signal when a key is depressed. Figure 10–9 shows how the key for number 9 is connected to the encoder to produce the correct BCD code. When the key is pressed, the switch is closed grounding the 9 input. Regardless of the other inputs (because of the priority encoding), the inverted BCD code for 9 will be generated. Inverters on the 74147 output lines in the figure change the code to the usual BCD representation for 9. The other keys are connected in the same manner, with each key switch going to its corresponding input pin on the 74147.

☐ DIGITAL COMPARATORS

Sometimes the action of a digital circuit depends on the relative magnitudes of two quantities. For instance, the example earlier of the thermostat re-

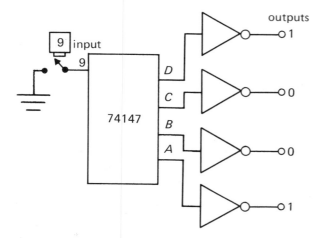

FIGURE 10-9. Keyboard Decoding

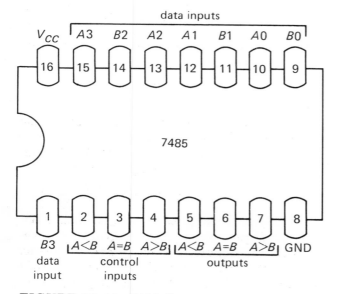

FIGURE 10-10. 7485 Comparator

quired the temperature measured by a thermal sensor to be compared with the temperature at which the heater is to turn on. In general, the magnitudes of the two inputs may be related by the expressions

$$A > B$$
$$A = B$$
$$A < B$$

Combinations of these relationships also give us

$$A \geq B$$
$$A \neq B$$
$$A \leq B$$

A general-purpose comparator is available in the 7485 integrated circuit. Each 7485 unit can make a comparison of four bits, but cascading permits numbers of any length to be compared. The circuit configuration is shown in Figure 10-10. Table 10-7 describes the functions of the comparator. Each bit of the two inputs is numbered, with $A3$ or $B3$ being the MSB and $A0$ or $B0$ being the LSB. For example,

A	$= 0101$	B	$= 1011$
$A3$	$= 0$	$B3$	$= 1$
$A2$	$= 1$	$B2$	$= 0$
$A1$	$= 0$	$B1$	$= 1$
$A0$	$= 1$	$B0$	$= 1$

Table 10-7 is somewhat complicated and is best understood by dividing it into sections. For now, ignore the control input column. Considering the first eight rows, we see that the numbers are unequal in all these cases. Because the comparisons begin with the MSBs, the larger number will be found as soon as one bit exceeds the other. In the example above, B is greater than A, because $B3 = 1$ while $A3 = 0$. In all eight rows, either the $A > B$ or $A < B$ output becomes 1.

The complications appear in the last five rows of the table. The inputs are equal in all these cases, and the output depends on the control inputs. The control inputs use identifications similar to those of the outputs, so be careful to distinguish one from the other. For the time being, do not be concerned about the meaning of the control inputs. Their function will become clear in the discussion on cascading comparators that follows.

Let us return to analyzing the table. When only one of the control inputs is a 1, then the outputs are the same as the control inputs. If the $A = B$ control input is 1, only the $A = B$ output is 1.

TABLE 10-7. 7485 Comparator Functions

Input										
Comparing				Control			Output			
$A3, B3$	$A2, B2$	$A1, B1$	$A0, B0$	$A>B$	$A=B$	$A<B$	$A>B$	$A=B$	$A<B$
$A3 > B3$	X[a]	X	X	X	X	X	1	0	0
$A3 < B3$	X	X	X	X	X	X	0	0	1
$A3 = B3$	$A2 > B2$	X	X	X	X	X	1	0	0
$A3 = B3$	$A2 < B2$	X	X	X	X	X	0	0	1
$A3 = B3$	$A2 = B2$	$A1 > B1$	X	X	X	X	1	0	0
$A3 = B3$	$A2 = B2$	$A1 < B1$	X	X	X	X	0	0	1
$A3 = B3$	$A2 = B2$	$A1 = B1$	$A0 > B0$	X	X	X	1	0	0
$A3 = B3$	$A2 = B2$	$A1 = B1$	$A0 < B0$	X	X	X	0	0	1
$A3 = B3$	$A2 = B2$	$A1 = B1$	$A0 = B0$	1	0	0	1	0	0
$A3 = B3$	$A2 = B2$	$A1 = B1$	$A0 = B0$	0	0	1	0	0	1
$A3 = B3$	$A2 = B2$	$A1 = B1$	$A0 = B0$	X	1	X	0	1	0
$A3 = B3$	$A2 = B2$	$A1 = B1$	$A0 = B0$	1	0	1	0	0	0
$A3 = B3$	$A2 = B2$	$A1 = B1$	$A0 = B0$	0	0	0	1	0	1

[a]X = don't care.

When the $A > B$ and $A < B$ control inputs are both 1s, all outputs are 0s. Finally, if all control inputs are 0, the $A > B$ and $A < B$ outputs are 1.

□ **EXAMPLE 10-4**

Show how the 7485 comparator can be used to produce a 1 output when $A \geq B$.

Solution The obvious solution is to OR the outputs $A = B$ and $A > B$.

□ **EXAMPLE 10-5**

How can eight-bit binary quantities be compared by combinations of 7485 circuits?

Solution Figure 10-11 shows a solution. Of importance in the figure are the interconnections of outputs and control inputs. (All other inputs, not shown in the figure, to the second-stage comparator are grounded.)

The upper first-stage comparator takes care of the most significant four bits, and the lower first-stage comparator handles the least significant four bits. For both comparators, the $A = B$ control input is tied high, while the other two control inputs are grounded. Only when all eight bits of both numbers are equal will the control input affect the outcome. Then, the $A = B$ output of lower comparator will be 1, and the two outputs of the upper comparator will be 0. These inputs into the second-stage comparator will produce a 1 at the $A = B$ output.

For all other situations, the inputs will be unequal. If the inequality is found in any of the most significant four bits, the output of the upper first-stage comparator will indicate which is larger. These outputs are connected to the second stage to generate the correct output. (For example, if $A > B$ is 1 from the first stage, $A3$ of the second stage is 1 and $B3$ of the second stage must be 0.)

If the most significant four bits are equal, the inequality of one of the least significant four bits will produce a 1 on either the $A > B$ or $A < B$ output of the lower first-stage comparator. Remembering that the $A3$ and $B3$ inputs to the second-stage comparator must be 0, we conclude that the output of the second stage will be the same as the control inputs. That is, if $A > B$ from the first stage is 1, the $A > B$ output of the second stage will be 1. In this circuit, the conditions in the last two rows of Table 10-7 are never allowed.

□ **ARITHMETIC LOGIC UNIT**

Many of the arithmetic, Boolean, and comparator operations that we have examined in the in-

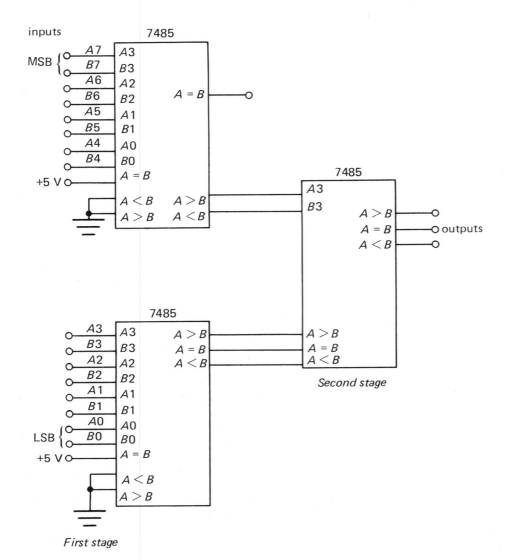

inputs

FIGURE 10–11.
Comparison of
Eight-Bit Quantities

dividual devices can all be found in one "super chip," the 74181 ALU. This single IC can add, subtract, compare, invert, AND, NAND, OR, NOR, and exclusive OR the two 4-bit inputs. Figure 10–12 shows the circuit. Table 10–8 gives a functional listing for the IC.

Table 10–8 is most easily analyzed by breaking it into pieces. From Figure 10–12, we note that there are five groups of inputs:

- $A3, A2, A1, A0$: A input (four bits);
- $B3, B2, B1, B0$: B input (four bits);
- $S3, S2, S1, S0$: selection input (four bits);
- M: mode selection (0 = Boolean logic, 1 = arithmetic);
- $\overline{C}_n$: carry-in from a lower stage (used with cascaded ALUs).

The various column headings in the table indicate which condition applies for these input values. The four left columns list all possible values for the selection input. The next column is used when $M = 0$; that is, when Boolean logic functions are to be performed. The next two columns apply when $M = 1$. Although called the arithmetic mode, logic functions are also included in these columns. The next to last column is used when there is no carry input ($C_n = 0$, so $\overline{C}_n = 1$), and the last column is applicable when there is an input carry ($C_n = 1$, so $\overline{C}_n = 0$). The output bits in Figure 10–12 are labeled $F3$ through $F0$. The C_{n+4} output is the carry-out for the MSB of any arithmetic operation.

Once the columns of the table are sorted out and associated with the elements of Figure 10–12, the use of the ALU is not complicated.

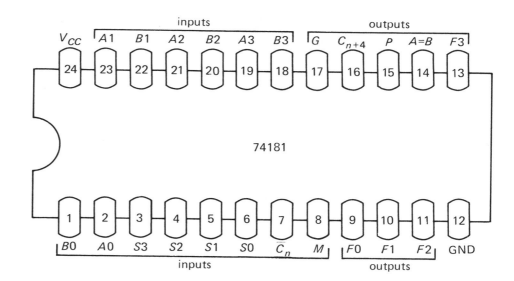

FIGURE 10-12.
74181 ALU

□ **EXAMPLE 10-6**

Determine the functions performed for the following inputs:

1. $S = 0110$
   $M = 0$
   $\overline{C}_n = 0$

2. $S = 1100$
   $M = 1$
   $\overline{C}_n = 1$

Solution

1. The mode selection is logic, so the $\overline{C}_n$ input is ignored. The selection ($S3 = 0$, $S2 = 1$, $S1 = 1$, $S0 = 0$) specifies that $F = A \oplus B$, the exclusive OR operation.

2. The mode is arithmetic, with no carry. The selection bits specify $F = A + A$. This operation doubles the A input.

TABLE 10-8. 74181 Arithmetic Logic Unit Functions

Selection				$M = 0$, Logic Functions	$M = 1$, Arithmetic Functions[a]	
$S3$	$S2$	$S1$	$S0$		$\overline{C}_n = 1$ (No Carry)	$\overline{C}_n = 0$ (With Carry)
0	0	0	0	$F = \overline{A}$	$F = A$	$F = A + 1$
0	0	0	1	$F = \overline{A \text{ OR } B}$	$F = A \text{ OR } B$	$F = (A \text{ OR } B) + 1$
0	0	1	0	$F = \overline{A}B$	$F = A \text{ OR } \overline{B}$	$F = (A \text{ OR } \overline{B}) + 1$
0	0	1	1	$F = 0$	$F = -1$	$F = 0$
0	1	0	0	$F = \overline{AB}$	$F = A + A\overline{B}$	$F = A + A\overline{B} + 1$
0	1	0	1	$F = \overline{B}$	$F = (A \text{ OR } B) + A\overline{B}$	$F = (A \text{ OR } B) + A\overline{B} + 1$
0	1	1	0	$F = A \oplus B$	$F = A - B - 1$	$F = A - B$
0	1	1	1	$F = A\overline{B}$	$F = A\overline{B} - 1$	$F = A\overline{B}$
1	0	0	0	$F = \overline{A} \text{ OR } B$	$F = A + AB$	$F = A + AB + 1$
1	0	0	1	$F = A \oplus B$	$F = A + B$	$F = A + B + 1$
1	0	1	0	$F = B$	$F = (A \text{ OR } B) + AB$	$F = (A \text{ OR } B) + AB + 1$
1	0	1	1	$F = AB$	$F = AB - 1$	$F = AB$
1	1	0	0	$F = 1$	$F = A + A$	$F = A + A + 1$
1	1	0	1	$F = A \text{ OR } B$	$F = (A \text{ OR } B) + A$	$F = (A \text{ OR } B) + A + 1$
1	1	1	0	$F = A \text{ OR } \overline{B}$	$F = (A \text{ OR } \overline{B}) + A$	$F = (A \text{ OR } \overline{B}) + A + 1$
1	1	1	1	$F = A$	$F = A - 1$	$F = 1$

[a]All arithmetic uses 2's complement.

□ EXAMPLE 10-7

Determine the output for each of the following combinations of input signals:

1. $S = B_{16}$
   $A = 6_{16}$
   $B = F_{16}$
   $M = 0$
   $\overline{C}_n = 0$

2. $S = 9_{16}$
   $A = 5_{16}$
   $B = 4_{16}$
   $M = 1$
   $\overline{C}_n = 0$

Solution

1. Converting to binary numbers, we have

$$S = 1011_2$$
$$A = 0110_2$$
$$B = 1111_2$$

The operation is $F = AB$ (logic mode). ANDing each bit of A with the corresponding bit of B gives

$$A = 0110$$
$$B = \underline{1111}$$
$$F = 0110 = 6_{16}$$

2. The operation is $F = A + B$ (arithmetic mode with no carry). Thus,

$$F = 5_{16} + 4_{16} = 9_{16}$$

Chapter Summary

□ A multiplexer acts as a data selector; a demultiplexer decodes the inputs.

□ Multiplexers use networks of gates to select the proper signal. Control inputs determine the selection. Strobe signals are sometimes provided to enable or disable the chip.

□ Demultiplexers use select inputs to designate where the signal will be routed. Strobe signals are often provided on demultiplexers.

□ Conversion between binary or decimal numbers and BCD numbers can be accomplished with an IC converter, such as the 7442.

□ Code converters are forms of demultiplexers adapted to specific functions.

□ Digital comparators indicate equality or inequality of the input numbers. If the numbers are not equal, the larger one is identified.

□ Arithmetic logic units can do arithmetic, execute Boolean operations, and compare the input quantities.

Problems

10-1. Find the BCD equivalents for the following decimal numbers:

a. 5
b. 199
c. 2673
d. 84005

10-2. What decimal numbers do the following BCD codes represent?

a. 0101 1001 1000
b. 1000 0001 0000 0100
c. 0010 0011 0111 0100
d. 0110 0101 0100 0010

10-3. With the inputs given below applied to the 74150 MUX, what will the output be?

a. strobe = 1
   $A = 1$
   $B = 1$
   $C = 1$
   $D = 0$
   $E13 = 0$
   $E14 = 1$
   $E15 = 1$

b. strobe = 0
   $A = 0$
   $B = 1$
   $C = 1$
   $D = 0$
   $E5 = 0$
   $E6 = 1$
   $E7 = 1$

10-4. What inputs to the 74154 DEMUX produce a low on output line 8?

10-5. Determine the output from Figure 10-8 for the following input conditions:

input 9 $= H$ input 7 $= H$
input 8 $= L$ input 6 $= L$

All other inputs are high.

10-6. How could an indication that A and B are unequal be produced by the 7485 comparator? What gates need to be placed on the outputs to generate a signal corresponding to $A \leq B$. (See Example 10-4.)

10-7. The inputs below are applied to the 74181 ALU. What function does the device perform in each case?

a. $S = 0101_2, M = 0, \overline{C}_n = 0$
b. $S = 0, M = 1, \overline{C}_n = 1$
c. $S = B_{16}, M = 1, \overline{C}_n = 0$

10-8. Find the F output of the 74181 for these input conditions:

a. $S = 1_{16}, M = 0, A = A_{16}, B = 3_{16}$
b. $S = 3_{16}, M = 1, A = 5_{16}, B = D_{16}, \overline{C}_n = 1$
c. $S = 9_{16}, M = 1, A = 5_{16}, B = 7_{16}, \overline{C}_n = 1$

10-9. If you want to subtract the B input to the 74181 from the A input, what other input settings are necessary?

10-10. The signals applied to the inputs of the circuit in Figure 10-11 are listed below. Find the value of the outputs from all first- and second-stage comparators.

$$A = F3_{16} \qquad B = F2_{16}$$

Chapter Eleven

Flip-Flops

All the circuits you have studied so far can be characterized by one distinguishing feature of the outputs. In these circuits, called **combinatorial circuits**, the outputs depend only on the present combination of inputs. **Flip-flops**, on the other hand, are classed as **sequential circuits**. Here the outputs are controlled not only by the inputs but also by the output state existing prior to the change of the input levels.

Another distinguishing feature of flip-flops is their ability to *store*, or hold, a particular value. The output of the flip-flop remains at the previous setting, even after the inputs are removed. As you recall, combinatorial circuits have no such memory characteristics. Instead, the output is valid only as long as the inputs are constant.

Chapter Objectives

Upon completion of this chapter, you should be able to:

- ☐ Analyze the operation of a debounced switch.
- ☐ Relate input levels to the outputs on a flip-flop timing diagram.
- ☐ Explain the action of a flip-flop by using state diagrams.
- ☐ Predict the output of an *RS* flip-flop for any combination of inputs.
- ☐ Show how a *JK* flip-flop functions by means of state tables.
- ☐ Distinguish between pulse and edge triggering.
- ☐ Describe the actions of *T* and *D* flip-flops.

☐ DEBOUNCED SWITCH

When a mechanical switch is used in conjunction with electronic circuits, unreliable switching occurs unless proper *conditioning* is provided. A conditioning circuit frequently selected is the **switch debouncer** of Figure 11-1. (The numerals in the figure identify pin numbers.)

The switching problem that must be avoided is illustrated in Figure 11-2a. As shown in the figure, the unconditioned switch can produce a very ragged transient. Because the contact in the switch is a spring, when the switch closes, the circuit can be made and broken several times. The output voltage thus varies considerably, and the circuit may react to several closures rather than to just one, as desired. Furthermore, as the switch is thrown, the output changes from +5 V to 0 V very slowly. The debounced switch, on the other hand, has a much improved transient performance, as shown in Figure 11-2b.

Using a NAND gate truth table (Table 11-1), we can readily determine the output levels for Figure 11-1. Note that if the gate has either or both inputs equal to 0, the output must be a 1. The upper gate in the figure has a 0 input to pin 1 because of the grounded switch. Therefore, the output of pin 3 must be 1. The lower gate has both inputs equal to 1. (A direct connection to the power supply on pin 5 and pin 3 is fed back to pin 4.) The output of the lower gate is 0, which feeds back to pin 2 of the upper gate. This feedback signal also guarantees that the upper gate output will be 1. In tabular form, we have so far

Input			
R	S	Output 1	Output 2
0	1	1	0

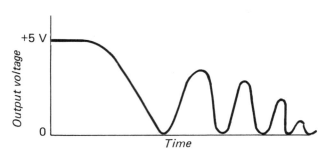

(a) Unconditioned-Switch Waveform

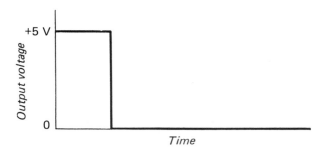

(b) Debounced-Switch Waveform

FIGURE 11-2. Switching Transients

TABLE 11-1. NAND Gate

Input		
A	B	Output
0	0	1
0	1	1
1	0	1
1	1	0

Note: Numerals identify pin numbers.

FIGURE 11-1. Switch Debouncer Constructed from 7400 NAND Gates

Now let the switch be thrown to position 2. While the switch is between the two positions, both gates have an input of 1 (on pins 1 and 5). The outputs can be found again by using the NAND gate truth table and also remembering the previous output states. We have

pin 1 = 1   pin 4 = 1
pin 2 = 0   pin 5 = 1

The 1 and 0 inputs to the upper gate hold its output at the 1 level, while two 1s into the lower gate keep its output at 0. This situation is called the **no-change input condition.**

Finally, the switch makes contact in the bottom position. Even if it bounces up immediately (because of the spring), contact will be long enough for the gates to react. Recall that the 7400 NAND gate has a propagation delay of only a few nanoseconds, which is much faster than the switch can bounce. Eventually, the switch does stay in position 2, but the output is already in the correct state.

The lower gate now has an input of 0 on pin 5, so its output level must rise to a 1. But before that level changed, the upper gate still had inputs of 1 and 0. So it will not respond until after the signal has propagated through the lower NAND gate. Sensing the new input on pin 2, the upper gate now has both inputs equal to 1, so its output goes to 0. The feedback of that output to pin 4 causes no additional response in the lower gate. Thus, the circuit outputs have reversed states.

Another feature of the debounced switch is that the switching time of the signal on output 1 is as fast as the TTL gates allow. Thus, it produces a crisp square wave rather than a slowly changing voltage (Figure 11-2b).

□ *RS* FLIP-FLOPS

The switch debouncer is an example of a **latch circuit.** A more general example of the latch circuit is an *RS flip-flop.* This flip-flop has two inputs: the S or *set* signal and the R or *reset* signal. Operation of the flip-flop is described by a **state table,** like that of Table 11-2. This table is best understood through the use of an *RS* flip-flop timing diagram.

Starting with an initial set condition (output 1 equal to 1), we can develop a timing diagram like the one in Figure 11-3. This diagram is based on Table 11-2. All inputs and outputs are ex-

TABLE 11-2. *RS* Flip-Flop State Table

Input		Output	
S	R	Output 1	Output 2
1	0	1	0
0	1	0	1
0	0	No change	No change
1	1	Forbidden state	Forbidden state

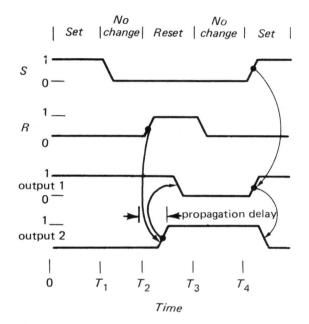

FIGURE 11-3. *RS* Flip-Flop Timing Diagram

plicitly shown. The situation shown between time 0 and time T_1 is a result of the initial conditions.

At time T_1, the S signal goes to 0. No change in the outputs is observed until time T_2. Then input R becomes a 1. After a small propagation delay, the change of the R signal causes output 2 to rise to 1 (indicated on the timing diagram by arrows). Following another small propagation delay, the change in output 2 causes output 1 to fall to 0.

At time T_3, the R input becomes 0, but the outputs do not vary. A rising S input at time T_4 causes output 1 to rise, which, in turn, causes output 2 to fall.

Observe that the various time intervals on the diagram are denoted by labels at the top. When both inputs are set to 0, the no-change situation prevails. When the reset input changes from 0 to 1, output 2 becomes a 1. This situation is called the **reset state**. When the S input makes a transition from 0 to 1, output 1 is forced to 1, or the **set state**.

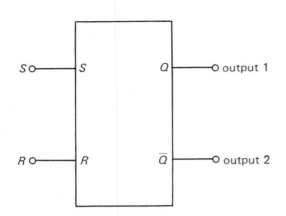

FIGURE 11-4. RS Flip-Flop Symbol

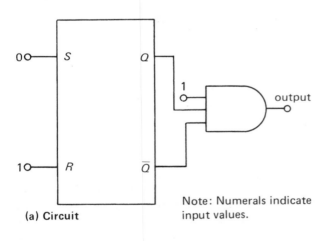

(a) Circuit

Note: Numerals indicate input values.

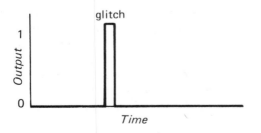

(b) AND Gate Output Timing Diagram

FIGURE 11-5. Flip-Flop and Gate Circuit with a Glitch

☐ FLIP-FLOP OUTPUTS

Figure 11-4 shows the schematic diagram symbol for an RS flip-flop. The outputs are labeled Q and $\overline{Q}$, corresponding to output 1 and output 2, respectively. As the nomenclature indicates, the Q and $\overline{Q}$ outputs *should* always be in opposite states. Opposite states for Q and $\overline{Q}$ are not always achieved, however. Refer to the last row of Table 11-2, labeled "forbidden state." This term is not meant to imply that any damage will result if both inputs are simultaneously set to 1. Rather, the meaning is that the Q and $\overline{Q}$ outputs under those circumstances are meaningless. For a particular RS flip-flop, the Q and $\overline{Q}$ outputs may both be the same, or they may be unpredictable when the forbidden state occurs. In any case, in this state the outputs are not opposites. Hence, this state must be avoided in normal operation.

Another time when the two outputs are equal was shown in Figure 11-3. Following T_2, output 2 ($\overline{Q}$) becomes a 1 before output 1 (Q) can fall to 0. This brief overlap can often be ignored, but it may cause problems in some cases.

Consider the circuit shown in Figure 11-5a. The inputs to the flip-flop have just changed to those shown (numbers indicate input values), and the expected output from the AND gate is a value of 0. After a propagation delay, both Q and $\overline{Q}$ are 1 for a very small period of time. If that time is about the same as the gate propagation time, a short pulse, or **glitch**, will appear on the output line (Figure 11-5b). Of course, the output level for the gate eventually reaches the expected value. But a glitch, such as the one produced here, can ripple through a logic network and cause false triggering of several gates. Therefore, glitch detection is an important factor in troubleshooting.

☐ EXAMPLE 11-1

An RS flip-flop currently has the following output levels:

$$Q = 1 \qquad \overline{Q} = 0$$

Determine the changes produced by the following inputs:

1. $S = 0$
2. $S = 0, R = 1$

Solution

1. For this case, there will be no change in Q or $\overline{Q}$. To reach this conclusion, refer to Table

11-2. The outputs could be in the given states only if the previous inputs were $S = 1$ and $R = 0$ or if both inputs were previously 0. No matter which input condition was the previous one, making S equal to 0 will produce no change in the output.

2. In this case, a reset condition is created. Output $\overline{Q}$ becomes 1 and Q becomes 0.

□ STATE DIAGRAM

An efficient way to depict the state table for a flip-flop is by using a **state diagram**. The diagram uses symbols to show each row of the table. Figure 11-6 shows a state diagram corresponding to Table 11-2.

In the diagram, each circle represents one of the output states of the flip-flop. The arrows indicate transitions between states with the input values written above. For example, an input of $S = 0, R = 1$ will cause the flip-flop to change from the set to the reset state. (This state transition matches the second row of Table 11-2.) Note that the no change combination of inputs is shown by an arrow going back into the current state; that is, if the flip-flop is in the set state, it remains in the set state.

The state diagram is often drawn in a simplified form as shown in Figure 11-7. Only inputs that cause transitions are shown above the arrows. That means in this case, all inputs producing no change do not appear.

□ EXAMPLE 11-2

From the state diagram in Figure 11-6, what combination of inputs will make the RS flip-flop change from the reset to the set state?

Solution The arrow on the diagram for the specified state change shows that $S = 1, R = 0$. So the answer is

$$S = 1$$
$$R = 0$$

One useful version of the RS flip-flop is provided by the 74279 integrated circuit. As Figure 11-8 shows, this package contains four RS flip-flops in a configuration almost identical to the circuit used in the switch debouncer.

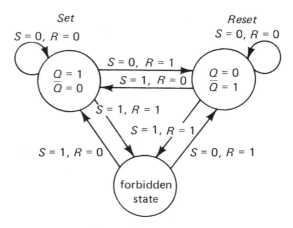

FIGURE 11-6. RS Flip-Flop State Diagram

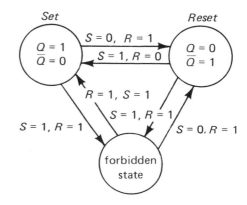

FIGURE 11-7. Simplified RS Flip-Flop State Diagram

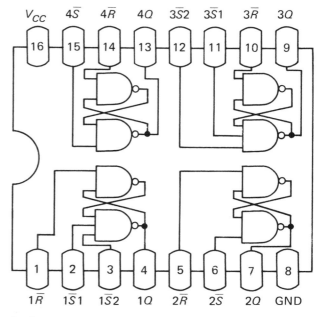

FIGURE 11-8. 74279 Quad RS Flip-Flop

To convert the voltage levels of the quad *RS* flip-flop circuit to the state table shown for the *RS* flip-flop, you must use an inverted input level (see Tables 11-3 and 11-4). The bar over the input signals indicates the inversion that takes place.

Several points should be noted from Tables 11-3 and 11-4. First, there is no $\overline{Q}$ output. Also, the inputs must be inverted for the "normal" state table to result. The first two rows of the state table (Table 11-4) are the same set and reset states discussed earlier. In the third row, the output is marked Q_0, which represents the Q output before the indicated input conditions were

established. In other words, this is the no-change condition. Finally, in the fourth row, the forbidden state is shown, in which the output is unstable. That is, it will not remain the same when the inputs go to the no-change state. As previously observed, the forbidden state would usually not be used in ordinary circuits.

TABLE 11-3. 74279 Flip-Flop Voltage Table

Input		
$\overline{R}$	$\overline{S}$	Output, Q
L	H	H
H	L	L
H	H	Q_0
L	L	H^a

^{a}Unstable state.

TABLE 11-4. 74279 *RS* Flip-Flop State Table

Input		Corrected Input		
R	S	$\overline{R}$	$\overline{S}$	Output, Q
0	1	1	0	1
1	0	0	1	0
1	1	0	0	Q_0
0	0	1	1	1^a

^{a}Unstable state.

TABLE 11-5. *JK* Flip-Flop State Table

Input		Output		
J	K	Q	$\overline{Q}$	State
1	0	1	0	Set
0	1	0	1	Reset
0	0	Q_0	$\overline{Q}_0$	No change
1	1	$\overline{Q}_0$	Q_0	Toggle

□ **EXAMPLE 11-3**

Explain how the 74279 IC could be used in place of the 7400 gates for a switch debouncer.

Solution For this situation, the switch could be connected so that switch terminal 1 goes to pin 5 and switch terminal 2 to pin 6 of the IC. The output is taken from pin 7. A $\overline{Q}$ output is not really necessary in a debounced switch, since only one voltage is called for. The Q output is sufficient.

□ *JK* FLIP-FLOPS

The *JK* flip-flop is undoubtedly used more widely than the *RS* flip-flop. The characteristics of the *JK* flip-flop are shown in its state table (Table 11-5).

This table is similar to earlier ones, except the inputs are designated *J* and *K*. One difference you will note is the lack of a forbidden state. Also, when both inputs are 1s, the outputs *exchange* values. As shown in the last row of the table, Q becomes $\overline{Q}_0$ and $\overline{Q}$ becomes Q_0.

□ **EXAMPLE 11-4**

Prior to the change in inputs, the outputs of a *JK* flip-flop are

$$Q = 1 \qquad \overline{Q} = 0$$

If both J and K are set to 1, what are the new output states?

Solution Q simply takes on the previous state of $\overline{Q}$ and vice versa. The final states are

$$Q = 0 \qquad \overline{Q} = 1$$

This state is often referred to as the **toggle input combination**. The toggle state eliminates a forbidden state for the *JK* flip-flop.

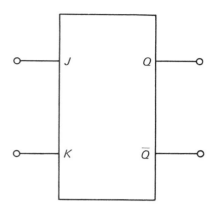

FIGURE 11-9. *JK* Flip-Flop Symbol

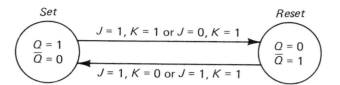

FIGURE 11-10. *JK* Flip-Flop State Diagram

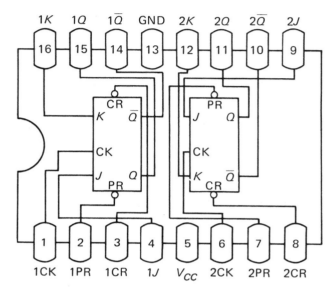

FIGURE 11-11. 7476 *JK* Flip-Flop

The schematic symbol for a *JK* flip-flop is shown in Figure 11-9. It is quite similar to the *RS* flip-flop symbol. The *J* terminal is the input used to set the flip-flop, while the *K* terminal causes the reset condition.

A state diagram can be readily drawn from Table 11-5. See Figure 11-10. Because the forbidden state has been removed, only the set and reset states appear. Remember that the no-change inputs are not shown on the diagram.

The 7476 IC is a typical example of the *JK* flip-flop. Its state table is shown in Table 11-6, and a diagram of the chip is illustrated in Figure 11-11.

The 7476 is a dual flip-flop package. This flip-flop has three extra terminals in addition to the inputs you have seen so far: the clock (CK), preset (PR), and clear (CR) inputs. These inputs also appear in the table.

We will examine the preset and clear inputs first. As their names indicate, these inputs can be used to establish a known initial condition before other inputs are applied to the flip-flop. You might want to accomplish this condition, for example, just after applying power to the circuit.

A 0 on the preset and 1 on the clear inputs produces the same state as a set input. This event occurs no matter what the levels of the other inputs are. (The X's on the table for "don't care" values of all other inputs indicate that the preset input will force the outputs to this state.) In the same way, a 0 on the clear and a 1 on the preset inputs establish the outputs in a clear state. If both the preset and clear inputs are 0, an unstable output state like the forbidden *RS* flip-flop state results. Usually, this state is avoided. Because negative logic is used on the preset and clear in-

TABLE 11-6. 7476 *JK* Flip-Flop

Input					Output	
Preset	Clear	Clock[a]	J^a	K^a	Q	$\overline{Q}$
0	1	X	X	X	1	0
1	0	X	X	X	0	1
0	0	X	X	X	1^b	1^b
1	1	⊓	0	0	Q_0	$\overline{Q}_0$
1	1	⊓	1	0	1	0
1	1	⊓	0	1	0	1
1	1	⊓	1	1	$\overline{Q}_0$	Q_0

[a]X = don't care.
[b]Unstable output condition.

puts (a 0 activates them), an inverter bubble is shown on the schematic for these signals (see Figure 11-11).

When the preset and clear inputs are both 1s, the normal *JK* flip-flop actions are enabled. At

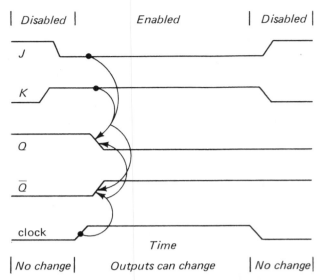

FIGURE 11-12. Clocked *JK* Flip-Flop Timing Diagram

this point, the clock input becomes important. The small "pulse" signal in the clock column of Table 11-6 indicates that the flip-flop can change in response to the *J* and *K* inputs only during the high-level pulse of the clock signal (which is, of course, a rectangular pulse train). This type of clocking is called **pulse triggering**. When the clock signal is low, the flip-flop is disabled and

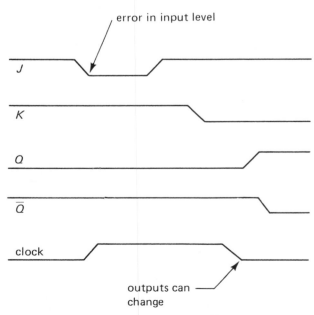

FIGURE 11-13. Negative Edge Triggering

cannot respond to changes in the *J* and *K* values (see Figure 11-12). The disable period is the time when new signal levels are applied. Because the flip-flop is disabled during that time, output levels remain constant. The clock input eliminates the possibility of a glitch during the time when inputs are changing. When the clock pulse is high, the 7476 implements the *JK* flip-flop state table.

☐ EDGE-TRIGGERED FLIP-FLOPS

In high-speed circuits, the time in which output levels can change becomes critical. In the 7476 flip-flop timing diagram, the outputs can switch at any time when the clock pulse is high. But sometimes this much time variation cannot be tolerated. Then, an **edge-triggered flip-flop** is used.

The 74112 is a *JK* flip-flop with negative edge triggering. As the name suggests, the output levels can change only during the brief interval when the clock pulse is going negative (Figure 11-13). At all other times, the output level is constant.

As the figure shows, even though the *J* input is erroneously allowed to go to 0 and return to 1, the outputs do not respond until the clock pulse makes its change from 1 to 0. (Positive edge triggering is used with other models of flip-flops. Then, the outputs change when the clock swings from 0 to 1.) Table 11-7 lists the states for the 74112 flip-flops.

TABLE 11-7. 74112 Negative Edge-triggered *JK* Flip-Flop

Input					Output	
Preset	Clear	Clock[a]	J	K	Q	$\overline{Q}$
0	1	X	X	X	1	0
1	0	X	X	X	0	1
0	0	X	X	X	1[b]	1[b]
1	1	↓	0	0	Q_0	$\overline{Q}_0$
1	1	↓	1	0	1	0
1	1	↓	0	1	0	1
1	1	↓	1	1	$\overline{Q}_0$	Q_0

[a]Negative edge triggering is symbolized by the arrow pointing down.
[b]Unstable output condition.

The 74112 has preset and clear inputs that work independently of the other inputs, as in previous flip-flops. The J and K inputs, at the time the clock falls, control the outputs just as any other JK flip-flop does.

□ AND-GATED *JK* FLIP-FLOPS

The 74102 AND-gated JK flip-flop, shown in Figure 11-14, is yet one more variation on the theme. This flip-flop also uses negative edge triggering. Preset and clear inputs are provided to initialize the device. The distinguishing feature of this device is in the IC inputs, which are ANDed together before being applied to the flip-flop itself. The inputs are

$$J = J1 \cdot J2 \cdot J3$$
$$K = K1 \cdot K2 \cdot K3$$

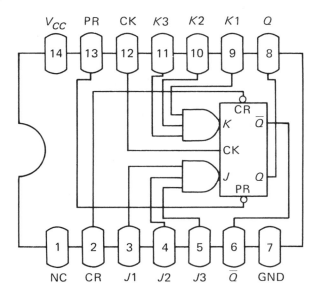

FIGURE 11-14. 74102 AND-Gated *JK* Flip-Flop

□ EXAMPLE 11-5

For the 74102 flip-flop, determine the outputs of pins 6 and 8 on the next falling clock signal for the inputs listed below:

preset $= 1$	clear $= 1$
$J1 = 0$	$K1 = 1$
$J2 = 0$	$K2 = 0$
$J3 = 1$	$K3 = 1$
$Q0 = 1$	$\bar{Q}0 = 0$

Solution The inputs to the flip-flop will be

$$J = 0 \cdot 0 \cdot 1 = 0$$
$$K = 1 \cdot 0 \cdot 1 = 0$$

The flip-flop will not change its output. So on the negative clock edge, the next output states remain the same as the preset ones.

□ *D* FLIP-FLOPS

The JK flip-flop can be modified as shown in Figure 11-15 to produce a new circuit called the *D flip-flop*. Because the J and K inputs are always forced into opposite states by the inverter, action is more limited for this device than for that of the original flip-flop. Only those input conditions corresponding to rows 1 and 3 of Table

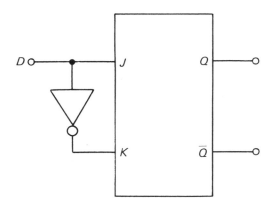

FIGURE 11-15. *D* Flip-Flop

TABLE 11-8. *D* Flip-Flop State Table

	Output	
Input, D	Q	$\bar{Q}$
0	0	1
1	1	0

11-5 are allowed. The resulting states for the new flip-flop are shown in Table 11-8.

On the clock pulse, the Q output becomes equal to the D input, *delayed* only by the propagation period. Hence, we have the name of the D

flip-flop. The *D* flip-flop is frequently used to store a value generated by other logic circuits. Its output is always the same as the input.

The 7474 IC is an example of a commercially available *D* flip-flop (see Figure 11–16). The 7474 is a dual *D* flip-flop with preset and clear inputs. It is triggered on the *positive* edge of the clock. The functions of this flip-flop are listed in Table 11–9.

For the 7474, the preset and clear inputs operate in the normal manner. The *D* input is transferred to the *Q* output on each transition of the clock from 0 to 1.

☐ *T* FLIP-FLOPS

The final type of flip-flop we will discuss is so simply constructed that it is not available from a commercial source. The *T flip-flop* is just a *JK* flip-flop with its input terminals wired together, as shown in Figure 11–17a. Now, the *J* and *K* inputs are always equal. So the *T* flip-flop states are limited to those shown in the last two rows of Table 11–5. Table 11–10 lists the possible *T* flip-flop states. The name of the circuit comes from its *toggling* of the outputs when the input is 1. The schematic symbol is shown in Figure 11–17b.

TABLE 11–10. *T* Flip-Flop State Table

	Output	
Input, T	Q	$\overline{Q}$
0	Q_0	$\overline{Q}_0$
1	$\overline{Q}_0$	Q_0

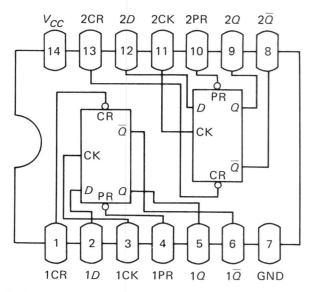

FIGURE 11–16. 7474 *D* Flip-Flop

TABLE 11–9. 7474 State Table

Input				Output	
Preset	Clear	Clock[a]	D	Q	$\overline{Q}$
0	1	X	X	1	0
1	0	X	X	0	1
0	0	X	X	1[b]	1[b]
1	1	↑	1	1	0
1	1	↑	0	0	1

[a]Positive edge triggering is symbolized by the arrow pointing up.

[b]Unstable output condition.

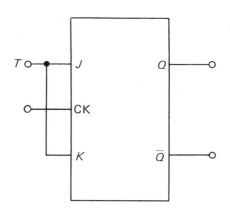

(a) Circuit

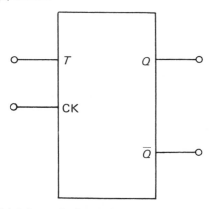

(b) Schematic Symbol

FIGURE 11–17. *T* Flip-Flop

□ **EXAMPLE 11-6**

The present states of a T flip-flop are $Q = 0$ and $\overline{Q} = 1$. What is the result of a T input of 1?

Solution The outputs toggle, so Q becomes 1 and $\overline{Q}$ changes to 0.

Chapter Summary

□ The outputs of sequential circuits, such as flip-flops, may depend on the previous output states as well as the current input levels. Flip-flops can store their last value after the inputs are removed.

□ Mechanical switches must be debounced for reliable operation in electronic circuits. An RS flip-flop is commonly used for that function.

□ A latch circuit is a form of the RS flip-flop. Its states are set, reset, no change, and forbidden. The latter state produces an unpredictable result.

□ Flip-flop operations are defined by a state table.

□ Outputs of a flip-flop are labeled Q and $\overline{Q}$, indicating that the outputs are never at the same logic levels (in normal operation).

□ A state diagram depicts the level changes of a state table.

□ The inputs to the 74279 RS flip-flop are inverted. This IC contains four RS flip-flops.

□ JK flip-flops have a toggle state in place of the forbidden state of the RS flip-flop. In other respects, the two devices are quite similar.

□ Preset and clear inputs are used to initialize the flip-flop outputs.

□ Clocked flip-flops may use either pulses or edge triggering; both positive and negative edge triggering are used.

□ Simple modifications of the JK flip-flop convert it to a D or a T flip-flop.

Problems

11-1. The switch of Figure 11-1 is in position 2 initially. Draw a timing diagram showing the change in outputs as the switch is thrown to position 1.

11-2. A negative edge-triggered clock is added to the RS flip-flop shown in Figure 11-5. Draw a timing diagram to show how the clock eliminates the glitch from the original circuit.

11-3. Draw a state diagram for the D flip-flop.

11-4. What are the outputs of an RS flip-flop if the S input is 1 and the R input is 0? The present outputs are $Q = 0$ and $\overline{Q} = 1$.

11-5. Construct the state diagram corresponding to Table 11-10.

11-6. The inputs to the 74279 flip-flop are high levels for both $\overline{R}$ and $\overline{S}$. What are the logic levels (not voltage levels) of the outputs? The previous output voltages were

$$Q = H \qquad \overline{Q} = L$$

11-7. For each situation below, find the outputs of the 7476 flip-flop. All input level changes occur while the clock is 0.

	Input				
	Preset	Clear	Clock	J	K
a.	0	1	⊓⊔	1	1
b.	1	1	⊓⊔	0	1

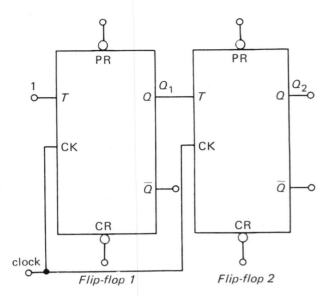

FIGURE 11-18.

11-8. Two T flip-flops are connected as shown in Figure 11-18. The input to the left flip-flop is always 1. Positive edge triggering is used, and the initial output of both flip-flops is 0. Draw a timing diagram showing the Q outputs of both flip-flops for the first five clock pulses.

11-9. Repeat Problem 11-8 for the initial conditions below.

Flip-flop	Output
1	1
2	0

11-10. By testing an unknown flip-flop, you obtain the voltage table given below. What type of flip-flop is it?

Input		Output	
1	2	Q	$\overline{Q}$
H	H	No change	No change
L	H	H	L
H	L	L	H
L	L	Unstable state	Unstable state

Chapter Twelve

Registers and Counters

As you learned in the previous chapter, flip-flops are capable of storing one bit of information. An obvious extension to this capability is to tie several flip-flops together to form a **register**. A register can store several bits as a unit (called a **word**). Common word lengths are 4, 8, and 16 bits. Of course, any other word length can be constructed by simply using the desired number of flip-flops.

Another important application of flip-flops is in **counters**. As the name suggests, a counter accumulates the total number of input pulses that have been received. As will be demonstrated, a counter can be used as a frequency divider as well. Because registers and counters are so often needed, they are available commercially. So you do not have to build them from component flip-flops whenever you need one of these circuits.

Chapter Objectives

Upon completion of this chapter, you should be able to:

- ☐ Describe how a register can be constructed by using flip-flops.
- ☐ Analyze the operation of register integrated circuits.
- ☐ Draw a timing diagram for a counter.
- ☐ Show how the count total for a given circuit can be changed by varying the connections on the IC.
- ☐ Discuss the cascading of counters to build multiple-digit counters.
- ☐ Explain how counters can be used as frequency dividers.
- ☐ Analyze both count-up and count-down counters.

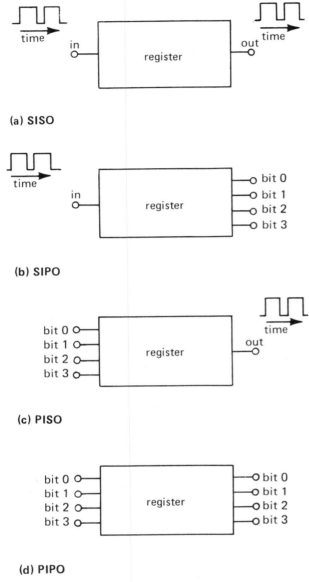

(a) SISO

(b) SIPO

(c) PISO

(d) PIPO

FIGURE 12-1. Register Input and Output

TABLE 12-1. SISO Register Dynamics

Input Bit Number	Input Value	Four-Bit Register Contents	Output Value
1	1	1000	0
2	0	0100	0
3	1	1010	0
4	0	0101	1 (first bit)
5	1	1010	0 (second bit)
6	0	0101	1 (third bit)

□ REGISTERS

Registers are classified by the method of input and output used. The input can consist of either a *serial* stream of bits or a *parallel* input in the form of a binary number. The output can also be in serial or parallel form.

Figure 12-1a shows a four-bit **serial-input–serial-output (SISO) register**. Note that there is only a single input and a single output terminal. The input pulses are usually synchronized with a clock signal that indicates the hold time for each bit. You can think of the SISO register as a pipeline. When one bit is accepted at the entrance to the pipeline (the input terminal), the bit at the end of the pipeline (output) is forced out. Therefore, one must synchronize a reading of the output pulses with reception of the input pulses.

Consider a four-bit SISO register. The register will hold values consisting of four bits, such as 0_{16}, 7_{16}, and D_{16}. After the register has been filled (that is, after four inputs have been received), the first input bit can be sensed at the output terminal (see Table 12-1). When the fifth input bit is accepted, the first bit is no longer available. The output is then equal to the value of the second input bit.

A **serial-input–parallel-output (SIPO) register** is shown in Figure 12-1b. Here, the input is the same as in the previous register, but all four bits are accessible simultaneously at the four output terminals. With this register, you do not have to wait for four bits to be received before the output becomes available. The circuitry is a little more complex in this register.

The **parallel-input–serial-output (PISO) register** in Figure 12-1c is just the reverse of the one described above. In this case, the bits are placed in the register all at once, but they can only be sampled on the output line serially. Most often, this register will be used in a *shifting* configuration (described later in this chapter).

The final configuration, a **parallel-input–parallel-output (PIPO) register**, is shown in Figure 12-1d. Now all bits are accepted at one time, and all bits also appear at the same time on the output terminals.

Serial Shift Register

An example of an SISO shift register can be built by using 4027 dual *JK* flip-flops as shown in

Figure 12-2 (power and ground connections are not shown in the figure). Because a clock controls each change of state, this is a **synchronous register**. Each of the 4027 ICs contains two JK flip-flops, so the four-bit register requires two of the 4027s (see Figure 12-2b). One of the inverters from a 4049 hex inverter is also needed.

Be sure to note the numbering of inputs and outputs on the register (see Figure 12-2b). The in- puts $J3$, $K3$, $J2$, $K2$, $J1$, $K1$, $J0$, and $K0$ refer to bit numbers 3 through 0, respectively. The out- puts $Q3$ through $Q0$ and $\overline{Q3}$ through $\overline{Q0}$ are also designated the same way. However, the bits on the data sheet of the individual 4027 (Figure 12-2a) are numbered for each flip-flop. On the pin diagram, $J1$ and $J2$ refer to the inputs of flip-flops 1 and 2, respectively. This somewhat confusing notation is widely used. So you must remember

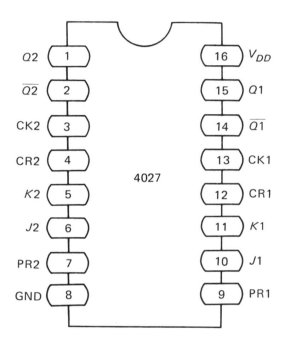

(a) **4027 JK Flip-Flop Pin Assignments**

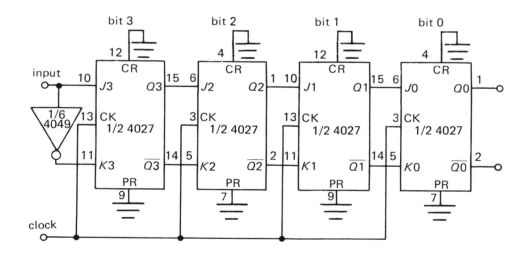

FIGURE 12-2.
Synchronous SISO
Four-Bit Shift
Register

(b) **Four-Bit Register (Power and Ground Connections Not Shown.)**

that the terminal designations on a register refer only to that one circuit, not to the particular IC data sheet.

To analyze the operation of this register, we must use the JK flip-flop state table, which is given in Table 12-2. Because the inverter is connected to the J and K inputs of the bit 0 flip-flop, only the second and third rows of the state table are applicable. If the input is a 1, after the clock pulse we have

$$J3 = 1 \quad K3 = 0 \quad Q3 = 1 \quad \overline{Q3} = 0$$

On the other hand, a 0 input gives

$$J3 = 0 \quad K3 = 1 \quad Q3 = 0 \quad \overline{Q3} = 1$$

after the clock pulse. The value stored in the bit 3 flip-flop is exactly equal to the input. (This result could also have been predicted by observing that the inverter changes the JK flip-flop to a D flip-flop, as was shown in Figure 11-15.)

Because the outputs of the bit 3 flip-flop ($Q3$ and $\overline{Q3}$) must be in opposite states, the inputs to all downstream flip-flops (bits 2, 1, and 0) must also be in opposite states. That is, $J2 = \overline{K2}$, $J1 = \overline{K1}$, and $J0 = \overline{K0}$. The Q output of each of these flip-flops will be equal to the J input, as rows 2 and 3 of Table 12-2 indicate.

From this observation, we can construct Table 12-3. This table attempts to show that one input moves the pattern to the right one column

on each clock pulse. After four clock pulses, the input has reached flip-flop 0 and its output terminal, $Q0$. For example, let the input bits during the first eight clock pulses be as shown in Table 12-4. Then, as shown in the last column of the table, the pattern has been shifted one bit to the right after each clock pulse.

Register States

Knowing how the shift register will react to any input allows us to prepare a state table for the circuit. Because there are four bits in the register, it can contain any value in the range 0000_2 through 1111_2, depending on the previous input stream. We call this the **present state** of the register. For a given input value and present state, the **next state** can be found by appending the new input on the left of the register and shifting the pattern

TABLE 12-4. Shift Register Example

Clock Pulse	Input	Register Content[a]			
		Q3	Q2	Q1	Q0
1	1	1	0	0	0
2	0	0	1	0	0
3	1	1	0	1	0
4	0	0	1	0	1
5	0	0	0	1	0
6	1	1	0	0	1
7	1	1	1	0	0
8	0	0	1	1	0

[a]Assuming that all flip-flops are initially cleared.

TABLE 12-2. JK Flip-Flop State Table

Input		Output	
J	K	Q	$\overline{Q}$
0	0	$Q0$	$\overline{Q0}$ (no change)
0	1	0	1
1	0	1	0
1	1	$\overline{Q0}$	$Q0$ (toggle)

TABLE 12-3. State Changes of the Shift Register

	Output			
Input	Q3 (Same as $J2$) at Clock Pulse 1	Q2 (Same as $J1$) at Clock Pulse 2	Q1 (Same as $J0$) at Clock Pulse 3	Q0 at Clock Pulse 4
0	0	0	0	0
1	1	1	1	1

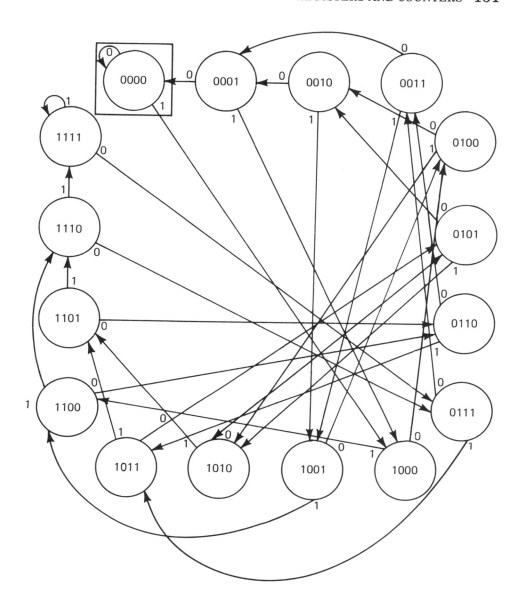

FIGURE 12-3. State
Diagram of Shift
Register

one bit. This method is carried out in developing
Table 12-5. If we read the present and next state
columns of this table as binary numbers, we can
draw a state diagram of it.

□ **EXAMPLE 12-1**

Use Table 12-5 to derive a state diagram for the
four-bit SISO shift register.

Solution From the first two rows of the state
table we have

$$0000_2 \rightarrow 0000_2 \quad \text{if the input is 0}$$
$$0000_2 \rightarrow 1000_2 \quad \text{if the input is 1}$$

Figure 12-3 shows these states boxed. Continu-

ing in the same way, we can draw the remainder
of the state diagram. The figure shows the complete diagram.

Using either the table or the diagram, we
can find the next state of the register if we know
the present state and the input.

□ **TIMING DIAGRAMS**

Another way to analyze register operation is with
a **timing diagram**. A timing diagram shows how
the individual flip-flops change states with time.
The state sequences cannot readily be found by
using timing diagrams, so the state table should

TABLE 12-5. Shift Register State Table

Present State	Input	Next State
0000	0	0000
	1	1000
0001	0	0000
	1	1000
0010	0	0001
	1	1001
0011	0	0001
	1	1001
0100	0	0010
	1	1010
0101	0	0010
	1	1010
0110	0	0011
	1	1011
0111	0	0011
	1	1011
1000	0	0100
	1	1100
1001	0	0100
	1	1100
1010	0	0101
	1	1101
1011	0	0101
	1	1101
1100	0	0110
	1	1110
1101	0	0110
	1	1110
1110	0	0111
	1	1111
1111	0	0111
	1	1111

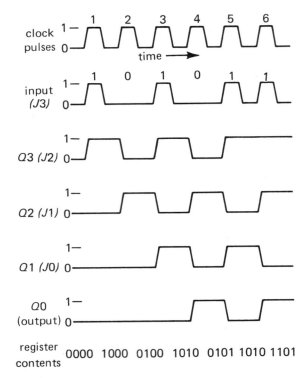

register contents 0000 1000 0100 1010 0101 1010 1101

FIGURE 12-4. Shift Register Timing Diagram

be derived before attempting to draw the timing diagram. The timing can then be determined from the state table.

The timing diagram of Figure 12-4 shows the operation corresponding to the sequence below (refer to Table 12-5).

Input	1	0	1	0	1	1
Next state	0000 →1000 →0100 →1010 →0101 →1010 →1101					

On the timing diagram, all outputs are low prior to clock pulse 1, corresponding to a reset of all flip-flops. An input signal of 1 is applied during the first clock pulse, causing $Q3$ to become 1, but all other outputs are 0. The register contains 1000_2. On the next clock, the input is 0, producing a 1 at output $Q2$ and a 0 at all other outputs. The content of the register is 0100_2. When clock pulse 3 occurs, the input is again 1, and a state transition to 1010_2 results. The 0 input on clock pulse 4 changes the contents to 0101_2. The input becomes 1 during clock pulse 5, causing the register to change to a value of 1010_2. On the final clock pulse, the input is 1, and the register contents become 1101_2. (The contents were 1010_2 during clock pulses 3 and 5. A return to the same state in this manner was simply a coincidence determined by the previous input sequence of bits.)

You have now seen that there are several ways to understand the operation of registers. Each method gives a different insight into the operation. Observation of the shifting demonstrates how the input pattern moves to the right (or left in a left-shifting register) and makes the SISO nature obvious. State tables are the most complete and powerful techniques to use in finding the next state of a register when you know the input and present state. A state diagram illustrates the state transitions in a form that is often easier to read than a state table. Finally, timing diagrams identify the signals you will observe on an oscilloscope connected to the inputs and outputs of the circuit.

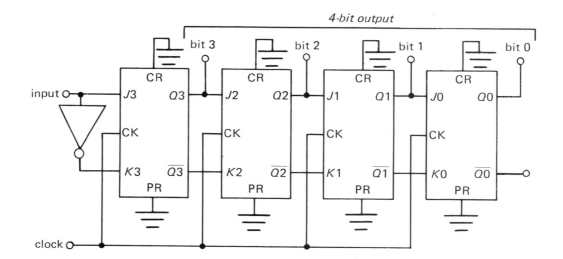

**FIGURE 12-5.
SIPO
Register**

□ **EXAMPLE 12-2**

Show how the SISO shift register can be converted to a SIPO configuration.

Solution The outputs of each flip-flop are readily available, so we simply attach leads to each flip-flop at the Q terminals, as shown in Figure 12-5.

An important application of SIPO registers is to convert serial data to parallel format. Many data communication systems require this **serial-to-parallel conversion.** For the register shown in Figure 12-5, the data would be converted as a four-bit word. After each set of four bits had been received, the data would be read out as a four-bit unit and stored, possibly in a computer memory.

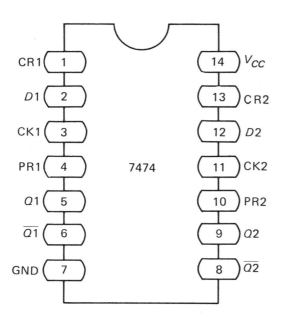

(a) 7474 Pin Assignments

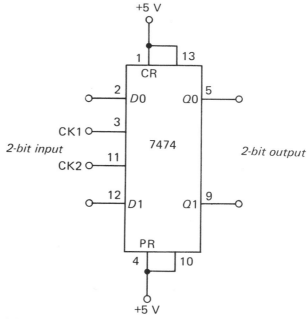

(b) PIPO Register

FIGURE 12-6. PIPO Register

☐ **EXAMPLE 12-3**

Using a 7474 dual D flip-flop (Figure 12-6a), construct a two-bit PIPO register.

Solution Using two D flip-flops, we connect the inputs and outputs in the register configuration shown in Figure 12-6b. Note that pins 2 and 12 are used for input.

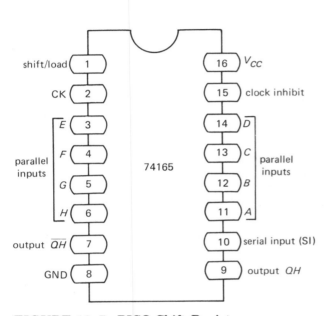

FIGURE 12-7. PISO Shift Register

☐ **INTEGRATED CIRCUIT REGISTER**

Instead of using several flip-flops to build a register, you can use a packaged device in a single IC, which will save time, money, and space. An example of such a circuit is the 74165 PISO shift register shown in Figure 12-7. The register can store eight bits.

Table 12-6 describes the operation of the register. The inputs are labeled A through H, while both the true (QH) and complemented ($\overline{QH}$) levels of the serial output are provided.

The eight parallel inputs are only accepted when the shift/load signal is low. At other times, the parallel input is disabled. The H input is immediately available at the output terminal. A serial-input terminal is provided, so this register can also be used as a SISO register. Shifting of the bits occurs on the positive transition of the clock. (The clock must first be enabled with a low level on the clock inhibit line.) The shift pattern can be shown as

Before shift	SI	A	B	C	D	E	F	G
	↓	↓	↓	↓	↓	↓	↓	↓
After shift	A	B	C	D	E	F	G	H

where SI is the serial-input value. The serial input takes the place of the A bit, and all other bits shift right one position.

TABLE 12-6. 74165 Function Table

Input					Output	
Shift/Load	Clock Inhibit	Clock	Parallel	Serial	QH	$\overline{QH}$
Low	X	X	$A, \ldots, H$	X	H	$\overline{H}$
High	Low	Low	X	X	$H0$	$\overline{H0}$
High	Low	↑	X	High	G	$\overline{G}$
High	Low	↑	X	Low	G	$\overline{G}$
High	High	X	X	X	$H0$	$\overline{H0}$

Notes: X = don't care.

    $H, \overline{H}$ = true and complement level of the H input.

    $G, \overline{G}$ = true and complement level of the G input.

    $H0, \overline{H0}$ = true and complement of the previous state of the H input (meaning no change in the output).

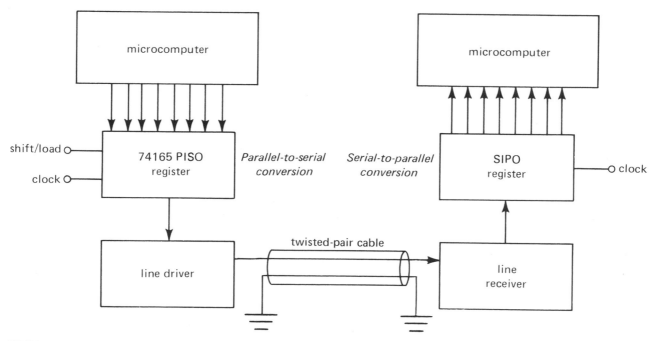

FIGURE 12–8. Simple Serial Communications Network Between Microcomputers

□ SERIAL DATA LINK

The 74165 register can be used to perform **parallel-to-serial conversion** for a data communications system. A typical network is shown in Figure 12–8. In this network, two microprocessors are to communicate over a twisted-pair (two-wire) cable. Since the link can only send one bit at a time, the parallel data must be converted to serial form at transmission. Upon receipt, the data are converted back to parallel for use by the second microcomputer.

□ BUS REGISTER

A **data bus** is a parallel communications channel that is widely used in microcomputers. If the bus is **bidirectional**, data can be sent or received over the same lines. Typically, many devices are connected to a bus, as shown in Figure 12–9a. This

situation requires provision to be made so that only one device transmits at any time. If two sending devices access the bus simultaneously, one may be trying to pull a data line high at the same time that the other is pulling the line low. The consequence of this conflict is, at the least, incorrect data on the bus, and, in some cases, the receivers can be damaged.

A register with a *three-state output* is needed to provide the interface to the bus. The 74LS374 is such a register. It is an eight-bit

TABLE 12–7. 74LS374 Register Functions

Output Control	Clock	D	Output, Q
	Input		
L	↑	H	H
L	↑	L	L
L	L	X	Previous output level
H	X	X	High impedance

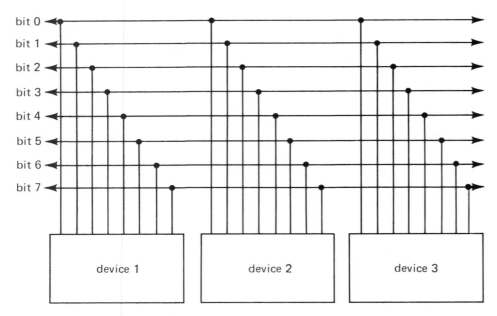

(a) Eight-bit Bidirectional Data Bus

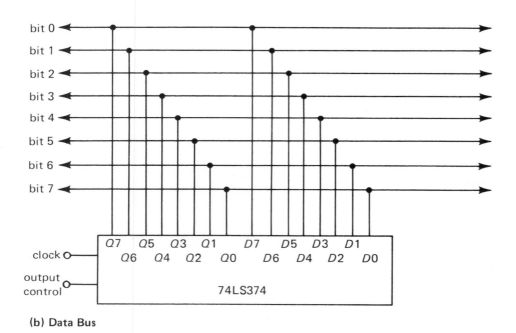

(b) Data Bus

FIGURE 12-9. Data Buses

PIPO register that uses D flip-flops in its construction. Table 12–7 describes its functions. The operation is a PIPO register as long as the output control signal is low. Each of the eight D inputs is accepted and appears at the corresponding Q output terminals on each positive-going clock transition. However, when the output control signal is high, the high-impedance state disconnects the device from the bus.

Figure 12–9b shows how this circuit can be used to send or receive data over the bus. Note that the 74LS374 can receive bus data at all times, but it will transmit only when the output control is low.

□ COUNTERS

Counters appear in circuits where a count of the number of input pulses must be tabulated. Digital clocks and watches are obvious users of counter circuits. If a clocking signal controls the counting transitions, the counter is said to be **synchronous**. If the counter is limited to powers of 2 (that is 2, 4, 8, 16, . . .), it is called a **binary** counter.

A simple count-by-2 circuit is shown in Figure 12-10a; its timing diagram is shown in Figure 12-10b. A JK flip-flop is connected as a T flip-flop. As the truth table (Table 12-8) demonstrates, a high output is generated only on alternate input pulses. We observe that the counter also divides by 2. The output is high only on every other input pulse. (Refer to Figure 11-11 for the pin diagram of the flip-flop.) A somewhat unusual feature of this counter is that the input pulses are applied to the clock input of the flip-flop, not to the J or K terminals.

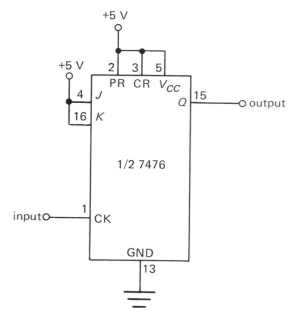

(a) Circuit

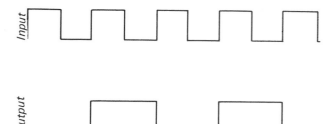

(b) Timing Diagram

FIGURE 12-10. Count-by-2 Circuit Using a T Flip-Flop

□ EXAMPLE 12-4

The count of a binary counter can be extended to any power of 2 by cascading the flip-flops. Figure 12-11 shows counters with capacities of 4 and 16 (power and ground connections not shown). Each cascaded stage receives its inputs on the clock terminal from the output of the previous stage. Because the count ripples along the chain, this configuration is called a **ripple counter**. In use, the output must not be sampled before the settling time following the application of a new input pulse.

Generally, the maximum count for any binary counter is

maximum count $= 2^s$
where $s =$ number of flip-flop stages

For example, in Figure 12-11a there are two stages; hence

$$\text{maximum count} = 2^2 = 4$$

In Figure 12-11b, with four stages, we have

$$\text{maximum count} = 2^4 = 16$$

TABLE 12-8. Count-by-2 Truth Table

Input	Output
⌐L	L
⌐L	H
⌐L	L
⌐L	H
⌐L	L
⌐L	H
⋮	⋮

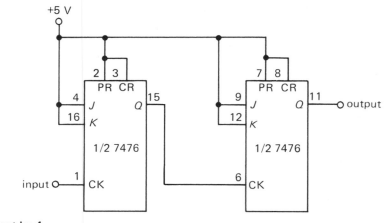

(a) Count by 4

Note: Power and ground connections not shown.

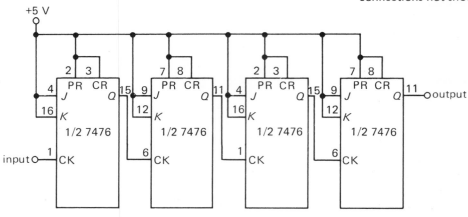

(b) Count by 16

FIGURE 12-11.
Ripple Counter

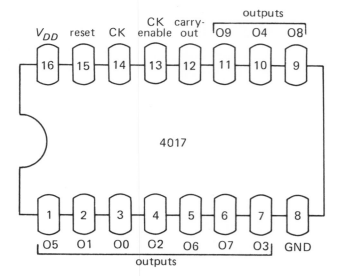

FIGURE 12-12. 4017 Decade Counter

☐ DECADE COUNTERS

Suppose the count we wish to accumulate is not a power of 2. For example, we often need to count by 10. This application is so frequently necessary that a wide variety of **decade** (count-by-10) **counter** ICs are found in the data books. The 4017 circuit of Figure 12-12 is a good example. The functions for this decade counter are given in Table 12-9.

In operation, the reset and clock enable lines of the counter must be low. Before the first clock input, and after a high reset pulse, the $O0$ line goes high. (All other outputs remain low.) The first clock pulse causes the $O1$ output to go high and $O0$ to fall. The following clock pulse makes the $O2$ line rise and the $O1$ line fall. The counting sequence continues in this manner until the $O9$

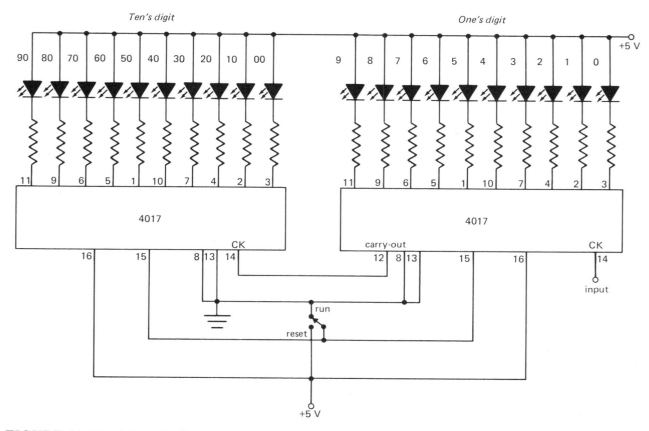

FIGURE 12-13. A 0-to-99 Counter

line is high. The next clock pulse recycles the counter back to $O0$. (The carry-out line goes high at that time also.) Cascading these counters makes it possible to accumulate higher totals that are powers of 10.

☐ **EXAMPLE 12-5**

Use the 4017 to build a counter that runs from 0 to 99.

Solution Figure 12-13 shows the circuit for this counter. The carry-out line from the lower stage becomes the input to the higher stage. The reset switch sets the initial count back to 0. By reading the two LEDs that are off (one for the units digit and the other for the tens digit), one finds the present total. The two LEDs are off because the two active outputs are high levels. The remaining outputs will be low, providing a ground for the current to flow into, which causes each of the other LEDs to light. The counter is reset by momentarily throwing the switch to the +5-V position. The high signal resets both counters. The switch is then placed in the grounded position to enable the counter.

TABLE 12-9. 4017 Decade Counter Functions

	Input		
Reset	Clock Enable	Clock	Output
H	X	X	All low
L	H	X	No change
L	L	⎍	$O0$ through $O9$ sequential count up

The 7490 decade counter is a popular counter because it is well suited for driving seven-segment LED displays (see Chapter 18). The pin

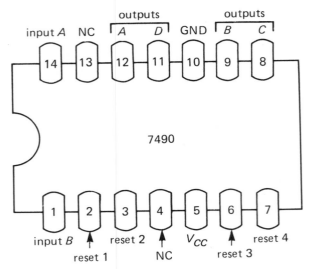

FIGURE 12-14. 7490 Decade Counter

diagram is shown in Figure 12-14, and its functions are listed in Table 12-10.

The flexibility of the 7490 IC can be seen by examining Figure 12-15. In addition to its ability to count by 10, with suitable connections, the 7490 can also serve as a divider by other numbers as well. These various configurations can be

realized because of the available outputs and the B input, which is a count-by-5 (bi-quinary) signal. Table 12-11 compares the different counts produced by use of either the A or B input.

☐ **EXAMPLE 12-6**

Use a timing diagram to show that the circuit in Figure 12-15b divides the input frequency by 6.

Solution Because output A (pin 12) is connected to input B (pin 1), we use the left-hand side of Table 12-11. Other important connections are the following:

☐ reset 1 (pin 2) and output A (pin 12)
☐ reset 3 (pin 6) and reset 4 (pin 7) grounded
☐ reset 2 (pin 3) and output C (pin 8)

The divide-by-6 count is obtained from output C.

The timing diagram is given in Figure 12-16. The counter increases its count in a normal fashion until outputs A and C both go high (on count 5 in Table 12-11). Counting from 0 through 5, inclusively, gives a total of six counts. Then both the reset 1 and reset 2 signals are high. According to rows 1 and 2 of Table 12-10, these two signals force all the counter output lines to go low. At that time, the count begins again, as Figure 12-16 shows.

TABLE 12-10. 7490 Decade Counter Functions

| | Input | | | | | Output | | | |
Row	Reset 1	Reset 2	Reset 3	Reset 4	Input A	D	C	B	A
1	H	H	L	X	X	L	L	L	L
2	H	H	X	L	X	L	L	L	L
3	X	X	H	H	X	H	L	L	H
4	X	L	X	L	Count	Accumulated total			
5	L	X	L	X	Count	Accumulated total			
6	L	X	X	L	Count	Accumulated total			
7	X	L	L	X	Count	Accumulated total			

Note: This table applies only when output A is connected to input B.

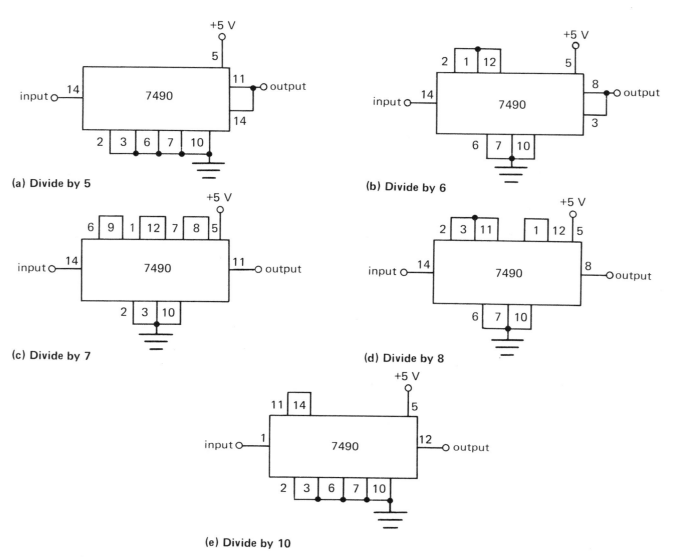

(a) Divide by 5

(b) Divide by 6

(c) Divide by 7

(d) Divide by 8

(e) Divide by 10

FIGURE 12-15. Counters Built from the 7490

TABLE 12-11. Inputs to the 7490

Using Input A, with Output A Connected to Input B					Using Input B, with Output D Connected to Input A				
	Output					Output[a]			
Count	D	C	B	A	Count	A	D	C	B
0	0	0	0	0	0	0	0	0	0
1	0	0	0	1	1	0	0	0	1
2	0	0	1	0	2	0	0	1	0
3	0	0	1	1	3	0	0	1	1
4	0	1	0	0	4	0	1	0	1
5	0	1	0	1	5	1	0	0	0
6	0	1	1	0	6	1	0	0	1
7	0	1	1	1	7	1	0	1	0
8	1	0	0	0	8	1	0	1	1
9	1	0	0	1	9	1	1	0	0

[a]Outputs are not used in the standard order $DCBA$ but in the order $ADCB$.

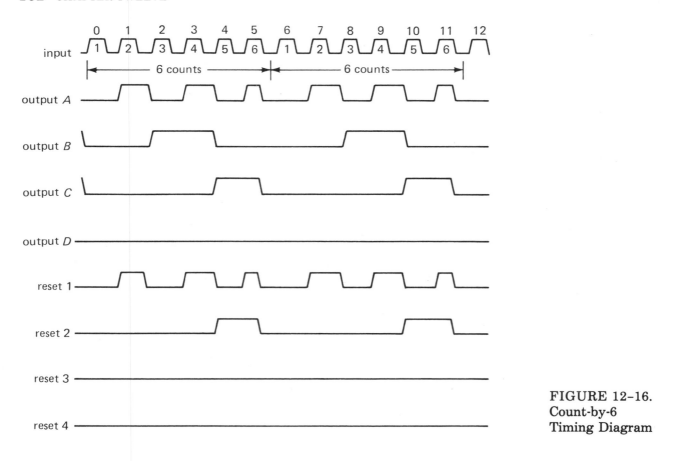

FIGURE 12–16.
Count-by-6
Timing Diagram

☐ **EXAMPLE 12-7**

A divider is needed in a digital clock to reduce the 60-Hz line frequency to seconds (one output per second). By combining counters described in this chapter, design the circuit.

Solution The circuit requires a series combination of a divide-by-6 and a divide-by-10 counter, which yields a total division by 60, as shown in Figure 12–17. Of course, it makes no difference which divider is placed first in the series. For the divide-by-6 followed by the divide-by-10 sequence shown in the figure, the output of the divide-by-6 circuit is 10 Hz, and the final frequency is 1 Hz.

☐ **UP-DOWN COUNTERS**

Often, we would like a counter to decrease the count rather than increasing it, as all the preceding examples have done. Figure 12–18 illustrates a counter that will count either up or down. If the count is to start from zero, a high signal is applied to the clear input to initialize the counter. (Inputs A, B, C, and D are the initial counts.) Alternatively, an initial count can be placed in the counter by setting the binary values on the D through A inputs (bit D is the most significant) and then setting the load command signal low (which sets $Q_A = A$, $Q_B = B$, $Q_C = C$, and $Q_D = D$). The outputs (D through A) then

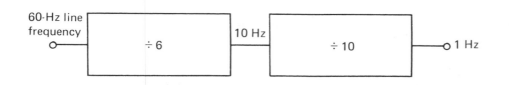

FIGURE 12–17.
Converting 60 Hz to
1 Hz with Dividers

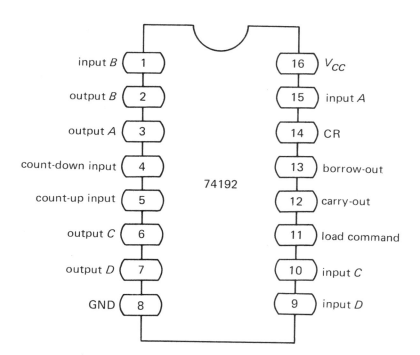

FIGURE 12–18.
74192 Decimal
Up-Down Counter

equal the input values. If the device is to count up, the input pulses are applied to pin 5. If the device is to count down, the input should be connected to pin 4. The carry-out signal is identical to the one described for the 4017 IC in a cascaded configuration (see Example 12–5). The **borrow-out signal** is used in the same manner, but it is applicable to cascaded count-down counters only.

A comparison of the use of count-up or count-down inputs and the carry or borrow outputs is provided in Figure 12–19. Figure 12–19a is a count-up circuit. The input pulses are routed to pin 5, and the carry signal (pin 12) goes from the lower stage to the count-up (pin 5) input of the upper stage. Note that the unused count-down input (pin 4) of both chips is tied to V_{CC} to disable this function.

The count-down circuit (Figure 12–19b) has its input connected to pin 4 of the lower stage. The borrow-out signal from that stage (pin 13) goes to the count-down (pin 4) input of the higher stage. The count-up inputs of both ICs are held high by V_{CC}.

The seven-segment LED decoder/driver (explained in Chapter 18) converts the BCD outputs of each counter to a display of that digit. The count-up IC begins its count at the initial input value, reaches 99, recycles to 0, then continues to count up. The count-down IC begins at the initial value, counts down to 0, recycles to 99, then continues to count down toward 0 again.

□ **EXAMPLE 12–8**

Construct a programmable single-digit counter that counts down from the initial value to 0 and then stops. A signal should be generated when the last count is reached.

Solution Figure 12–20 shows the circuit for this counter. Interesting features include the LED, which lights when the final count is reached (as indicated by the low borrow signal). The present

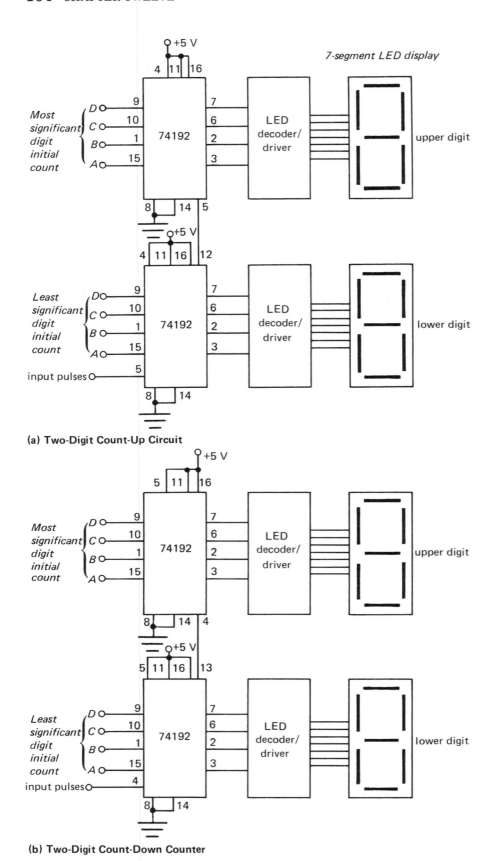

7-segment LED display

(a) Two-Digit Count-Up Circuit

(b) Two-Digit Count-Down Counter

**FIGURE 12–19.
Comparison of
Count-up and
Count-down
Counters**

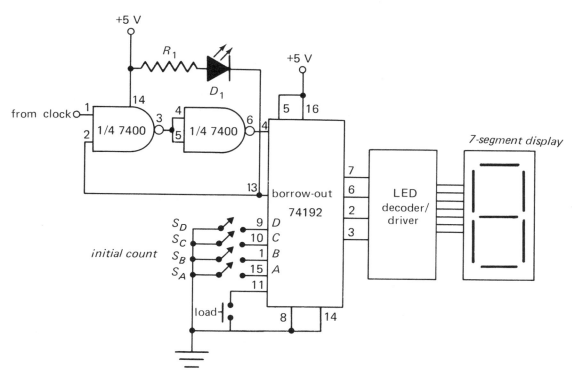

FIGURE 12-20. Programmable Counter

count is always shown in the seven-segment displays. The four switches on the input terminals place the initial count in the device. Closing each switch generates a 0, while opening each produces a 1. The push-button switch is pressed after the proper number has been set into the S_A through S_D inputs to cause the initial count to be loaded into the counter.

Chapter Summary

☐ Registers can use either serial or parallel inputs and outputs of the bit stream. The type of input and output determines whether a register is classified as SISO, SIPO, PISO, or PIPO.

☐ Synchronous registers accept inputs and change outputs only on the clock pulse.

☐ A shift register can move its contents left or right one bit at a time.

☐ The state table of a register or counter shows the next state for a given present state and input. A state diagram graphically depicts the state table.

☐ Timing diagrams show the dynamic operation of a register or counter. A timing diagram simulates the display that would be observed on an oscilloscope monitoring the circuit.

☐ Serial-to-parallel converters are in actuality SIPO registers. PISO registers convert parallel data to serial data.

☐ Registers are used on data buses to buffer information being sent or arriving over the bus.

☐ Counters tabulate the number of input pulses received. Synchronous counters change outputs only on the true clock signal, but ripple counters generate the output asynchronously.

☐ Binary counters are limited to powers of 2. Other common count totals are 10 (decade) and 12. With suitable connections, any other count total can be accumulated.

☐ A counter can also be used as a frequency divider.

☐ Use of cascaded counters is necessary to achieve totals higher than an individual counter stage can hold.

☐ Up-down counters can count up or count down.

Problems

12-1. Draw a timing diagram of the SIPO register shown in Figure 12-5 as it receives an input data stream of 1, 0, 1, 1, 0. The individual flip-flops are reset to 0 prior to receiving the first bit. The outputs of each flip-flop, clock, and input signals should be shown in the diagram.

12-2. Construct a block diagram for a data transmission network that provides the following functions:

a. A four-bit bidirectional data bus that interconnects two 4-bit registers and a parallel-to-serial converter;

b. A line driver and receiver for transmission over a 50-m twisted-pair cable;

c. A receiving four-bit data bus that passes the incoming signals to a microprocessor or to a register (do not forget to convert from serial back to parallel data format).

12-3. The outputs of a 74192 counter are connected as shown in Figure 12-21. The switch S_1 is thrown to the upper position to clear. Draw the output timing diagram, showing the voltage levels and the time between changes in the output signal. The clock frequency is 1 kHz. The counter is initially reset to 0. (Hint: Note that the resistors on pins 8 and 3 are connected in parallel and are of equal value. What is their equivalent resistance? Continue combining resistors in this fashion and also apply Thevinin's theorem.)

12-4. Explain why the LED in Figure 12-20 lights when the final count is reached.

12-5. Draw a timing diagram for the counter shown in Figure 12-15c to verify that it does divide by 7.

12-6. Figure 12-15e employs the bi-quinary mode of input, as listed in the right-hand side of Table 12-11. With a timing diagram, show that the output frequency is 1/10 of the input frequency.

12-7. What is the total count that can be accumulated in a five-stage binary counter?

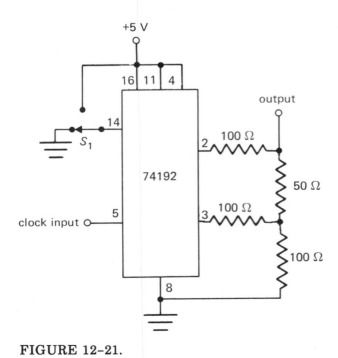

FIGURE 12-21.

12-8. Use the idea illustrated in Figure 12-17 to change a 60-Hz line frequency to seconds, minutes, hours, and days in a digital clock. Draw a block diagram of your circuit. (Hint: What count will you need to convert 24 hours to one day?)

12-9. Design a counter that starts with an initial value of 49, counts to 9999, then recycles to 0 and counts to 9999. The last sequence continues to repeat from that point on. You should use 74192 counters.

12-10. Expand the programmable counter of Figure 12-20 so that it can count to 99 before halting.

Chapter Thirteen

Operational Amplifiers

In contrast to the devices studied thus far, which were digital components, the **operational amplifier** is an analog component. Operational amplifiers (op amps) are as fundamental to analog circuits as combinatorial gates are to digital circuits. Op amps were once used mostly in analog computers to perform such operations as addition, multiplication, integration, and differentiation. However, op amps today are employed in a variety of circuits. The characteristics of op amps—high input impedance, high gain, and low output impedance—make them popular with designers. Because TTL-compatible power supply voltages are supplied on many op amps, their use in hybrid digital-analog circuitry is growing ever more common.

As a technician, you will need to understand both analog and digital components in order to maintain modern electronic equipment. In this chapter we will construct a model of an idealized op amp. That model will then be used to analyze real op amps, with suitable modifications being made in the model to account for the nonidealized behavior of real components.

Chapter Objectives

Upon completion of this chapter, you should be able to:

- ☐ Classify linear circuits into their respective families.
- ☐ List the characteristics of ideal op amps.
- ☐ Derive parameters of inverting and noninverting amplifiers.
- ☐ Show how op amps can be used to build differential amplifiers, summing amplifiers, integrators, and differentiators.
- ☐ Explain how finite open-loop gain affects op amp performance.
- ☐ Estimate the errors generated by the common-mode rejection ratio of an op amp.
- ☐ Use a Bode plot to illustrate gain performance of an op amp.
- ☐ Describe how offset inputs can eliminate errors.
- ☐ Discuss op amp bandwidth characteristics.
- ☐ Explain how the large-signal limit impacts op amp performance.
- ☐ Determine whether an amplifier will exhibit stability or oscillation in operation.
- ☐ Discuss the phase shift variation of op amps with changing frequency.

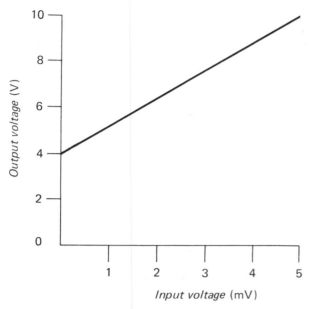

FIGURE 13-1. Output Versus Input in a Linear Circuit

☐ LINEAR CIRCUITS

The output of a **linear circuit** is related to the inputs by a straight-line (linear) graph on Cartesian coordinates. Figure 13-1 shows a generalized plot of a linear operation. As you know from mathematics, the equation for a linear plot is

$$V_{out} = aV_{in} + b \qquad \qquad \textbf{(13-1)}$$

where

V_{in} = input voltage
a = slope of the line
b = y intercept

The operational amplifier is the key to most linear circuits, though the amplifier is often combined with other components (all within a single integrated circuit).

Typical families of linear circuits are shown in Figure 13-2. All relate to analog signals, but the data conversion devices also have digital in-

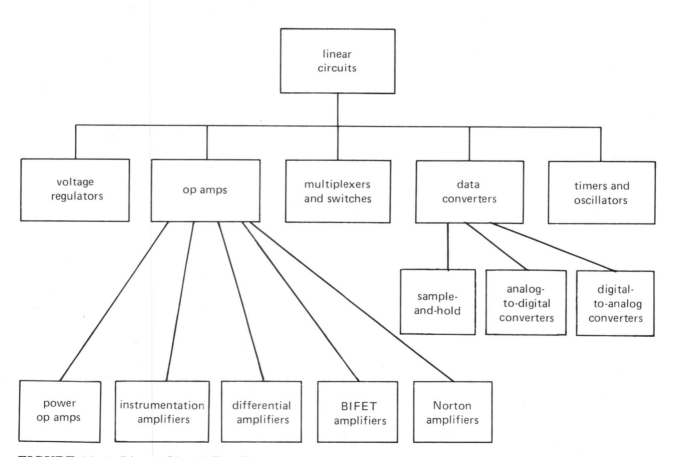

FIGURE 13-2. Linear Circuit Families

(a) 20-Pin DIP

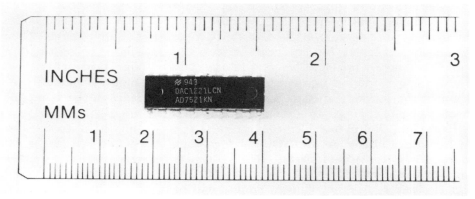

(b) 18-Pin DIP

FIGURE 13–3.
Linear Circuit
Packaging

(c) Other Common Forms of DIPs

terfaces as well. Each of the families illustrated in the figure will be described in a brief sentence or two. More detail for specific components is provided later in this chapter and in those that follow.

A steady voltage that does not vary with minor changes on the power supply line voltage can be provided by means of **voltage regulators**. Op amps have already been mentioned, and some specialized types are shown in the figure. Use of field effect transistors in the input circuitry gives **BIFET amplifiers** especially high input impedance as well as good high-frequency response. **Norton amplifiers** form general-purpose video amplifiers that offer high speed and wide bandwidth. **Analog multiplexers** and switches offer the same type of service as the digital MUX we previously examined, but in these devices, the signals routed are analog. Changing information from analog to digital representation and back again is the purpose of **data conversion** equipment. Within this group are **sample-and-hold (S/H) circuits**, **digital-to-analog converters (DAC)**, **analog-to-digital converters (ADC)**, and **voltage-to-frequency converters (V/F)**. Finally, **timers** supply clock signals for synchronous operation of digital circuits. All these linear circuits will be analyzed in later chapters, except for the op amp, which is the subject of the present chapter.

For the facilitation of their use in printed circuits or wire-wrapped cards, linear components are packaged much like digital devices. As Figures 13-3a and b show, the components are often available in plastic or ceramic DIPs. Other common forms (see Figure 13-3c) are the "can," "top hat," heat tab, and three-lead plastic packages. These latter packages are found mostly in voltage regulation circuits. Because they can generate a lot of heat, a heat sink is generally re-

quired with them. A good thermal contact between the circuit package and the heat sink is guaranteed if a silicone grease is applied to both surfaces before attaching them.

☐ IDEALIZED OP AMPS

The study of op amps is best begun by examining a model that approximates the operation of the actual components. The model, an idealized op amp, simplifies the operation, so we can concentrate on the most important principles. Later, we will discuss the ways in which real amplifiers differ from the model.

The op amp symbol is shown in Figure 13-4. The amplifier has two input terminals and one output terminal. The input marked by the minus sign is called the **inverting input**, while the plus sign designates the **noninverting input**. Power supply terminals are shown by lines joining the sides of the triangle, though the power contacts are often omitted in a diagram when they are not important to the discussion. One of the power supply voltages is positive $(+V_{CC})$ and the other is either negative $(-V_{CC})$ or ground. Numbers on the various inputs and outputs (if shown) indicate the pins on the IC, just as they did in digital circuits.

The output of the op amp responds to the difference in voltage between the input terminals. Hence, the op amp is often said to have **differential inputs**. An equivalent circuit for the op amp is shown in Figure 13-5. A positive signal applied to the inverting input produces a negative voltage at the output terminal. On the other hand, a positive signal applied to the noninverting terminal causes the output to be positive.

The **open-loop gain** (A_{vo}) of the ideal op amp is assumed to be infinite. The open-loop gain is

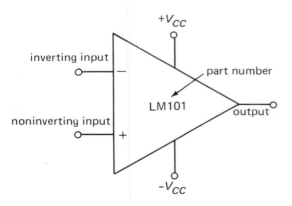

FIGURE 13-4. Op Amp Symbology

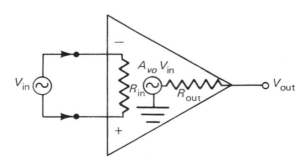

FIGURE 13-5. Equivalent Circuit for an Op Amp

the amplification provided when there is no feedback of a portion of the amplifier output signal to the input. *Input resistance* (R_{in}) is also infinite in this model. Because of this high resistance, no current can flow into the op amp. The *output resistance* (R_{out}) in the amplifier model is 0 Ω. The op amp is also assumed to have a **bandwidth** that is infinite, meaning that the output response is independent of the frequency of input signals. Finally, we require the ideal amplifier to have **zero offset**. That is, the output voltage (V_{out}) is zero if the input voltage (V_{in}) is also zero.

Because of the high gain, a small (essentially zero) input voltage can produce a large output level. The output is related to the input by the equation

$$V_{out} = A_{vo}V_{in} \qquad (13\text{--}2)$$

At first you may think that the equivalent circuit implies a lesser output voltage, considering the drop across the output resistance (R_{out}). Remember, however, that resistor has a zero value, so there is no voltage drop across it.

Inverting Amplifier

An op amp is never used in isolation. Instead, it is combined with external components, which provide the stability necessary for reliable operation. A common circuit is the **inverting amplifier**, which receives its input signal at the inverting terminal through resistor R_1. The noninverting terminal is grounded, while a fraction of the output voltage is fed back by resistor R_2 (see Figure 13-6).

The operation of this circuit can be readily analyzed with the idealized amplifier parameters. Because the amplifier has infinite gain, V_{out} will be nonzero even if the input voltage is almost 0 V. The feedback loop provides a signal that is 180° out of phase with the input at the inverting terminal, maintaining the differential voltage, V_D, at 0 V. This value of V_D implies that V_{in} must be completely dropped across R_1, so

$$I_{in} = \frac{V_{in}}{R_1} \qquad (13\text{--}3)$$

Because R_{in} of the amplifier is infinite, the current flowing into the amplifier (I_1 on the diagram) must be zero.

Note that a V_D of 0 V in effect places the point labeled "point 1" on the diagram at *virtual ground*. (The noninverting terminal is grounded, and there is no potential difference between the

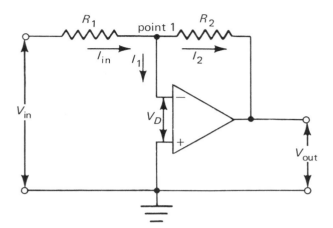

FIGURE 13-6. Inverting Amplifier

two input terminals. Therefore, the inverting input is effectively grounded as well.)

With $I_1 = 0$, we have

$$I_2 = I_{in} \qquad (13\text{--}4)$$

and V_{out} must be the voltage drop across R_2:

$$V_{out} = -I_2R_2 \qquad (13\text{--}5)$$

The output is negative because the signal is on the inverting input. Rewriting Equation 13-5, we have

$$I_2 = \frac{-V_{out}}{R_2} \qquad (13\text{--}6)$$

But from Equation 13-4, we know that I_2 and I_{in} are equal. So from Equations 13-3 and 13-6, we obtain

$$\frac{V_{in}}{R_1} = \frac{-V_{out}}{R_2} \qquad (13\text{--}7)$$

If we define the gain with feedback, A_{vf}, to be

$$A_{vf} = \frac{V_{out}}{V_{in}}$$

then rearranging Equation 13-7 gives

$$A_{vf} = \frac{V_{out}}{V_{in}} = \frac{-R_2}{R_1} \qquad (13\text{--}8)$$

Thus the gain of the inverting amplifier is a linear equation controlled by the negative ratio of R_2 to R_1.

□ EXAMPLE 13-1

What is the range of values of the gain with feedback for the inverting op amp?

Solution If R_2 is zero, we have

$$A_{vf} = \frac{0}{R_1} = 0$$

If R_1 is zero, then

$$A_{vf} = \frac{-R_2}{0} = -\infty$$

If $R_1 = R_2$, the gain is

$$A_{vf} = \frac{-R_2}{R_1} = \frac{-R_1}{R_1} = -1$$

The gain with feedback can range from zero to infinity. If both resistors are of equal value, the gain is -1 (unity gain). The gain is always negative, because the inverting input is the signal source.

Noninverting Amplifier

If the input signal is connected to the noninverting input of the amplifier, we have the circuit of Figure 13-7, a **noninverting amplifier**. Two resistors are needed in this circuit, with R_2 providing feedback.

Because of this feedback, V_D is again zero, meaning that once more the two input terminals are at the same voltage. This zero differential voltage could only occur if R_1 has a potential drop equal to V_{in}. So

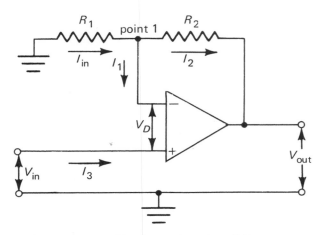

FIGURE 13-7. Noninverting Amplifier

$$I_{in} = \frac{V_{in}}{R_1} \tag{13-9}$$

Point 1 is then at the potential of the noninverting terminal.

Furthermore, we know that

$$I_1 = 0 \quad \text{and} \quad I_3 = 0 \tag{13-10}$$

because the op amp has infinite input resistance. Consequently, we have

$$I_2 = I_{in} \tag{13-11}$$

The output voltage can be found to be

$$V_{out} = I_2(R_1 + R_2) \tag{13-12}$$

$$\text{or} \quad V_{out} = I_{in}(R_1 + R_2) \tag{13-13}$$

Substituting the expression for I_{in} from Equation 13-9 into Equation 13-13, we obtain

$$V_{out} = \frac{V_{in}}{R_1}(R_1 + R_2) \tag{13-14}$$

Hence the gain with feedback is

$$A_{vf} = \frac{V_{out}}{V_{in}} = \frac{R_1 + R_2}{R_1} \tag{13-15}$$

This gain is also linearly related to the values of the two resistors. Because the noninverting input is the signal terminal, the output signal is in phase with that of the input.

□ EXAMPLE 13-2

What is the range of values of the gain for the noninverting amplifier?

Solution If R_2 is zero, we have a gain of

$$A_{vf} = \frac{R_1 + 0}{R_1} = \frac{R_1}{R_1} = 1$$

If R_1 is zero, the gain becomes

$$A_{vf} = \frac{0 + R_2}{0} = \infty$$

If $R_1 = R_2$, we have

$$A_{vf} = \frac{R_1 + R_1}{R_1} = \frac{2R_1}{R_1} = 2$$

Thus the gain can range from one (unity gain) to infinity.

Differential Amplifier

Two separate signals can be applied to an op amp, as Figure 13-8 illustrates. This configuration is called a **differential amplifier**. We will find that it is convenient to select the resistors so that

$$R_1 = R_3 \quad \text{and} \quad R_2 = R_4$$

From the basic parameters of the idealized op amp, we can readily show that

$$V_D = 0 \quad I_1 = 0 \quad I_2 = 0 \qquad \text{(13-16)}$$

The output voltage is the sum of two component voltages:

$$V_{\text{out}} = V_{\text{out}_1} + V_{\text{out}_2} \qquad \text{(13-17)}$$

where

V_{out_1} = voltage produced by V_{in_1}
V_{out_2} = voltage produced by V_{in_2}

Observe that V_{out_1} is the same as the voltage that appeared in the inverting amplifier. So from Equation 13-7, we have

$$V_{\text{out}_1} = -V_{\text{in}_1}\left(\frac{R_2}{R_1}\right) \qquad \text{(13-18)}$$

The noninverting amplifier analysis can be used to find the contribution to the output from V_{in_2}. From Equation 13-14, we have

$$V_{\text{out}_2} = V_+\left(\frac{R_1 + R_2}{R_1}\right) \qquad \text{(13-19)}$$

where

V_+ = voltage between R_3 and R_4

The voltage divider formed by R_3 and R_4 allows us to write an equation for V_+ in terms of V_{in_2}:

$$V_+ = V_{\text{in}_2}\left(\frac{R_4}{R_3 + R_4}\right) \qquad \text{(13-20)}$$

Substituting this expression for V_+ into Equation 13-19, we obtain

$$V_{\text{out}_2} = V_{\text{in}_2}\left(\frac{R_4}{R_3 + R_4}\right)\left(\frac{R_1 + R_2}{R_1}\right) \qquad \text{(13-21)}$$

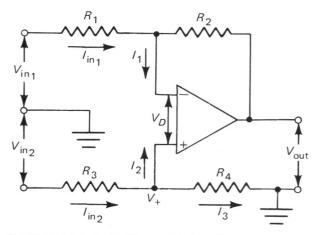

FIGURE 13-8. Differential Amplifier

Because we chose $R_1 = R_3$ and $R_2 = R_4$, we have

$$V_{\text{out}_2} = V_{\text{in}_2}\left(\frac{R_2}{R_1 + R_2}\right)\left(\frac{R_1 + R_2}{R_1}\right)$$

or

$$V_{\text{out}_2} = V_{\text{in}_2}\left(\frac{R_2}{R_1}\right) \qquad \text{(13-22)}$$

Returning to the sum of the two voltages given in Equation 13-17, we substitute into that equation the expressions found in Equations 13-18 and 13-22 and obtain

$$V_{\text{out}} = -V_{\text{in}_1}\left(\frac{R_2}{R_1}\right) + V_{\text{in}_2}\left(\frac{R_2}{R_1}\right)$$

or

$$V_{\text{out}} = \left(V_{\text{in}_2} - V_{\text{in}_1}\right)\left(\frac{R_2}{R_1}\right) \qquad \text{(13-23)}$$

Thus the gain with feedback is

$$A_{vf} = \frac{V_{\text{out}}}{V_{\text{in}_2} - V_{\text{in}_1}} = \frac{R_2}{R_1} \qquad \text{(13-24)}$$

if $V_{\text{in}_1} \neq V_{\text{in}_2}$

The meaning of these equations becomes clear if we note, from Equation 13-23, that the output voltage is zero when the two input voltages are equal. That is, signals common to both inputs (called the **common-mode input**) are canceled out. The **common-mode gain** is therefore zero. (In the discussion of real op amps later in the chapter, we will see that a common-mode gain of exactly zero is not achievable, and the amplifier performance is degraded as a result.)

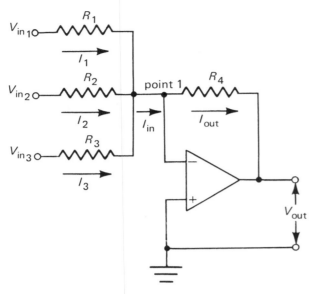

FIGURE 13-9. Summing Amplifier with Inverting Inputs

Summing Amplifier

Several signals can be received by an op amp, as Figure 13-9 shows. The analysis of the summing amplifier follows the same procedure used earlier. Again, we observe that point 1 is at virtual ground and because of infinite input resistance,

$$I_{out} = I_{in} \qquad (13\text{-}25)$$

The input current is the sum of component currents:

$$I_{in} = I_1 + I_2 + I_3$$

or

$$I_{in} = \frac{V_{in_1}}{R_1} + \frac{V_{in_2}}{R_2} + \frac{V_{in_3}}{R_3} \qquad (13\text{-}26)$$

and

$$I_{out} = \frac{-V_{out}}{R_4} \qquad (13\text{-}27)$$

The minus sign results from the inverting input. Combining Equations 13-25, 13-26, and 13-27, we obtain

$$V_{out} = - \left[V_{in_1}\left(\frac{R_4}{R_1}\right) + V_{in_2}\left(\frac{R_4}{R_2}\right) + V_{in_3}\left(\frac{R_4}{R_3}\right) \right]$$

$$(13\text{-}28)$$

The size of resistor R_4 *scales*, or multiplies, the input levels by a constant. The gains of each individual input channel are

$$\frac{R_4}{R_1}, \qquad \frac{R_4}{R_2}, \qquad \text{and} \qquad \frac{R_4}{R_3}$$

respectively. Any number of additional input channels can be connected in parallel with the existing three to increase the capacity of the summing amplifier. The same type of scaling will also be found on the new channels.

Integrator

An integrating circuit can also be constructed from an op amp. Figure 13-10 shows such a circuit. The input goes to the inverting terminal, and a capacitor is used in the feedback loop. The input and output currents are equal for the same reasons as those given previously:

$$I_{in} = I_{out} \qquad (13\text{-}29)$$

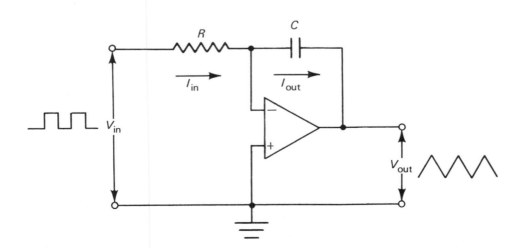

FIGURE 13-10. Integrator

The capacitor in the feedback loop causes the constant current at the peaks of the input square wave to generate a *linear ramp signal* (which is the integral of the input) while charging the capacitor.

The fundamental equation relating the current flowing through a capacitor and the voltage across it is

$$\Delta V_{\text{out}} = \frac{-I_{\text{out}}\Delta t}{C} \qquad (13\text{-}30)$$

Recall that

$$I_{\text{in}} = \frac{V_{\text{in}}}{R} \qquad (13\text{-}31)$$

Substituting the expressions from Equations 13-29 and 13-31 into Equation 13-30, we have

$$\Delta V_{\text{out}} = \frac{-V_{\text{in}}\Delta t}{RC} \qquad (13\text{-}32)$$

So the change in output is linear. The change in output voltage per unit of time is

$$\frac{\Delta V_{\text{out}}}{\Delta t} = \frac{-V_{\text{in}}}{RC} \qquad (13\text{-}33)$$

□ **EXAMPLE 13-3**

The integrator has an input resistor of 300 Ω and a feedback capacitor of 1 μF. The initial output voltage is 0 V. If the input signal is steady at +5 V, what is the level of the output signal after 150 μs?

Solution Using Equation 13-32, we have

$$\Delta V_{\text{out}} = \frac{-(5)(1.5 \times 10^{-4})}{(3 \times 10^{2})(10^{-6})}$$
$$= -2.5 \text{ V}$$

Differentiator

Interchanging the positions of the resistor and capacitor of the integrator produces a new circuit called the **differentiator**. The schematic is shown in Figure 13-11.

By this time, you should be quite familiar with the analytical technique. The input and output currents are equal:

$$I_{\text{in}} = I_{\text{out}} \qquad (13\text{-}34)$$

From the equation relating capacitor voltage and current (13-30), we have

$$I_{\text{in}} = \frac{\Delta V_{\text{in}}C}{\Delta t} \qquad (13\text{-}35)$$

Using the inverting input terminal, we have

$$V_{\text{out}} = -I_{\text{out}}R \qquad (13\text{-}36)$$

Putting the information in these three equations together, we obtain

$$V_{\text{out}} = \frac{-\Delta V_{\text{in}}RC}{\Delta t} \qquad (13\text{-}37)$$

V_{out} is zero except when the input is changing. (The value of ΔV_{in} is zero except when there is a change in that signal.)

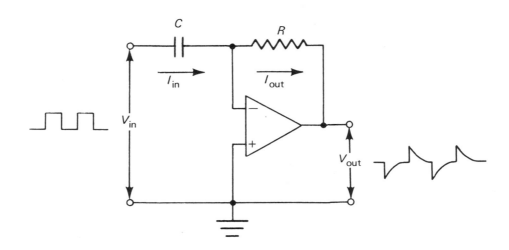

FIGURE 13-11.
Differentiator

□ EXAMPLE 13-4

Show that the output of a differentiator is a series of pulses of alternating polarity when the input is a square wave. The values of the circuit parameters are

$$R = 5 \text{ k}\Omega \quad \text{and} \quad C = 100 \text{ pF}$$

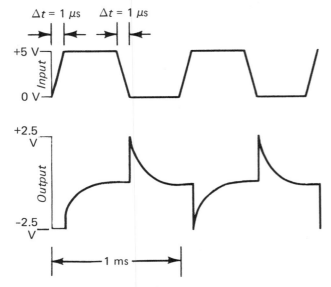

Note: Time axis not to scale.

FIGURE 13-12. Input and Output Signals of a Differentiator

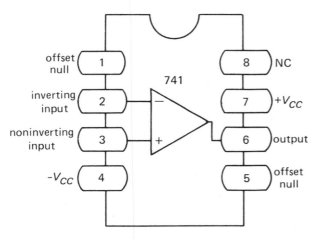

FIGURE 13-13. 741 Op Amp

Solution Let the input be as shown in Figure 13-12. So $\Delta t = 1$ μs. For the input signal transition from 0 to 5 V, the output is

$$V_{\text{out}} = \frac{-5(5 \times 10^3)(10^{-10})}{10^{-6}}$$
$$= -2.5 \text{ V}$$

Once the input is steady at $+5$ V, $\Delta V_{\text{in}} = 0$, so $V_{\text{out}} = 0$. During the input signal transition from $+5$ to 0 V,

$$V_{\text{out}} = \frac{-(-5)(5 \times 10^3)(10^{-10})}{10^{-6}}$$
$$= 2.5 \text{ V}$$

The output is 0 V while the square wave is at 0 V because ΔV_{in} is 0 V during that time. The resulting output is shown in Figure 13-12.

Applications of Basic Op Amp Configurations

The widely used 741 op amp will serve as an example to show how the circuits we have studied can be realized. The 741 is an 8-pin DIP, as Figure 13-13 shows. This op amp can also be obtained packaged in a metal can, 10-pin or 14-pin DIP. (The extra pins are not used.) Pin 2 is the inverting input and pin 3 the noninverting input. The output is available at pin 6. The positive power supply goes to pin 7, while the negative supply goes to pin 4. Use of the offset null will be described later. The two power supply voltages can be any values within the range of ± 5 to ± 18 V. Both positive and negative voltages are normally equal but of opposite polarity.

The inverting amplifier is shown in Figure 13-14a. The inverted output is related to the input voltage by the resistor ratio. That is,

$$V_{\text{out}} = -\left(\frac{R_2}{R_1}\right) V_{\text{in}}$$

A noninverting amplifier is shown in Figure 13-14b. Here the input signal goes to the noninverting input. In this case,

$$V_{\text{out}} = \left(\frac{R_1 + R_2}{R_1}\right) V_{\text{in}}$$

☐ EXAMPLE 13-5

Analyze the 741 op amp as a **unity-gain amplifier**. (Such amplifiers are often seen in the coupling to a circuit with low impedance.) Figure 13–15 shows the circuit.

Solution The operation can be analyzed in our usual way. We need only note that R_1 is infinite (open circuit), as compared to the input resistor value in a normal noninverting amplifier, and R_2 is zero. Thus

$$A_{vf} = \frac{R_1 + R_2}{R_2} = \frac{R_1 + 0}{R_1} = 1$$

Therefore,

$$V_{out} = V_{in}$$

A unity-gain amplifier is also called a **voltage follower** because of the direct relationship of the output with the input.

☐ REAL OP AMPS

Obviously, many of the assumptions that were made in formulating the idealized op amp model cannot be provided by actual components. The effects of relaxing these parameters will be investigated in this section.

One of the more important parameters is the open-loop gain, which was specified to be infinite in our model. So in this section, we will first consider finite open-loop gain to show how the amplifier equations must be changed to accommodate this factor. Next we will examine the less-than-perfect rejection of common-mode signals. How gain varies with finite bandwidth will be analyzed by using a Bode plot. Finally, we will consider second-order errors such as offset voltage, large signal limit, stability, and phase issues.

Finite Open-Loop Gain

An infinite open-loop gain was used in the idealized op amp model. However, actual op amps have dc open-loop gains on the order of 100 dB (decibels). This gain will not be constant, either. Gain varies from one op amp to another (even though they have the same part number) because of temperature changes, loading effects, and variations in supply voltage. It varies mostly because of the input signal frequency, though. This latter effect is most pronounced, so we will concentrate on it.

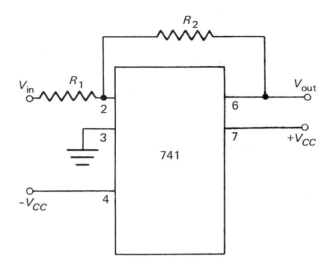

(a) Inverting Amplifier

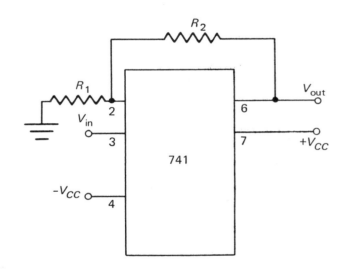

(b) Noninverting Amplifier

FIGURE 13–14. Using the 741 in Circuits

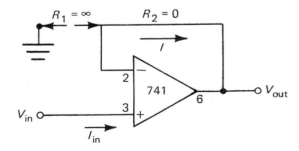

FIGURE 13–15. Unity-Gain Amplifier

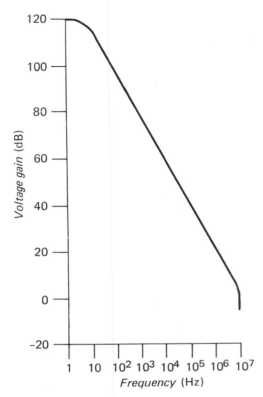

FIGURE 13-16. Gain Versus Frequency

The gain variation with frequency is shown in the graph of Figure 13-16. This graph is called a **Bode plot**. In the linearly decreasing portion of the curve, gain decreases by 20 dB per decade. (A **decade** is a change in frequency by one order of magnitude.)

Recall from the definition of a decibel that

$$\text{voltage gain (dB)} = 20 \log A_{vo} = 20 \log \left(\frac{V_{\text{out}}}{V_{\text{in}}}\right) \qquad \textbf{(13-38)}$$

If the open-loop gain is 10^5, then, in decibels, we have

$$\begin{aligned}\text{gain (dB)} &= 20 \log (10^5) \\ &= 20(5) \\ &= 100 \text{ dB}\end{aligned}$$

From Figure 13-16, we observe that the gain is higher at lower bandwidths. At a 10-Hz bandwidth, the gain for this op amp is greater than 100 dB, while at 10 MHz, it drops to 0 dB. Using Equation 13-38, we can show that 0 dB is a unity gain:

$$0 = 20 \log \left(\frac{V_{\text{out}}}{V_{\text{in}}}\right)$$

Dividing both sides by 20, we obtain

$$\log \left(\frac{V_{\text{out}}}{V_{\text{in}}}\right) = 0$$

Hence,

$$\left(\frac{V_{\text{out}}}{V_{\text{in}}}\right) = 1$$

In other words, it is possible to achieve an open-loop gain of 100 dB by limiting the signal bandwidth to 10 Hz. But gain falls to 0 dB if the bandwidth is increased to 10 MHz.

Noninverting Amplifier with Finite Gain

Let us take another look at the noninverting amplifier configuration without requiring that the open-loop gain, A_{vo}, be infinite. Without an infinite value for A_{vo}, the differential voltage between the inputs (labeled V_e here, where e represents "error") is no longer 0 V. For example, if A_{vo} is 10^5 and V_{out} is -1 V, we have

$$V_{\text{out}} = (A_{vo})(V_e)$$

or

$$V_e = -\frac{V_{\text{out}}}{A_{vo}} = -\frac{(-1)}{10^5} = 10 \ \mu\text{V}$$

Not a large error, but not zero by any means.

In general, we can write

$$V_{\text{in}} - V_e = \left(\frac{R_1}{R_1 + R_2}\right) V_{\text{out}} \qquad \textbf{(13-39)}$$

where

$$V_e = V_{\text{in}} - \beta V_{\text{out}}$$

$$\frac{R_1}{R_1 + R_2} = \beta$$

$$= \text{feedback attenuation factor}$$

That is, β is the ratio of the feedback signal to the input signal. Then

$$V_{\text{out}} = A_{vo} V_e$$

And from Equation 13-39, we have

$$V_{\text{out}} = A_{vo}(V_{\text{in}} - \beta V_{\text{out}}) \qquad \textbf{(13-40)}$$

Because the input voltage to the op amp is reduced by the small differential voltage, we have

$$V_{\text{out}} = A_{vo} V_{\text{in}} - A_{vo} \beta V_{\text{out}}$$

or

$$V_{\text{out}}(1 + A_{vo}\beta) = A_{vo} V_{\text{in}}$$

The closed-loop gain can then be written as

$$A_{cl} = \frac{V_{\text{out}}}{V_{\text{in}}} = \frac{A_{vo}}{1 + A_{vo}\beta} \qquad \textbf{(13–41)}$$

We can compare this gain with that of the idealized op amp. Dividing numerator and denominator of Equation 13–41 by $A_{vo}\beta$, we obtain

$$A_{cl} = \frac{1/\beta}{(1/A_{vo}\beta) + \beta}$$
$$= \left(\frac{1}{\beta}\right)\left[\frac{1}{1 + (1/A_{vo}\beta)}\right]$$

If A_{vo} is large (say 10^5), the term $1/A_{vo}\beta$ is small. So we can use the approximation

$$\frac{1}{1 + \Delta} = 1 - \Delta \qquad \text{(if } \Delta \text{ is small)}$$

in this equation, giving

$$A_{cl} \approx \left(\frac{1}{\beta}\right)\left(1 - \frac{1}{A_{vo}\beta}\right) \qquad \textbf{(13–42)}$$

Comparing this equation with Equation 13–15, we have

$$A_{vf} = \frac{R_1 + R_2}{R_1} \qquad \text{(idealized)}$$
$$A_{cl} = \left(\frac{1}{\beta}\right)\left(1 - \frac{1}{A_{vo}\beta}\right) \qquad \text{(finite gain)}$$

We note, then, that

$$\frac{1}{\beta} = \frac{R_1 + R_2}{R_1}$$

which is the gain of the idealized amplifier. Thus $1/A_{vo}\beta$ is the error term. If $1/A_{vo}\beta$ is small, the values obtained from the two gain equations will be quite close.

☐ **EXAMPLE 13–6**

Compare the size of the errors in two noninverting amplifiers, one with an open-loop gain of 10^5 and one with a gain of 10. $R_1 = 5\ \text{k}\Omega$ and $R_2 = 1\ \text{k}\Omega$.

Solution For an open-loop gain of 10^5, we have

$$A_{vf} = \frac{1}{\beta} = \frac{5 \times 10^3 + 10^3}{5 \times 10^3} = 1.2$$
$$A_{cl} = 1.2\left[1 - \frac{1}{(10^5)\left(\dfrac{5 \times 10^3}{5 \times 10^3 + 10^3}\right)}\right]$$
$$= 1.2\,(1 - 1.2 \times 10^{-6})$$
$$= 1.199998$$
$$\text{percent error} = \frac{A_{vf} - A_{cl}}{A_{vf}} = 0.00012\%$$

For an open-loop gain of 10, we have

$$A_{cl} = 1.2\left[1 - \frac{1}{10\left(\dfrac{5 \times 10^3}{5 \times 10^3 + 10^3}\right)}\right]$$
$$= 1.2(1 - 0.12)$$
$$= 1.056$$
$$\text{percent error} = \frac{A_{vf} - A_{cl}}{A_{vf}} = 12\%$$

Note that the error depends on both A_{vo} and β. The entire term $1/A_{vo}\beta$ must be small compared to one for the error to be minimized.

Several different terms are used to describe gain in op amps. Be sure to keep them straight. Table 13–1 lists the various types of gain for a noninverting op amp and gives the equations used to find the gain. Loop gain and noise gain are sometimes used in place of closed-loop gain.

The inverting amplifier gain is also affected by an open-loop gain that is less than infinite. The equations for the various gain terms are listed in Table 13–2. Note that the closed-loop gains of the inverting and noninverting amplifiers are not equal. However, the loop gain, noise gain, and feedback attenuation factor are the same for both.

Common-Mode Rejection Ratio

In our analysis of the idealized op amp, we assumed that the summation point (point 1 in Figure 13–7) was at virtual ground. In Figure 13–7, a virtual ground is not possible because of the error voltage V_e. This error is called the **common-mode voltage** resulting from an imbalance in the circuit. (Recall from the discussion of the differential op amp that, ideally, signals present at both inputs at the same time should produce no output.)

A measure of how well an op amp minimizes this error is the **common-mode rejection ratio (CMRR)**. By definition,

$$\text{CMRR} = \frac{\text{open-loop gain}}{\text{common-mode gain}} = \frac{A_{vo}}{A_{cm}} \qquad \textbf{(13–43)}$$

TABLE 13-1. Noninverting Op Amp Gains with Finite Open-Loop Gain

Term	Definition	Symbol	Equation
Open-loop gain	Gain of basic amplifier without feedback but with loading	A_{vo}	None (measured parameter)
Closed-loop gain	Gain including the effects of noise and loop gain	A_{cl}	$\dfrac{A_{vo}}{1 + A_{vo}}$ or approximately $\left(\dfrac{1}{\beta}\right)\left(1 - \dfrac{1}{A_{vo}\beta}\right)$
Loop gain	Net gain around the broken feedback loop, as seen from the feedback network input terminal back to the amplifier output	—	βA_{vo}
Signal gain	Closed-loop voltage gain of the applied signal(s)	—	$\left(\dfrac{R_1 + R_2}{R_1}\right)\left[\dfrac{1}{1 + (1/A_{vo}\beta)}\right]$
Noise gain	Reciprocal of the feedback loop attenuation	$\dfrac{1}{\beta}$	$\dfrac{R_1 + R_2}{R_1}$

TABLE 13-2. Inverting Op Amp Gains with Finite Open-Loop Gain

Term	Symbol	Equation
Open-loop gain	A_{vo}	None (measured parameter)
Closed-loop gain	A_{cl}	$\left(-\dfrac{R_2}{R_1}\right)\left[\dfrac{1}{1 + (1/A_{vo}\beta)}\right]$
Loop gain	—	βA_{vo}
Signal gain	—	$\left(-\dfrac{R_2}{R_1}\right)\left[\dfrac{1}{1 + (1/A_{vo}\beta)}\right]$
Noise gain	$\dfrac{1}{\beta}$	$\dfrac{R_1 + R_2}{R_1}$

Only if the common-mode gain is zero do we achieve the ideal infinite rejection ratio

$$\text{CMRR} = \frac{A_{vo}}{0} = \infty$$

The CMRR enters the closed-loop gain equation for the noninverting op amp as another error term:

$$A_{cl} = \left(\frac{1}{\beta}\right)\left[1 - \left(\frac{1}{A_{vo}\beta} + \frac{1}{\text{CMRR}}\right)\right] \quad (13\text{-}44)$$

Common-mode errors only occur in noninverting op amps. There can be no common-mode error in an inverting op amp configuration, so no CMRR error term can appear in its closed-loop gain equation.

□ EXAMPLE 13-7

Find the error produced in the closed-loop gain of a noninverting amplifier with the following characteristics:

$$\beta = 0.01$$
$$A_{vo} = 5 \times 10^4$$
$$\text{CMRR} = 50 \text{ dB}$$

Solution We must first convert the CMRR to a voltage ratio:

$$50 \text{ dB} = 20 \log\left(\frac{V_{\text{out}}}{V_{\text{in}}}\right)$$

$$\log\left(\frac{V_{\text{out}}}{V_{\text{in}}}\right) = 2.5$$

$$\frac{V_{\text{out}}}{V_{\text{in}}} = 10^{2.5}$$

The error is

$$\begin{aligned}
\text{error} &= \frac{1}{A_{vo}\beta} + \frac{1}{\text{CMRR}} \\
&= \frac{1}{(5 \times 10^4)(10^{-2})} + \frac{1}{10^{2.5}} \\
&= 5.16 \times 10^{-3} \\
&= 0.5\%
\end{aligned}$$

Using Bode Plots

For any particular model of the op amp, the open-loop gain is fixed. Although A_{vo} varies with the frequency, this variation is unchanged for a given op amp. Tailoring the gain response to an application is controlled by the β chosen. Since β is determined by the external resistors, it is these components that allow us to balance gain against bandwidth in a given configuration.

Figure 13–17 is a Bode plot of the open-loop gain, the feedback attenuation factor, and the noise gain for a typical amplifier. The constant portion of A_{vo} occurs at frequencies less than 10 Hz. At that frequency, gain is down by -3 dB, which is $1/\sqrt{2}$ times the original signal level. That is,

$$-3 \text{ dB} = 20 \log\left(\frac{V_{\text{out}}}{V_{\text{in}}}\right)$$

$$\log\left(\frac{V_{\text{out}}}{V_{\text{in}}}\right) = -0.15$$

$$\frac{V_{\text{out}}}{V_{\text{in}}} = \frac{1}{1.414} = \frac{1}{\sqrt{2}} = 0.707$$

The 3-dB level is called the **half-power point** because the power is half that of the original level. This result can be obtained by using the decibel equations for power instead of voltage, as we have done so far in this chapter. Thus

$$-3 \text{ dB} = 10 \log\left(\frac{P_{\text{out}}}{P_{\text{in}}}\right)$$

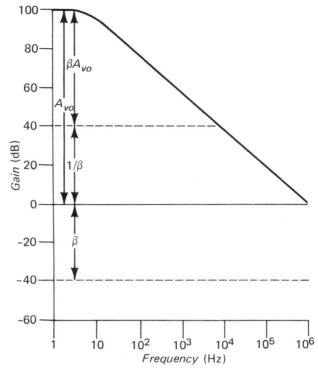

FIGURE 13–17. Bode Plot of Open-Loop Gain and β

where

$$P_{\text{out}} = \text{output power}$$
$$P_{\text{in}} = \text{input power}$$

Then

$$\log\left(\frac{P_{\text{out}}}{P_{\text{in}}}\right) = -0.3$$

$$\frac{P_{\text{out}}}{P_{\text{in}}} = \frac{1}{2}$$

The open-loop gain decreases by 20 dB per decade until it reaches unity gain (0 dB) at 1 MHz.

The feedback attenuation factor β is plotted as a negative gain, because the signal gain is decreased by that amount. The broken line for β in Figure 13–17 shows a -40-dB attenuation, which is independent of frequency. The plot for noise gain, $1/\beta$, is simply the β line reflected above the 0-dB level.

Loop gain is the product of β and A_{vo}. But on a logarithmic plot, the values are added because of the rule for multiplying logarithms:

$$\log(A_{vo}\beta) = \log A_{vo} + \log \beta$$

In Figure 13-17, the open-loop gain is the distance between the $1/\beta$ line and the A_{vo} plot.

□ **EXAMPLE 13-8**

What is the loop gain for an op amp with the characteristics shown in Figure 13-17 at a frequency of 5 Hz?

Solution   From the graph, we have

$$A_{vo} = 100 \text{ dB}$$
$$\beta = -40 \text{ dB}$$
$$\beta A_{vo} = 60 \text{ dB}$$

Another use of Bode plots is to find the **gain-bandwidth product** (GBP) for an amplifier circuit (see Figure 13-18). By definition,

$$\text{GBP} = (A_{vo})(\text{BW}) \qquad \text{(13-45)}$$

where
   BW = bandwidth at −3-dB points

From the graph, we can obtain the value for A_{vo} and convert it from decibel to voltage ratios at bandwidths of 100 Hz and 100 kHz. For the 100-Hz bandwidth, $A_{vo} = 80$ dB. So

$$80 \text{ dB} = 20 \log \left(\frac{V_{\text{out}}}{V_{\text{in}}} \right)$$
$$\frac{V_{\text{out}}}{V_{\text{in}}} = 10^4$$

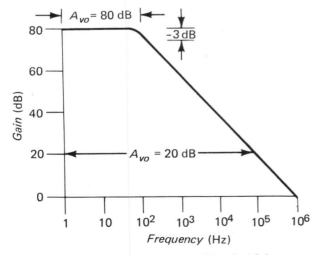

FIGURE 13-18. Gain Versus Bandwidth

TABLE 13-3. Gain-Bandwidth Product

A_{vo} (dB)	Ratio	Bandwidth at −3-dB Point (Hz)	GBP
0	1	10^6	10^6
20	10	10^5	10^6
40	10^2	10^4	10^6
60	10^3	10^3	10^6
80	10^4	10^2	10^6

Using Equation 13-45, we obtain

$$\text{GBP} = (10^4)(10^2) = 10^6$$

For the 100-kHz bandwidth, $A_{vo} = 20$ dB. So

$$20 \text{ dB} = 20 \log \left(\frac{V_{\text{out}}}{V_{\text{in}}} \right)$$
$$\frac{V_{\text{out}}}{V_{\text{in}}} = 10$$
$$\text{GBP} = (10)(10^5) = 10^6$$

Thus the gain-bandwidth product is *constant*. That is, we can select an amplifier with high gain or wide bandwidth, but not both. Increasing one variable causes the other to decrease in proportion. Table 13-3 lists other gains and bandwidths for this amplifier.

Offset Voltage

The **offset voltage** (V_{os}) is a small signal that must be applied to the inputs of an op amp to cause the output voltage to become 0 V (null) when the input voltage is 0 V. The offset voltage can be considered as another input, as shown in Figure 13-19a. In this circuit,

$$V_{\text{out}} = A_{vo} (V_{\text{in}} + V_{os})$$
$$= (A_{vo})(V_{os}) \quad \text{when} \quad V_{\text{in}} = 0 \text{ V}$$

The 741 op amp we examined in Figure 13-13 had two pins (pins 1 and 5) for the inputs of the offset voltage. These inputs permit **offset nulling**, as shown in Figure 13-19b. The offset voltage is set by adjusting the 25-kΩ potentiometer until the output voltage is 0 V when $V_{\text{in}} = 0$ V. Observe that the potentiometer is attached to the positive power supply voltage in this circuit.

The offset voltage is not constant; it will drift with changes in temperature. The change in output voltage with change in temperature is given by

$$\frac{\Delta V_{\text{out}}}{\Delta T} = A_{vo} \left(\frac{\Delta V_{\text{os}}}{\Delta T} \right) \qquad \textbf{(13–46)}$$

where

ΔT = change in temperature (°C)

$\dfrac{\Delta V_{\text{os}}}{\Delta T}$ = change in offset voltage per °C change in temperature

A typical value for $\Delta V_{\text{os}}/\Delta T$ is 25 μV/1°C.

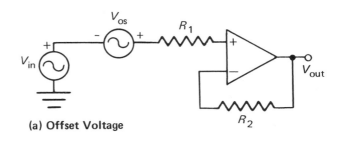

(a) Offset Voltage

Large-Signal Limit

At high frequencies, the output voltage lags behind changes in the input signal. This effect is especially pronounced in sinusoidal signals that vary rapidly. As Figure 13–20 illustrates, a sine wave has its maximum rate of change when it is passing through zero from either below or above. This performance factor of an op amp is called its **large-signal limit.**

If the large-signal limit is exceeded, the output appears as a triangular wave rather than as an amplified sine wave. The maximum frequency that does not exceed the large-signal limit is

$$f_{\text{max}} = \frac{\text{SR}}{2\pi V_p} \times 10^6 \qquad \textbf{(13–47)}$$

where

SR = slew rate of the op amp in V/μs (found in the data sheet)

V_p = peak output voltage

The large-signal limit is the maximum frequency for which the op amp will reliably reproduce input signals. If good fidelity in the output is necessary, the circuit should use an op amp that exceeds the highest frequency of the input in its large-signal limit.

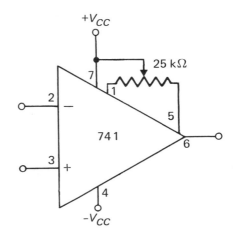

(b) Offset Nulling

FIGURE 13–19. Offset Voltage

□ **EXAMPLE 13–9**

Find the large-signal limiting frequency for an op amp with a slew rate of 0.7 V/μs and a peak output voltage of 15 V.

Solution   From Equation 13–47, we have

$$f_{\text{max}} = \frac{0.7 \times 10^6}{2\pi(15)} = 7.43 \text{ kHz}$$

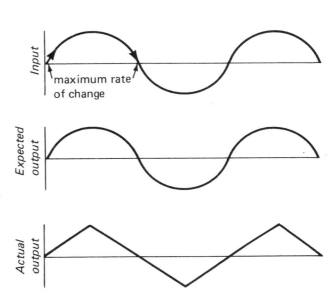

FIGURE 13–20. Large-Signal Limit

Stability

If we apply a 10-Hz input signal to the circuit of Figure 13–21 and then increase the frequency, an interesting effect will be observed. At some higher frequency, the phase of the output will reverse and become a negative-going voltage when a positive input is applied. As we continue to raise the frequency, the amplifier will begin to oscillate.

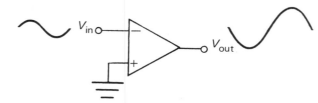

FIGURE 13–21. Phase Reversal and Stability

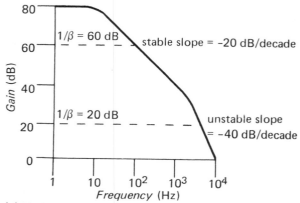

(a) Variable-Gain Slope

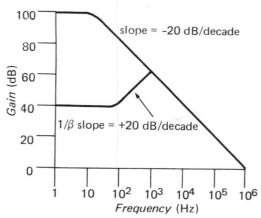

(b) Variable Slope in $1/\beta$

FIGURE 13–22. Using a Bode Plot to Determine Stability

The effect of this phase error can be seen in the closed-loop gain equation,

$$A_{cl} = \frac{A_{vo}}{1 + A_{vo}\beta}$$

If the denominator ever becomes zero, the gain becomes infinite, which is the cause of amplifier's oscillation. How can this occur? If $1 + A_{vo}\beta = 0$, then $A_{vo}\beta = -1$. In other words, there is a 180° *phase reversal* in the loop gain. (This problem is worst for $\beta = 1$.)

To guarantee that an amplifier will not oscillate, we require *unconditional stability* in the design. Unconditional stability will be realized when the $1/\beta$ curve on the Bode plot intersects the open-loop gain curve with a net slope of less than −40 dB per decade. Thus, to check for stability, we add the two slopes and compare the result to −40 dB per decade. (The slope is the decrease in the gain divided by the frequency change.) We use the equation

net slope = slope of A_{vo} + slope of $1/\beta$ (13–48)

Consider the intersection of the A_{vo} curve with a $1/\beta$ of 60 dB, as shown in Figure 13–22a. Here

slope of A_{vo} = −20 dB/decade
  slope of $\frac{1}{\beta}$ = 0
  net slope = −20 + 0 = −20 dB/decade

So we have unconditional stability.

Now look at the intersection of the steeper portion of A_{vo} with the $1/\beta = 20$ dB line. Here

slope of A_{vo} = −40 dB/decade
  slope of $\frac{1}{\beta}$ = 0
  net slope = −40 + 0 = −40 dB/decade

So unconditional stability is not guaranteed.

Often, the $1/\beta$ frequency response is not flat, as shown in Figure 13–22b. However, the net slope is still found in the same manner. The intersection of the two gains gives

slope of A_{vo} = −20 dB/decade
  slope of $\frac{1}{\beta}$ = 20 dB/decade
  net slope = −20 + 20 = 0 dB/decade

Again, we have unconditional stability.

Another way of looking at the stability issue is from the point of view of *phase shift*. The plot

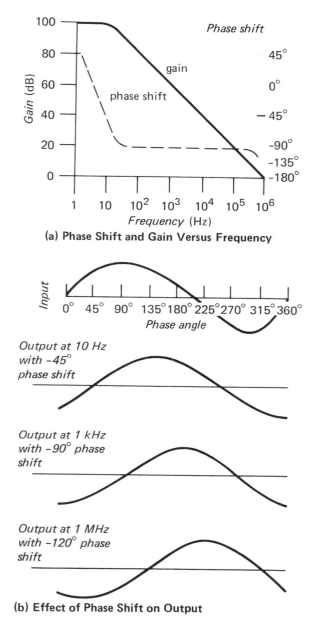

(a) Phase Shift and Gain Versus Frequency

(b) Effect of Phase Shift on Output

FIGURE 13-23. Phase Shift Versus Frequency

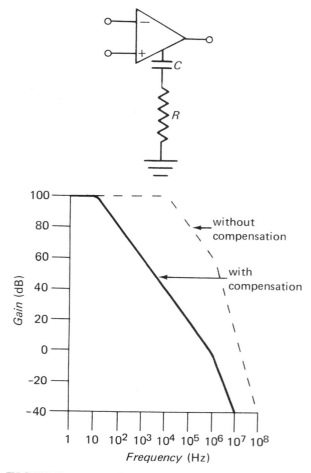

FIGURE 13-24. Compensation Effects on Gain

in Figure 13-23a shows how the phase of the output signal changes with frequency. The phase of the output (as compared to the input signal) is −45° at the point when the open-loop gain is down 3 dB (see Figure 13-23b). The phase change reaches a constant level of −90° where the gain is dropping by −20 dB per decade. In a general-purpose op amp, the maximum phase change is less than −135° (typically −120°) as the gain reaches 0 dB. Note that at some higher frequency

the phase error will be −180°, which is where oscillation will begin.

Many op amps are **internally compensated** to reduce the effects of phase change with frequency. These devices have a desirable −90° phase shift and a gain roll-off of −20 dB/decade. Earlier models of op amps required **external compensation**, as shown in Figure 13-24. The value of the resistor and capacitor shown in the figure can be found by using the relationship

$$f_{-90} = \frac{10}{2\pi RC}$$

where

f_{-90} = frequency at phase shift of −90°

The compensation is not without cost, however. While stability is improved, the open-loop gain is reduced, as the Bode plot in Figure 13-24 shows. The uncompensated amplifier has a

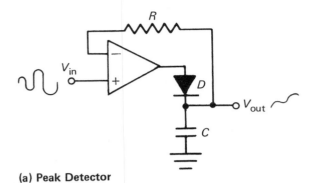

(a) Peak Detector

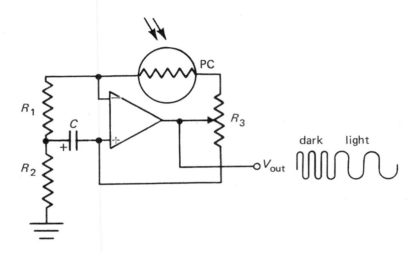

(b) Light Sensor

FIGURE 13–25.
Op Amp Circuits

100-dB gain at 10 kHz, but the gain at that frequency is reduced to 40 dB in the compensated circuit.

Applications of Op Amps

The universal applicability of op amps makes them useful in performing many jobs. For instance, the **peak detector** of Figure 13–25a holds the output at the highest level of the input signal. The noninverting amplifier produces an output signal that is in phase with the input. The diode eliminates the negative-going transitions of the signal, while the capacitor is charged to the highest voltage of the signal. This voltage is maintained until a higher voltage is available to increase the charge on the capacitor.

The **light sensor** in Figure 13–25b takes advantage of the oscillation that can occur in an op amp. When light shines on the photocell (PC), the frequency of oscillations decreases. When the photocell is in the dark, the frequency increases.

Chapter Summary

☐ The output of a linear circuit is related to the input by a straight-line plot.

☐ The op amp is an analog component that has two inputs, one inverting and the other noninverting, and a single output terminal. The voltage between the input terminals is called the differential voltage.

☐ The open-loop gain of an op amp is the gain without feedback.

☐ The idealized op amp has infinite open-loop gain, bandwidth, and input resistance. The output resistance is zero. When the input voltage is 0 V, the output is also 0 V (zero offset).

☐ In the inverting amplifier, the input signal is applied to the inverting input terminal. In contrast, the noninverting amplifier uses the noninverting input terminal.

☐ The differential amplifier generates a signal that represents the difference of the two inputs. The summing amplifier adds the voltages on each channel as scaled by the feedback resistor. Op amps are also capable of integrating or differentiating waveforms.

☐ Finite loop gain in real op amps produces an error term, which reduces the open-loop gain. The noninverting amplifier has a second error term, which is a result of the common-mode rejection ratio.

☐ Bode plots allow us to predict the performance of an amplifier at various frequencies. The plot shows how external feedback networks affect the open-loop gain.

☐ The gain-bandwidth product of an amplifier is constant. Thus one can achieve high gain or wide bandwidth in a single amplifier, but not both.

☐ The offset voltage of an op amp is used to null the output voltage. Offset voltage varies with temperature.

☐ The large-signal limit sets a maximum frequency for which the output signal of an op amp can track the input changes.

☐ Stability of an amplifier is based on phase change. An amplifier that is unconditionally stable will not oscillate. Compensation networks (internal or external) are used to provide stability, but gain is reduced as a result.

Problems

13-1. Use the idealized op amp parameters to find the gain with feedback for the amplifiers of Figures 13-26a and 13-26b. The input voltage is a sine wave with ±0.2-V peak voltage and a frequency of 10 Hz. Sketch the output signal of each amplifier.

13-2. Input voltages to the circuit in Figure 13-8 are listed below. If R_3 is 2 kΩ and R_4 is 15 kΩ, what is the output voltage?

$$V_{in_1} = 3.8 \text{ V} \qquad V_{in_2} = 4.2 \text{ V}$$

13-3. Suppose the output voltage of the summing amplifier of Figure 13-9 is not to exceed −10 V. Input voltages are in the range of 0 to 5 V. Determine the value you would recommend for R_4 if the other resistor values are

$$R_1 = 500 \text{ Ω} \qquad R_2 = 750 \text{ Ω} \qquad R_3 = 300 \text{ Ω}$$

13-4. Compare the closed-loop gain, the loop gain, the signal gain, and the noise gain of an inverting and a noninverting amplifier that both

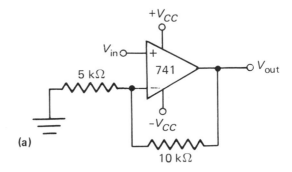

(a)

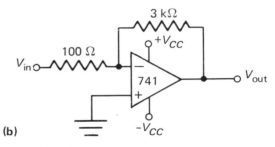

(b)

FIGURE 13-26.

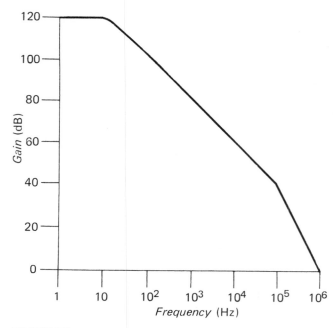

FIGURE 13-27.

use the same op amp in a unity-gain configuration.

13-5. What offset voltage would be needed for an amplifier with the characteristics shown in Figure 13-17? The input signal frequency is 1 kHz, and an input signal of 0 V results in an output of 0.15 mV.

13-6. The peak output voltage of an op amp is 12 V. If the amplifier has a slew rate of 0.4 V/μs, what is the large-signal limiting frequency?

13-7. Will an amplifier with a noise gain of 27 dB from dc to 1 MHz oscillate if the open-loop gain is as shown in Figure 13-27? Would your answer change if the noise gain were the one shown in Figure 13-22b?

13-8. Find the gain-bandwidth product for an op amp with the characteristics shown in Figure 13-23a. What is the bandwidth for that amplifier if the open-loop gain is 30 dB?

13-9. An op amp requires external compensation for phase stability. If a 10-kΩ resistor is to be used, what size would you recommend for the capacitor?

13-10. A 0.2-V sine wave is applied to the amplifier of Figure 13-23. The frequency is 1 kHz. Sketch the output signal, showing its phase relative to the input and its amplitude.

Chapter Fourteen
Signal Conditioning

Sometimes the signals issued by electronic devices are not clear or are not compatible with the equipment they serve. For instance, signals provided by sensors located at remote equipment sites are often noisy and distorted. Control devices issue commands in the form of outputs that may lack the current drive necessary to interface with an actuator or motor. In both situations, the signals must be modified, or **conditioned**, so that they meet the criteria of the systems involved. Signal-conditioning circuits are designed to accomplish these tasks. Important measures of performance include **speed**, accuracy, power, and interface compatibility.

Signal-conditioning devices can be packaged as integrated circuits, hybrid circuits, modules, or even entire circuit boards. Figure 14-1 shows the internal construction of a **hybrid circuit**. Several individual chips are contained in the package, in contrast to the monolithic structure of an IC.

In this chapter, we will study the problems associated with signal conditioning, including transducer interfacing, signal amplification, analog multiplexing, signal routing, switching, and filtering.

Chapter Objectives

Upon completion of this chapter, you should be able to:

☐ List applications of signal-conditioning circuits in a typical data acquisition process.

☐ Compare the features of instrumentation amplifiers with those of operational amplifiers.

☐ Draw a block diagram of an analog multiplexer used in a multichannel sampling system.

☐ Determine the safe operating points for power op amps.

☐ Show how voltage comparators can be used as drivers and zero-crossing detectors.

☐ Explain the operation of a smoke detector IC that implements a combination of signal-conditioning functions.

☐ Select the components of an active filter.

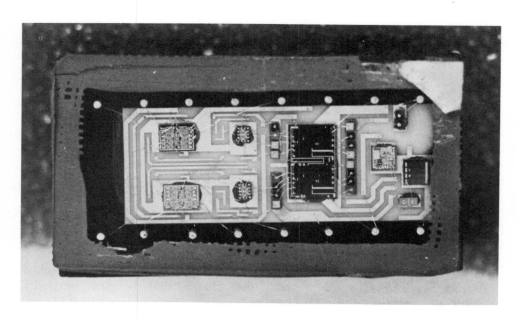

FIGURE 14-1.
Hybrid Circuit

☐ SIGNAL CONDITIONING IN PROCESS CONTROL

Industrial processes monitored by electronic controls must provide signals that represent the status of the operation. They must also maintain safe limits with commands issued from the controlling circuit. The monitoring sensor uses a **transducer**, which converts physical measures (such as temperature, pressure, and liquid levels) into electrical signals. The commands from the control circuits cause **actuators** to open or close valves, move a machine arm, or turn on a motor.

An industrial process control system is shown in the block diagram of Figure 14-2. The noisy signals from the sensor are smoothed and amplified by the *instrumentation amplifier*, which gets its input from a *filter*. Then the signal goes to an *analog multiplexer*. Several signals are received at the multiplexer, but only one signal at a time is routed to the *sample-and-hold circuit (S/H)*. The S/H maintains the signal at a constant level long enough for the *analog-to-digital converter (ADC)* to sample it. The converted signal is sent to the *microcomputer*, which decides what the proper response is to be. The computer produces a digital output signal that is changed to an analog voltage by the *digital-to-analog converter (DAC)*. That voltage is boosted by the *power amplifier* and used to drive an *actuator* that changes settings in various stages of the process. The *reference* provides a precise voltage to the ADC and

DAC, which they use for comparison with their internal voltages for the conversion process. The devices associated with digital and analog conversion will be covered in Chapter 15, while Chapter 19 examines power supplies and controls. The remaining elements in this system are the subject of this chapter.

☐ INSTRUMENTATION AMPLIFIERS

An **instrumentation amplifier** is a dc amplifier with feedback for voltage gain and configured for data acquisition. Characteristics of these amplifiers are high gain and extremely high input impedance. (Typical impedance values are 10^{10} Ω for amplifiers fabricated from bipolar transistors and 10^{13} Ω for those built from field effect transistors.) Other key performance measures are high speed, low noise, minimum drift, and low power consumption.

Instrumentation amplifiers are built for either *single-ended* or *differential* input. The **single-ended amplifier** provides only one input terminal, which may be inverting or noninverting. The other input to the amplifier is grounded. High signal levels can be applied to the single-ended amplifier, with full-scale (that is, peak-to-peak) voltages from 10 to 20 V typical. Conversely, the **differential amplifier** is limited to low-level signals (10 mV to 1 V, full-scale).

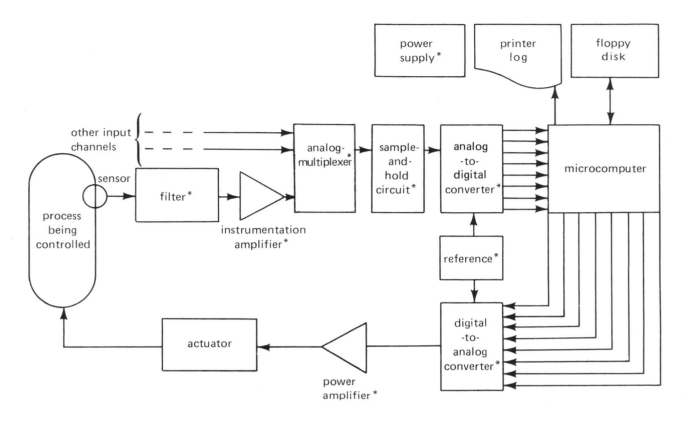

*Elements containing linear circuits

FIGURE 14-2. Process Control Block Diagram

Because there are two inputs, the input signal is the differential voltage.

The advantage of the differential amplifier is that it nulls common-mode signals. Such signals are especially troublesome when ground loops provide a source of noise from other channels that will mix in (see Figure 14-3). The disadvantage of the differential amplifier, also shown in the figure, is the necessity to use two output channels from a multiplexer instead of one. Both types of instrumentation amplifiers are widely used with such sensors as thermocouples, strain gauges, and pressure transducers.

Characteristics of Differential Amplifiers

The special features of the differential instrumentation amplifier are best appreciated by looking at an example. Figure 14-4 shows the same sensor providing signals to an op amp (Figure 14-4a) and to an instrumentation amplifier (Figure 14-4b) through a coaxial cable. For the op amp, the output voltage is

$$V_{out} = -A_{cl}(V_{in} + V_g) \qquad (14-1)$$

where

V_g = noise signal

The output of the instrumentation amplifier is

$$V_{out} = -A_{cl}V_{in} + \frac{V_g}{CMRR} \qquad (14-2)$$

where

CMRR = common-mode rejection ratio

The CMRR varies with frequency, usually decreasing by 20 dB per decade. Typical values are 120 dB at low frequency, falling to 80 dB at 100 Hz.

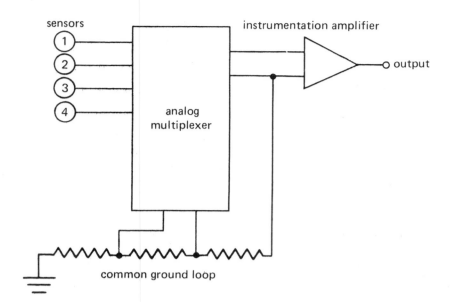

FIGURE 14–3.
Analog Multiplexer
with Differential

The differential gain for the instrumentation amplifier can be found by using the equation

$$A_{\text{diff}} = KA_i(V_2 - V_1) \qquad (14\text{–}3)$$

where

K = a design-controlled coefficient
A_i = internal amplifier gain
V_2 = noninverting input voltage
V_1 = inverting input voltage

□ **EXAMPLE 14–1**

Compare the noise performance of an op amp with that of an instrumentation amplifier if both have a closed-loop gain of 100. The input voltage is 50 mV and the noise signal is 2 mV. The CMRR of the instrumentation amplifier is 110 dB.

Solution The output of the op amp, from Equation 14–1, is

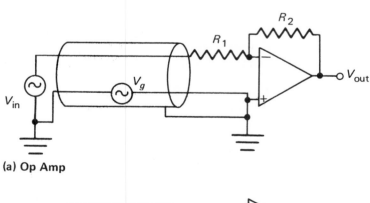

(a) Op Amp

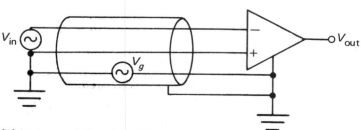

(b) Instrumentation Amplifier

FIGURE 14–4. Op Amp Compared to Instrumentation Amplifier

$$V_{out} = 100(50 \times 10^{-3} + 2 \times 10^{-3})$$
$$= 5.2 \text{ V}$$

The error is

$$\text{error} = \frac{V_{out} - V_{out} \text{ (without noise)}}{V_{out} \text{ (without noise)}}$$
$$= \frac{5.2 - 5}{5}$$
$$= 4\%$$

The instrumentation amplifier output is

$$V_{out} = -100(50 \times 10^{-3}) + \frac{2 \times 10^{-3}}{10^{110/20}}$$
$$= 5 + 6.3 \times 10^{-9}$$

The error is

$$\text{error} = \frac{(5 + 6.3 \times 10^{-9}) - 5}{5}$$
$$= 0.000001\%$$

Input Impedance and Frequency

The input impedance of an instrumentation amplifier is not independent of frequency, as shown in Figure 14-5. The roll-off varies from 10^{13} to 10^7 Ω for FET amplifiers. It varies from 10^{10} to 10^8 Ω for bipolar transistor amplifiers. The rating of amplifiers using FETs is better at low frequencies, but a crossover occurs at 10 Hz. At that point, the bipolar amplifier offers better performance.

☐ ANALOG MULTIPLEXERS

An **analog multiplexer (MUX)** performs the same function as a digital multiplexer: One of many inputs is routed to the single output. The difference is that here signals are analog not digital. An analog multiplexer is, in effect, a bank of switches that connects the desired input channel to the output. Each channel is addressed by its unique digital code. Switching time is measured in nanoseconds. Before the next switch closes, the previously closed switch should open to prevent routing of two signals to the output at once. This type of operation is called **break-before-make**.

Because the analog multiplexer does not actually contain a physical switch, its characteristics are a little different from those of a normal switch. The resistance of the channel, when the

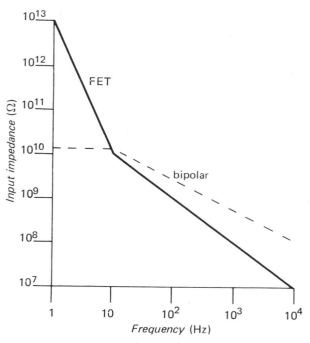

FIGURE 14-5. Roll-off of Input Impedance with Frequency

circuit is closed, is on the order of 100 Ω. Switching time from on to off is faster than the time from off to on. The switching off time is about 0.2μs, while the switching on time is 2μs, one order of magnitude longer.

The LF11508 eight-channel MUX shown in Figure 14-6 is a typical example of the device. The input signals are connected to the pins identified as $S1$ through $S8$ (Figure 14-6a). The switch-addressing pins are $A0$ through $A2$. Before any switch will respond to its address, the chip must be enabled by a high EN signal. Table 14-1 lists the functions of the IC. Figure 14-6b shows a useful way to visualize the routing of the inputs. As specified by the input address, only one of the eight switches will close. That signal can then be sampled at the output terminal D.

☐ EXAMPLE 14-2

An application of the analog multiplexer is depicted in Figure 14-7. There are eight input sensors attached to the multiplexer inputs (see Figure 14-7a). The unity-gain amplifier provides a buffer to the ADC, and it also performs another function. When the MUX enable signal is high,

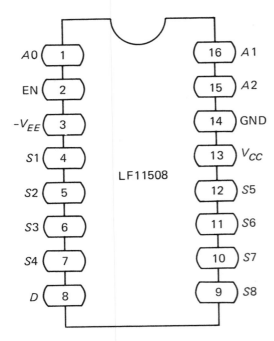

(a) Pin Assignments

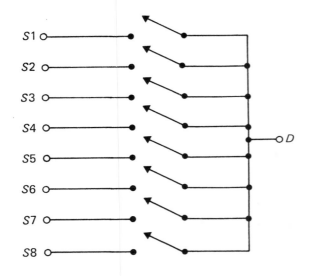

(b) Equivalent Circuit

FIGURE 14-6. LF11508 Eight-Channel Multiplexer

TABLE 14-1. LF11508 Functions

| EN | Address | | | Switch On |
	A2	A1	A0	
L	X[a]	X[a]	X[a]	None
H	L	L	L	S1
H	L	L	H	S2
H	L	H	L	S3
H	L	H	H	S4
H	H	L	L	S5
H	H	L	H	S6
H	H	H	L	S7
H	H	H	H	S8

[a]X = don't care.

The capacitor cannot discharge, so this constant signal is available for the ADC to sample when the microcomputer issues the command (see Figure 14-7b). Afterward, the microcomputer addresses another channel and again enables the MUX. This voltage will differ from that presently stored on the capacitor, which will charge or discharge as necessary to become equal to the applied voltage. Then the process repeats. Thus, the op amp and capacitor comprise a sample-and-hold circuit, which is covered in detail in the next chapter.

□ POWER OPERATIONAL AMPLIFIERS

When there is a requirement for high output voltage and current, a **power op amp** is often the best component to choose for the job. These amplifiers are encountered driving dc motors, providing voltage to the linear-deflection amplifier of a cathode ray tube (CRT), supplying voltages to speakers in audio equipment, and varying the voltage in programmable power supplies. Output current exceeds 50 mA with a supply voltage of 44 V or more (±22 V with dual supplies). Both hybrid and monolithic IC packagings are used.

Power op amps do not offer high gain, and the differential input voltage must be limited to less than that of the supply voltage. Manufacturers provide information on these limits in the form of **safe operating area (SOA) curves**, such as

the chosen input voltage (with a range of 0 to 10 V) will charge the capacitor to that value. Then the EN signal goes low, opening the channel switch. The capacitor sees high impedance from both the op amp and the MUX output channel (because the switches on all channels are open).

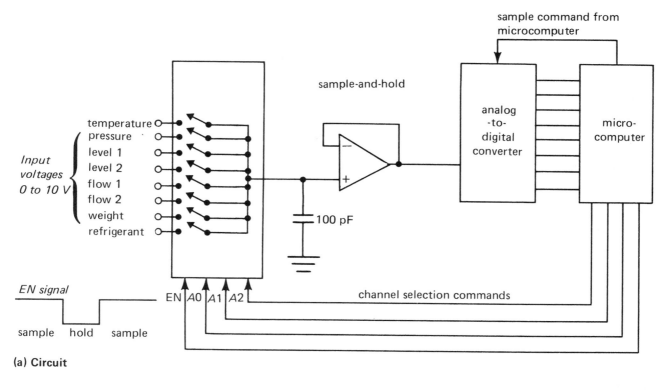

(a) Circuit

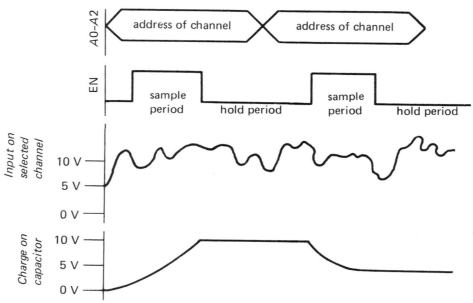

(b) Timing Diagram

FIGURE 14-7. Eight-Channel Data-sampling Circuit

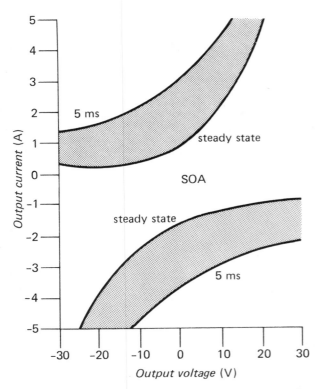

FIGURE 14-8. Safe Operating Area Curve of a Power Op Amp

the curve in Figure 14-8. This graph plots output voltage against output current. When output current is positive, the amplifier is supplying current to the load. A negative output current means that the power supply is sinking current from the load.

There are two curves on each half of the plot. The one labeled "5 ms" is the short-time capacity (less than 5 ms) that the amplifier can safely handle. These values are to be expected in start-up transients. The steady state curve gives the long-time operating limits for the amplifier.

Let's consider an example. If a ±35-V supply is used, suitable maximum output voltage limits would be ±30 V. (Generally, the maximum output voltage is 5 V less than the supply.) If the load is 15 Ω, we have

$$I_{\text{outMAX}} = \frac{V_{\text{outMAX}}}{R_L} \qquad (14\text{-}4)$$

where

V_{outMAX} = steady state maximum output voltage

R_L = load resistance

So

$$I_{\text{outMAX}} = \frac{30}{15} = 2 \text{ A}$$

which is within the safe steady state limits.

Reactive loads require additional consideration, because transients of the load may act as a short to the power supply. (Supply voltages are sometimes called *supply rails*. So you may hear reference to "a short to the rails.") In a reactive load, a motor will generate an electromotive force (EMF) that depends on its speed. Although Equation 14-4 is always true, the R_L of the motor is not constant. The resistance of the motor can drop rapidly when the motor is running or rise sharply when the motor reverses.

Figure 14-9a shows a simple motor drive circuit. The internal resistance of the motor is R_m. During the first 5 ms after starting, the worst-case voltage-current combination occurs, as shown in Figure 14-9b. The output voltage reaches 10 V and the supply must sink −2 A during that interval. Referring to Figure 14-8, we see that for 5 ms or less this combination of voltage and current can be tolerated. The steady state values of 10 V and 1 A are also within the acceptable range.

The diodes shown on the schematic are not needed for motor operation. They protect the amplifier against excessive positive or negative EMF from the motor. The diodes *clamp* the voltages to the supply rails, protecting the amplifier from damage. Some power amplifiers are made with these diodes as internal components in order to protect the amplifier.

□ AUDIO POWER AMPLIFIERS

Good fidelity is especially important in amplifying signals broadcast through a speaker. The input waveform should not be altered or distorted in the power amplifier that drives a speaker. The LM386 **audio amplifier** is a stand-alone IC suited for battery-operated AM-FM radios, tape players, intercoms, TV audio, and ultrasonic drivers. It offers voltage gains in the range of 20 to 200.

Figure 14-10a shows the pin assignments for the LM386. The chip can drive an 8-Ω speaker directly. Power supply voltages in the range of

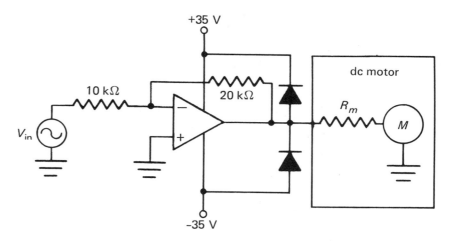

(a) dc Motor Circuit

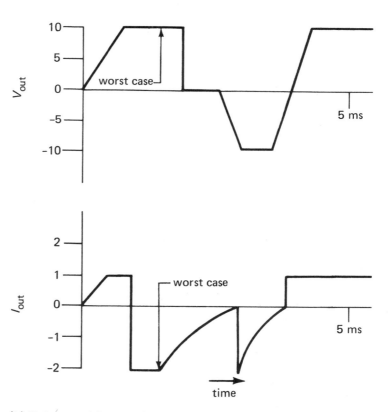

FIGURE 14–9.
Reactive-Load
Effects

(b) Voltage and Current Output Transients

+4 to +12 V are acceptable. Pins 1 and 8 control the amount of gain produced by the amplifier. If both pins are open, an internal capacitor sets the gain at 20, as shown in Figure 14–10b. Connecting a capacitor between those pins increases the gain to 200, as shown in Figure 14–10c. If a resistor is placed in series with that capacitor, any gain between 20 and 200 can be realized. For example, a 1.2-kΩ resistor, in series with a 10-μF capacitor, produces a gain of 50. The input potentiometer in both circuits serves to control the input level.

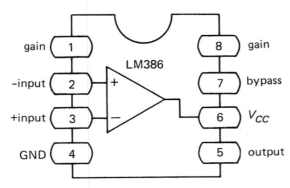

(a) Pin Assignments

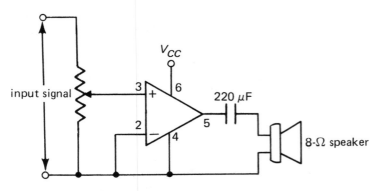

(b) Basic Amplifier with Gain of 20

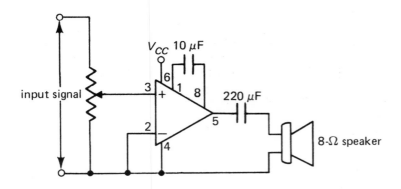

(c) Amplifier with Gain of 200

FIGURE 14–10.
Audio Power
Amplifier

□ VOLTAGE COMPARATORS

A voltage comparator—a circuit that compares two voltages and indicates which is higher—can be built from an op amp. However, it is usually more convenient to select a packaged device such as the LM339 quad comparator. As shown in Figure 14–11a, there are four comparators within the IC. A single power supply can be used, with V_{CC} in the range of +2 to +36 V.

Two circuits using the LM339 are illustrated in Figures 14–11b and 14–11c. The first schematic uses the comparator as a CMOS driver. Drivers are needed when signals must run for long distances—that is, more than a foot (30 cm). A similar driver for TTL circuits is shown in the second circuit. In both cases, the input signal is applied to the noninverting terminal. The wiring to comparators must be routed carefully. If the output wires are too close to the inputs, the

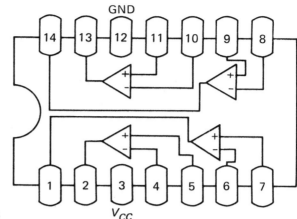

(a) Pin Assignments

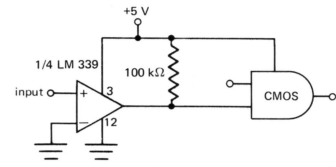

(b) CMOS Driver

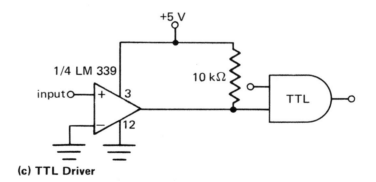

(c) TTL Driver

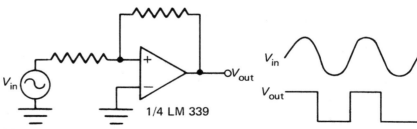

(d) Zero-crossing Detector

FIGURE 14–11.
Voltage Comparator

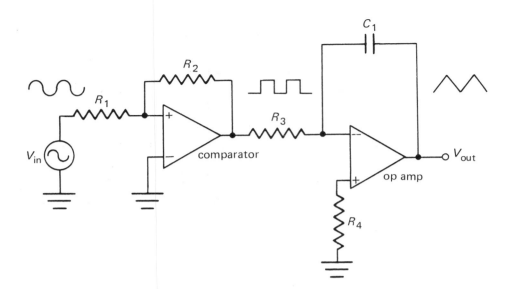

FIGURE 14–12.
Function Generator

comparators will oscillate. All pins of unused comparators should be grounded.

Another use of comparators is shown in Figure 14–11d. A **zero-crossing detector** switches its output level from high to low, or vice versa, each time the input signal passes through the zero voltage level. The output voltage shift occurs because the inverting input is grounded, causing the differential voltage to change sign every time the input goes through 0 V.

Function generators that produce square, triangular, and sine waves can also be built by using comparators. To change a square wave to a triangular wave, we just integrate it. Figure 14–12 shows a function generator offering all these waveforms.

The LM1801 **smoke detector** is a sophisticated combination of a comparator, a low-battery-voltage sensor, a timing circuit, and a driver for the alarm horn. The pin assignments for the device are shown in Figure 14–13a. This chip is used with an ionization type of smoke detector. The comparator inputs provide a comparison of the output from the ionization chamber with the system ground, as shown in Figure 14–13b. When smoke is present, the chamber voltage changes, causing the comparator output to change levels and sound the horn.

Normally, a 9-V battery is used in the smoke detector, but battery voltages up to +14 V or dc line voltages are also acceptable. A battery voltage of less than 8.2 V sounds the low-voltage alarm, with the biasing of the 7.5-MΩ and 2.7-MΩ

resistors, as shown. Other bias values will trip at other voltages.

The smoke detector can be connected in parallel to make a maximum network of eight detectors. When one of the alarms is tripped, they all sound. The LM1801 also generates a regulated +6-V supply to power the ionization chamber.

☐ ACTIVE FILTERS

The purpose of a **filter** is to sharply attenuate an input signal at a specified frequency. Various filter performance curves are plotted in Figure 14–14. In each case, the relative gain is plotted against frequency. The **low-pass filter** (Figure 14–14a) reduces any signal above the high-frequency cutoff (f_H), measured at the −3-dB gain point. A **high-pass filter** (Figure 14–14b) passes all signals higher than the lower cutoff frequency (f_L), again specified at the −3-dB level. A **band-pass filter** (Figure 14–14c) is a combination of the high- and low-pass filters. Only frequencies between f_L and f_H are not attenuated. A bandpass filter can be constructed by cascading a high-pass and a low-pass filter stage. Yet another possible combination of filtering is the **band rejection**, or **notch**, filter. This circuit removes frequencies in the range between f_L and f_H. Figure 14–14d shows how the outputs of a high-pass and a low-pass filter are fed to a summing amplifier to form a notch filter.

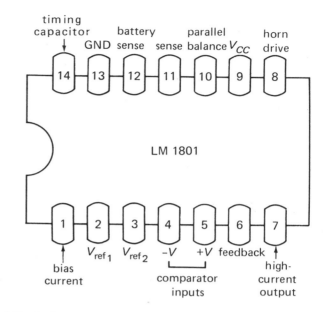

(a) Pin Assignments

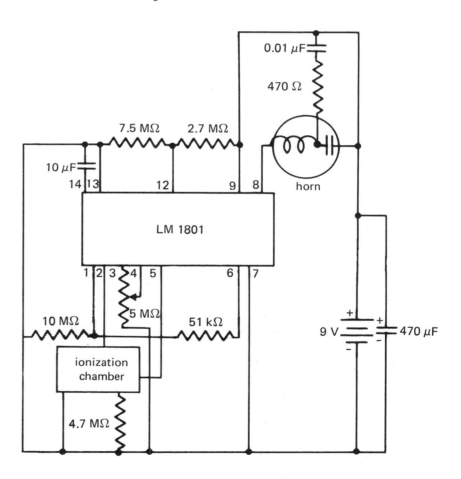

FIGURE 14-13.
Smoke Detector

(b) Complete System

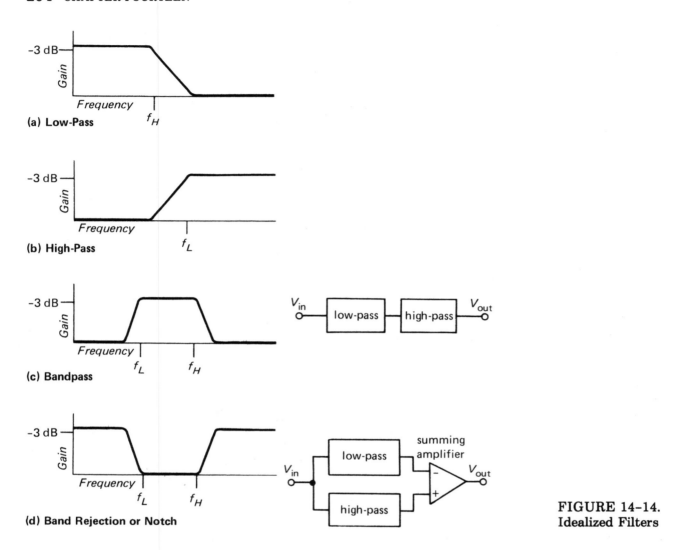

FIGURE 14-14.
Idealized Filters

If these filters are constructed with op amps (as well as resistors, capacitor, and inductors), a much sharper cutoff can be achieved in a single stage than is possible from the use of passive elements alone. These components are called **active filters**, after the active device they contain (namely, the operational amplifier). A generalized active filter is shown in Figure 14-15. The selection of the various impedances in the circuit determines its frequency response characteristics. (Some of these impedances can be zero.)

The sharpness of the cutoff for a filter depends on the **quality factor Q** of the filter. The quality factor for a bandpass filter is

$$Q = \frac{f_o}{f_H - f_L} = \frac{f_o}{\text{BW}} \qquad (14\text{-}5)$$

where

$$\begin{aligned}
f_o &= \text{center frequency} \\
f_H &= \text{upper cutoff frequency} \\
f_L &= \text{lower cutoff frequency} \\
f_H - f_L &= \text{bandwidth (BW) of the filter}
\end{aligned}$$

The bandwidth of the filter is symmetrical about f_o. That is, f_L is the same distance below f_o that f_H is above the center frequency on a logarithmic scale. From Equation 14-5, we have

$$\begin{aligned}
f_H &= f_o + \frac{\text{BW}}{2} \\
f_L &= f_o - \frac{\text{BW}}{2}
\end{aligned} \qquad (14\text{-}6)$$

Figure 14-16 shows how the filter gain varies with frequency for different values of Q. It

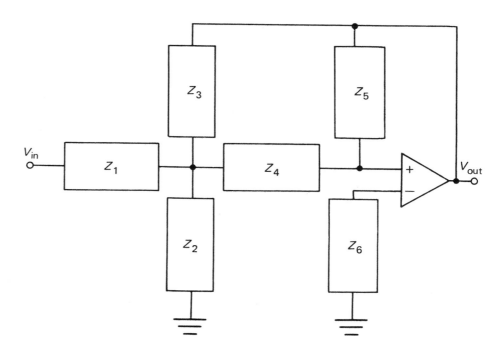

FIGURE 14-15.
Generalized Active
Filter

may seem that a high Q is best, but that is not always the case. If the quality factor is too high, there will be peaking (overshoot) in the filter characteristics near the cutoff point. Usually, a flat response is more desirable, which means that Q should be held to 10 or less as a trade-off for flat response (at the sake of a very sharp cutoff). Sharper cutoff can be achieved by cascading filter stages.

Another parameter of interest is the gain that the op amp offers to frequencies that are not attenuated. Those frequencies are said to be in the **passband** of the filter. The effect the filter has on those frequencies is expressed as the passband gain H_o.

The subject of active filtering is so extensive that we can only give an introduction to some possible designs here. For more complete discussions, refer to the references listed in the Appendix.

Examples of low-pass, high-pass, and band-pass active filter circuits are shown in Figures 14-17a, 14-17b, and 14-17c. Table 14-2 lists the formulas to use in calculating values of parameters for these filters. Simplifying assumptions have been made in developing these formulas, which will provide filters of satisfactory performance. All are second-order filters, meaning that they offer cutoff rates of 40 dB per decade. In all cases, Q is less than 10, and passband gain is

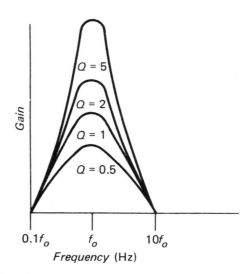

FIGURE 14-16. Effects of Q on Gain

never unity for a flat response near cutoff. For proper loading and biasing, the values of the resistors in these filters should be limited to the range of 10 kΩ to 10 MΩ. Capacitor values from 25 pF to 900 pF will provide satisfactory operating characteristics.

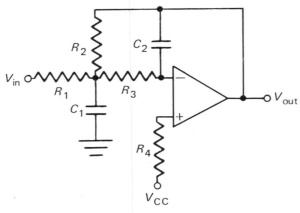

(a) Low-Pass Filter

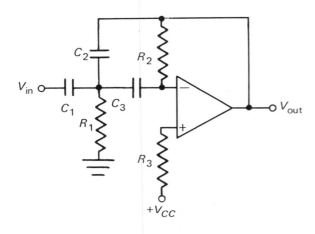

(b) High-Pass Filter

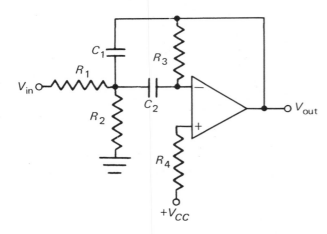

(c) Bandpass Filter

FIGURE 14–17. Filter Circuits

□ **EXAMPLE 14–3**

Find the values for all passive elements of a bandpass active filter with a center frequency of 1 kHz, with a Q of 5, and with unity passband gain.

Solution From the specified values, the upper and lower cutoff frequencies can be found from the equation

$$Q = \frac{f_o}{\text{BW}}$$

So

$$\text{BW} = \frac{f_o}{Q} = \frac{1000}{5} = 200$$

$$f_H = 1000 + \frac{200}{2} = 1100 \text{ Hz}$$

$$f_L = 1000 - \frac{200}{2} = 900 \text{ Hz}$$

The capacitor values should be calculated first. We can pick any value for C_1, so let it be 500 pF. Then $C_2 = C_1 = 500$ pF.

The resistor values are found next.

$$R_1 = \frac{Q}{2\pi f_o C_1 H_o} = \frac{5}{(2\pi)(10^3)(500 \times 10^{-12})(1)}$$
$$= 1.6 \text{ M}\Omega$$

$$R_2 = \frac{Q}{2\pi f_o C_1 (2Q^2 - H_o)}$$
$$= \frac{5}{2\pi(10^3)(500 \times 10^{-12})(50 - 1)}$$
$$= 32.5 \text{ k}\Omega$$

$$R_3 = \frac{Q}{\pi f_o C_1} = \frac{5}{\pi(10^3)(500 \times 10^{-12})} = 3.2 \text{ M}\Omega$$

$$R_4 = 2R_3 = 6.4 \text{ M}\Omega$$

□ **EXAMPLE 14–4**

Design a low-pass active filter with a gain of 1 and a cutoff frequency of 1 kHz. V_{in} is biased at a dc level of $+V_{CC}/2$.

Solution Again, capacitor values are found first. Let C_1 be 300 pF. Then

$$C_2 = \frac{C_1}{4Q^2(H_o + 1)} = \frac{300}{4(0.5)(2)}$$
$$= 75 \text{ pF}$$

The resistor values are found next.

$$R_2 = \frac{1}{4\pi f_H Q C_2} = \frac{1}{4\pi(10^3)(0.707)(75 \times 10^{-12})}$$
$$= 1.5 \text{ M}\Omega$$

$$R_1 = \frac{R_2}{H_o} = \frac{1.5 \times 10^6}{1}$$
$$= 1.5 \text{ M}\Omega$$

$$R_3 = \frac{1}{4\pi f_H Q C_2 (H_o + 1)}$$
$$= \frac{1}{4\pi(10^3)(0.707)(75 \times 10^{-12})(2)}$$
$$= 750 \text{ k}\Omega$$

$$R_4 = 2\left(\frac{R_1}{2} + R_3\right)$$
$$= 2\left(\frac{1.5 \times 10^6}{2} + 750 \times 10^3\right)$$
$$= 3 \text{ M}\Omega$$

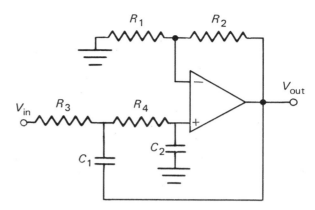

FIGURE 14-18. Second-Order Butterworth Low-Pass Filter

TABLE 14-2. Active Filter Characteristics

Parameter	Low-Pass	High-Pass	Bandpass
Passband gain, H_o	$\dfrac{R_2}{R_1}$	$\dfrac{C_1}{C_2}$	$\dfrac{1}{(R_1/R_3)[1 + (C_1/C_2)]}$
f_H	$\dfrac{1}{2\pi}\sqrt{\dfrac{1}{R_2 R_3 C_1 C_2}}$	---	$f_o + \dfrac{\text{BW}}{2}$
f_L	---	$\dfrac{1}{2\pi}\sqrt{\dfrac{1}{R_1 R_2 C_2 C_3}}$	$f_o - \dfrac{\text{BW}}{2}$
Q	0.707	0.707	$\dfrac{f_o}{\text{BW}}$
f_o	---	---	$\dfrac{1}{2\pi C}\sqrt{\dfrac{R_1 + R_2}{R_1 R_2 R_3}}$
C_1	Any convenient value	Any convenient value	Any convenient value
C_2	$\dfrac{C_1}{4Q^2(H_o + 1)}$	$\dfrac{C_1}{H_o}$	C_1
R_1	$\dfrac{R_2}{H_o}$	$\dfrac{1}{2\pi f_L Q C_1 [2 + (1/H_o)]}$	$\dfrac{Q}{2\pi f_o C_1 H_o}$
R_2	$\dfrac{1}{4\pi f_H Q C_2}$	$\dfrac{Q(2H_o + 1)}{2\pi f_L C_1}$	$\dfrac{Q}{2\pi f_o C_1 (2Q^2 - H_o)}$
R_3	$\dfrac{1}{4\pi f_H Q C_2 (H_o + 1)}$	$2R_2$	$\dfrac{Q}{\pi f_o C_1}$
[a]R_4	$2\left(\dfrac{R_1}{2} + R_3\right)$	---	$2R_3$

[a]R_4 for a low-pass filter for V_{in} biased at the dc level of $+V_{CC}/2$; otherwise select $R_4 = R_2 + R_3$.

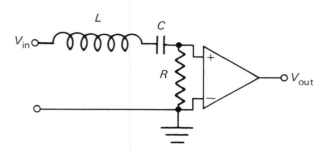

FIGURE 14–19. Active Resonant Filter

There are several other designs used in active filters. The **Butterworth filter** in Figure 14–18 is a low-pass filter. The narrow-bandpass filter in Figure 14–19 uses active resonance to achieve very sharp cutoff. The center, or **resonant, frequency** for this filter is

$$f_o = \frac{1}{2\pi\sqrt{LC}} \qquad (14\text{–}7)$$

The large inductances sometimes required in this design are a disadvantage, so the RC filters described earlier find wider application.

Chapter Summary

☐ Process control systems require status and command signals in order to monitor and adjust operations. Transducers convert physical quantities to electrical signals in the sensors. Commands are executed by actuators, motors, and mechanical linkages. Instrumentation amplifiers smooth and amplify sensor signals, which are often multiplexed into an analog-to-digital converter. A digital subsystem computes the correction factors needed and feeds them back as commands through a digital-to-analog converter and power amplifier.

☐ Instrumentation amplifiers feature high gain and very high input impedance. Single-ended instrumentation amplifiers accept large peak-to-peak input voltages. Differential instrumentation amplifiers permit inputs of low levels only. In differential amplifiers, common-mode signals are strongly attenuated.

☐ Analog multiplexers allow one of many input signals to be selected and routed to the output terminal.

☐ Power op amps offer considerable current drive. Thus they are suitable for controlling motors and other high-current circuits. Power op amps should be restricted to the limits of the safe operating area curve.

☐ Audio op amps find applications in radio, TV, and hi-fi products. Audio amplifiers must accurately amplify the applied signal so that the sound produced by the speaker is not distorted.

☐ Packaged voltage comparators are economical circuits that can detect variations in the input signals. Comparators are the basis for zero-crossing detectors. Another use of comparators is in function generators that produce square wave and triangular wave outputs.

☐ A smoke detector and alarm is a combination of linear circuits. The main component is a comparator, which detects changes in the voltage from the ionization chamber.

☐ Active filters attenuate input signals. They can act as low-pass, high-pass, bandpass, or notch networks. The filter characteristics results from the passive elements used with the op amp.

Problems

14-1. Compare the noise performance of an instrumentation amplifier with an op amp. The closed-loop gain of both amplifiers is 120. The signal level is 75 mV and the noise is 6 mV. The instrumentation amplifier has a common-mode rejection ratio of 110 dB.

14-2. What is the differential gain of an instrumentation amplifier with an internal gain of 1000 if V_1 is 5 V and V_2 is 5.07 V? The design coefficient K is 0.98.

14-3. Determine which of the sensor signals in Figure 14-7a is sampled if the address lines have the following levels applied:

a. $A0 = L, A1 = H, A2 = L$
b. $A0 = L, A1 = H, A2 = H$

14-4. Would operation of a power op amp be acceptable under the conditions listed below? Explain your answer.

output voltage $= 15$ V
load resistance $= 5$ Ω

14-5. Draw a block diagram of an audio amplifier that will boost the power of a 50-mW signal to 1 W. Use an 8-Ω speaker in your design.

14-6. Sketch the output of the zero-crossing detector of Figure 14-11d if the input is as shown in Figure 14-20.

14-7. Find the values of all resistors and capacitors to be used in an active low-pass filter if the 3-dB upper cutoff frequency is 1 kHz and the gain is unity. The input voltage is biased at the dc level of $+V_{CC}/2$. Use a value of 250 pF for C_1.

14-8. Design a high-pass filter with a cutoff frequency of 500 Hz; let C_1 be 500 pF.

14-9. A bandpass filter with a lower cutoff frequency of 900 Hz must be designed. If Q is 5 and the center frequency is 1 kHz, find the upper cutoff frequency. What is the bandwidth? Compute the values of the components for the filter, using a value of 500 pF for C_1.

14-10. A notch filter is constructed as shown in Figure 14-14d. The lower cutoff frequency is 500 Hz and the upper frequency is 1500 Hz. Find the value of each component of the low-pass and high-pass filter if both have a gain of unity and a value of 400 pF for C_1.

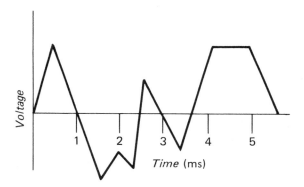

FIGURE 14-20.

Chapter Fifteen
Data Conversion

The last of the circuits necessary for digital control of analog processes is the data acquisition module. In the previous chapters, we have already mentioned the converters of interest. An **analog-to-digital converter (ADC)** changes the time-varying input signal to a numeric value representing its amplitude. Transforming a number into a proportional voltage or current is the job of a **digital-to-analog converter (DAC)**. When signals are varying rapidly, a **sample-and-hold (S/H) circuit** is often used to maintain the input steady while an ADC accomplishes the conversion. All these components will be analyzed in this chapter, including the interpretation of important specifications for each.

Chapter Objectives

Upon completion of this chapter, you should be able to:

☐ Define the terms resolution and dynamic range.
☐ Distinguish between unipolar and bipolar codes.
☐ Explain the principles of operation of the various types of converters.
☐ Give the meaning of converter specifications.
☐ Describe the operation of sample-and-hold circuits and explain why they are needed.
☐ Draw a block diagram of a voltage-to-frequency converter.

☐ RESOLUTION AND DYNAMIC RANGE

Every one of the converters we will study uses numbers in either their input or their output. The manufacturers do not limit their choice to a single number system (such as binary) but select from many numeric representations.

Two frequently used number systems are the binary and the binary-coded decimal (BCD) systems. Depending on the choice of code and the number of bits in the number, the smallest value that can be written varies. The smallest increment that a given code can represent is called the **resolution** of that code. The size of the increment is the **quanta** (derived from the same Latin word that **quantize** is derived from) of the converter. The largest number that can be represented is the **dynamic range** of the converter.

Table 15–1 lists examples of the resolution and dynamic range for several codes. To read this table, you must understand that the code is always a fraction of a **reference voltage**. The reference voltage is a precisely controlled input to the converter that must remain constant. Any variation in the reference voltage will cause errors in the output. For a DAC, the output voltage is

$$V_{out} = KV_{ref} \tag{15-1}$$

where

$$V_{ref} = \text{reference voltage}$$
$$K = \text{fractional code}$$

☐ EXAMPLE 15–1

Use Table 15–1 to find the DAC output voltage for four-bit binary codes, if the reference voltage is 5 V.

Solution First, let us look at some binary examples. If the code is 0000_2, then

$$V_{out} = (0.0000_2)(5) = 0 \text{ V}$$

For the code 0001_2,

$$
\begin{aligned}
V_{out} &= (0.0001_2)(5) \\
&= (0.0625_{10})(5) \\
&= 0.3125 \text{ V}
\end{aligned}
$$

Note that a radix point is inserted to the left of the binary number, making the code a fraction.

For the code 1101_2,

$$
\begin{aligned}
V_{out} &= (0.1101_2)(5) \\
&= (0.8125_{10})(5) \\
&= 4.06 \text{ V}
\end{aligned}
$$

Finally, using the largest code of 1111_2, we have

$$
\begin{aligned}
V_{out} &= (0.1111_2)(5) \\
&= (0.9375_{10})(5) \\
&= 4.6875 \text{ V}
\end{aligned}
$$

We observe that the maximum, or *full-scale*, code can never be equal to exactly 1.0_2. Consequently, the full-scale output voltage is always less than the reference voltage. This difference, known as the **quantizing error**, is always the value of one quantum. As we saw above, the size of the quanta of a four-bit binary code is one least significant bit (LSB). A code of 0001_2 produced a voltage of 0.3125 V. That voltage is exactly the size of the full-scale deficit, as can be shown by adding the quanta size to the full-scale voltage:

$$
\begin{array}{ll}
4.6875 & \text{(full-scale voltage)} \\
+0.3125 & \text{(size of quanta)} \\
\hline
5.0000 & \text{(reference voltage)}
\end{array}
$$

In summary, the maximum output is always less than the reference voltage by the value of one LSB—the resolution of the converter.

TABLE 15–1. Resolution and Dynamic Range

Number of Bits	BCD Decades	Resolution of LSB		Dynamic Range	
		Binary	BCD	Binary	BCD
4	1	0.0625	10^{-1}	15	9
8	2	3.906×10^{-3}	10^{-2}	255	99
10	—	9.77×10^{-4}	—	1023	—
12	4	2.44×10^{-4}	10^{-3}	4096	999

□ **EXAMPLE 15-2**

Show how a four-bit BCD code operates in a converter with a reference voltage of 5 V.

Solution   The BCD code 0000 gives

$$V_{out} = (0.0000_{BCD})(5)$$
$$= (0_{10})(5)$$
$$= 0\ V$$

The BCD code 0001 gives

$$V_{out} = (0.0001_{BCD})(5)$$
$$= (0.1_{10})(5)$$
$$= 0.5\ V$$

As the table shows, the value of the LSB represents a code of 0.1_{10}. Finding the output generated by a BCD code of 0111, we obtain

$$V_{out} = (0.0111_{BCD})(5)$$
$$= (0.7_{10})(5)$$
$$= 3.5\ V$$

What is the full-scale output of the BCD code?

$$V_{out} = (0.1001_{BCD})(5)$$
$$= (0.9_{10})(5)$$
$$= 4.5\ V$$

Again, the full-scale output shows the quantizing error. If we add the value of the LSB to the full-scale voltage, we obtain

0.5	(value of LSB)
+4.5	(full-scale output)
5.0	(reference voltage)

The evaluation procedure of Example 15-2 is used regardless of the input coding. The steps are as follows:

1. Write the output in terms of a product of the fractional code and the reference voltage (Equation 15-1).
2. Convert the code to its true decimal representation.
3. Carry out the arithmetic.

□ UNIPOLAR AND BIPOLAR CODES

The codes that we have used so far permit us to have output voltages that range between 0 V and the positive reference voltage. If a negative reference voltage is selected, then Equation 15-1 will produce an output between 0 V and some negative value. Both of these cases are examples of **unipolar codes**, because the output is limited to only positive or only negative voltages. Most often, the code for zero (such as 0000_2) represents 0 V in a unipolar code.

Suppose, however, that we wish the converter to generate both positive and negative voltages. In such a **bipolar code**, the value for 0 V must be somewhere in the middle of the range.

Consider a trivial two-bit binary bipolar code. If we choose a 2's complement system, then we have the following codings:

01_2: most positive number; maximum positive voltage

00_2: 0 V

11_2

10_2: most negative number; maximum negative voltage

Table 15-2 lists examples of two 8-bit codes. The 2's complement code is just an extension of our simple example above. The **offset binary code** assigns the code number $0000\ 0000_2$ to the full-

TABLE 15-2. Bipolar Codes

2's Complement	Offset Binary	±10-V Range (Volts)
0111 1111	1111 1111	+9.922
⋮	⋮	⋮
0100 0000	1100 0000	+5
⋮	⋮	⋮
0000 0001	1000 0001	+0.078
0000 0000	1000 0000	0
1111 1111	0111 1111	−0.078
⋮	⋮	⋮
1100 0000	0100 0000	−5
⋮	⋮	⋮
1000 0001	0000 0001	−9.922
1000 0000	0000 0000	−10

scale negative voltage and the largest code number, $1111\ 1111_2$, to the full-scale positive voltage. (Note that because there is one more negative code value than positive code value, the negative full-scale voltage is slightly larger than the positive one.)

Converting between 2's complement and offset binary is easy. We just complement the most significant bit (MSB). For example:

2's Complement		Offset Binary
0111 1111	=	1111 1111
	complement	
0000 0000	=	1000 0000
1000 0000	=	0000 0000

☐ EXAMPLE 15-3

What output voltage would a 2's complement code of $1011\ 1111_2$ produce if the range is ± 10 V? Find the equivalent offset binary code.

Solution   From Equation 15-1, we have

$$V_{\text{out}} = (0.1011\ 1111_2)(-10\ \text{V})$$

A negative voltage is used because the 2's complement has a sign bit of 1. Converting the binary fraction to a decimal fraction, we have

$$V_{\text{out}} = (0.496_{10})(-10) = -4.96\ \text{V}$$

The offset binary code is produced by complementing the sign bit, which gives $0011\ 1111_2$.

☐ CONVERTER FUNDAMENTALS

Converters can be thought of as electronic realizations of the equations we have been applying. The digital-to-analog converter, shown in Figure 15-1, performs a **transfer function** that changes the digital input to an analog output. The output can be either a current or a voltage, though almost all newer designs produce a voltage. A voltage form of output is chosen because it is then much easier to interface the DAC to other circuit components. The digital input may be from 4 to 12 bits. More input bits mean greater resolution, but the expense and complexity of the converter goes up accordingly.

The analog output voltage is produced between the *output terminal* and the *analog ground*, which should be a high-quality ground. This ground serves as the system ground point. The *digital ground* is the return line for the digital inputs.

The analog-to-digital converter in Figure 15-2 just reverses the order of inputs and outputs. The same number of pins is required. The

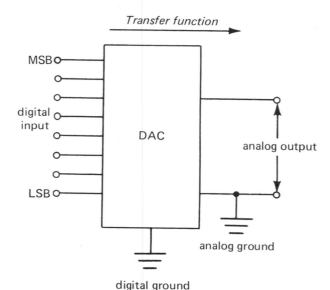

FIGURE 15-1. General Digital-to-Analog Converter

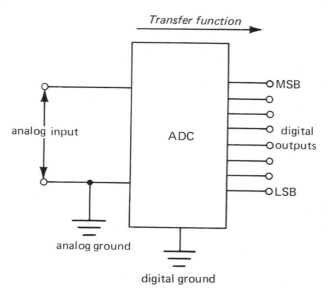

FIGURE 15-2. General Analog-to-Digital Converter

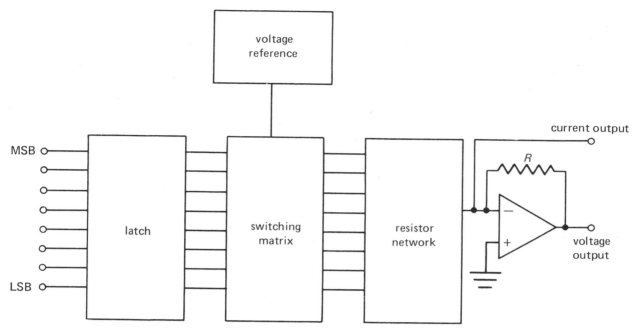

FIGURE 15–3. *N*-Bit DAC

transfer function in the ADC generates a digital output that matches the analog voltage.

☐ DIGITAL-TO-ANALOG CONVERTERS

There are several ways to realize a DAC by using electronic parts, but all the designs are based on the concepts shown in Figure 15–3. Here an arbitrary number of input bits are applied to the *N*-bit converter (as mentioned above, *N* is usually between 4 and 12). The digital number is latched and used to generate *N* voltages that operate a *switching matrix*. The voltage reference (further discussed in Chapter 19) is routed to the *resistor network* under control of the switches. The output of the resistor network is a current that is proportional to the input. This current is the output of the type of DACs that provide a current output. DACs with voltage outputs feed the current into an op amp, which performs the conversion of current to voltage.

Weighted-Ladder DAC

The **weighted-ladder DAC** is the easiest of these converters to understand. The example in Figure

15–4 uses a four-bit input. However, these lines can be increased to any desired number. Each of the input bits controls its individual switch. These switches operate just like those of the analog multiplexer. If the control bit is 1, the switch connects the reference voltage to the line attached to the inverting input of the op amp. Should the control bit be 0, the switch grounds that line.

The weighted resistor values give this converter its name. Any convenient size of resistor is selected for the MSB line. Then for each of the lower bits, the resistor value is doubled, as we move down the "ladder." As the figure shows, if we start with a 10-kΩ resistor on the MSB (bit 3), then the next lower bit (bit 2) uses a 20-kΩ resistor. Bit 1 doubles the resistance again to 40 kΩ. Finally, the LSB has an 80-kΩ resistor, twice that of bit 1. In general, for bit *x* (starting the numbering with 0 for the LSB) the resistor is

$$R_x = (2^{N-x})R \qquad (15-2)$$

where

N = bit number of the MSB
R = MSB resistor value
x = bit number for the unknown resistor

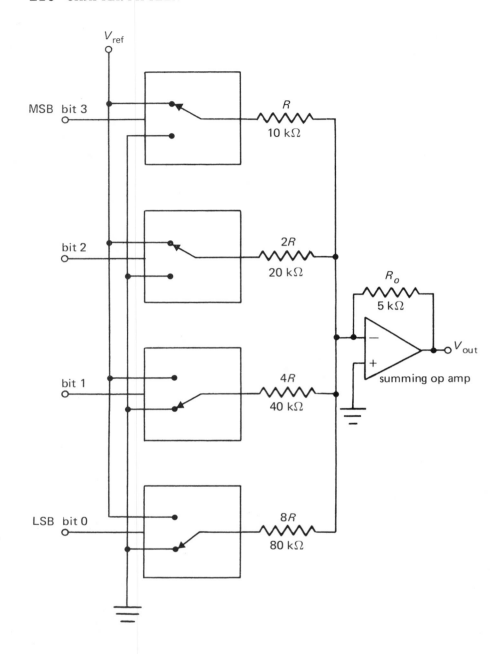

FIGURE 15–4.
Weighted-Ladder
DAC

□ EXAMPLE 15–4

What size of resistor should be used on the LSB of a four-bit weighted-ladder DAC if the MSB resistor is 10 kΩ?

Solution   The MSB is bit 3, and the LSB is bit 0. So

$$R_x = (2^{3-0})(10^4)$$
$$= (2^3)(10^4)$$
$$= 80 \text{ k}\Omega$$

The currents from the switches are summed by the op amp. As you know from your study of op amps, the output voltage is

$$V_{out} = I_T R_o \qquad (15-3)$$

where

I_T = total current at the inverting input to the amplifier

R_o = output resistance

The output resistor can be used to scale the output voltages according to the equation

$$F = 2\left(\frac{R_o}{R}\right) \qquad (15\text{-}4)$$

where

F = scale factor
R_o = output resistor value
R = MSB resistor value

For the DAC in Figure 15-4, the scale factor is unity:

$$F = 2\left(\frac{5 \times 10^3}{10 \times 10^3}\right)$$
$$= 2\left(\frac{1}{2}\right)$$
$$= 1$$

For other combinations, F can scale the output voltage up (if $R_o > R/2$) or down (if $R_o < R/2$).

☐ **EXAMPLE 15-5**

The DAC in Figure 15-4 uses a $+5$-V reference voltage. What output is produced by an input of 8_{16} if R_o is 5 kΩ?

Solution Because all switches except the one on the MSB are grounded ($8_{16} = 1000_2$), the current, from Ohm's law, is

$$I_T = \frac{V_{ref}}{10 \times 10^3}$$
$$= \frac{5}{10^4}$$
$$= 500\ \mu\text{A}$$

From Equation 15-3, we have

$$V_{out} = (500 \times 10^{-6})(5 \times 10^3)$$
$$= 2.5\text{ V}$$

As a check, we will use Equation 15-1 to see if we arrive at the same answer.

$$V_{out} = (0.1000_2)(5)$$
$$= (0.5_{10})(5)$$
$$= 2.5\text{ V}$$

☐ **EXAMPLE 15-6**

Repeat the problem in Example 15-5 but use an input of A_{16}.

Solution Now we have two switches closed, because

$$A_{16} = 1010_2$$

From bit 3, the current is

$$\frac{V_{ref}}{10 \times 10^3} = \frac{5}{10^4} = 500\ \mu\text{A}$$

From bit 1, the current is

$$\frac{V_{ref}}{40 \times 10^3} = \frac{5}{4 \times 10^4} = 125\ \mu\text{A}$$

Summing these currents, we have

$$I_T = 500 + 125 = 625\ \mu\text{A}$$

Therefore, from Equation 15-3, we obtain

$$V_{out} = (625 \times 10^{-6})(5 \times 10^3)$$
$$= 3.125\text{ V}$$

Again using Equation 15-1 as a check, we obtain

$$V_{out} = (0.1010_2)(5)$$
$$= (0.625_{10})(5)$$
$$= 3.125\text{ V}$$

Table 15-3 lists all four-bit DAC transformations. You should verify several of them by using both Equations 15-1 and 15-3 to be sure that you understand how to use these important equations.

TABLE 15-3. Four-Bit DAC Transformations

Unipolar Binary Input	Generalized Output	Output with Reference of $+5$ V
0000	0	0
0001	$0.0625\,V_{ref}$	0.3125
0010	$0.125\,V_{ref}$	0.625
0011	$0.1875\,V_{ref}$	0.9375
0100	$0.25\,V_{ref}$	1.25
0101	$0.3125\,V_{ref}$	1.5625
0110	$0.375\,V_{ref}$	1.875
0111	$0.4375\,V_{ref}$	2.1875
1000	$0.5\,V_{ref}$	2.5
1001	$0.5625\,V_{ref}$	2.8125
1010	$0.625\,V_{ref}$	3.125
1011	$0.6875\,V_{ref}$	3.4375
1100	$0.75\,V_{ref}$	3.75
1101	$0.8125\,V_{ref}$	4.0625
1110	$0.875\,V_{ref}$	4.375
1111	$0.9375\,V_{ref}$	4.6875

R–2R-Ladder DAC

Finding precision resistors that meet the criteria of the weighted-resistor DAC is very difficult, so another implementation of the converter is more common. The **R–2R ladder**, shown in Figure 15-5, uses only two values for the resistors regardless of the number of stages. This converter also uses the same switching matrix as the weighted-resistor DAC. The currents produced by each bit are summed at the op amp. The output scale factor F is computed differently from that of the previous converter, however. It is

$$F = \frac{R_o}{R} \qquad\qquad (15\text{--}5)$$

where

R_o = output resistor value
R = smaller resistor value in the R–$2R$ ladder

Referring to the figure, we see that 10 kΩ and 20 kΩ are the resistances that appear in the ladder. The individual currents can be found by using Thevenin's theorem. Starting at the grounded 20-kΩ resistor, we form a parallel

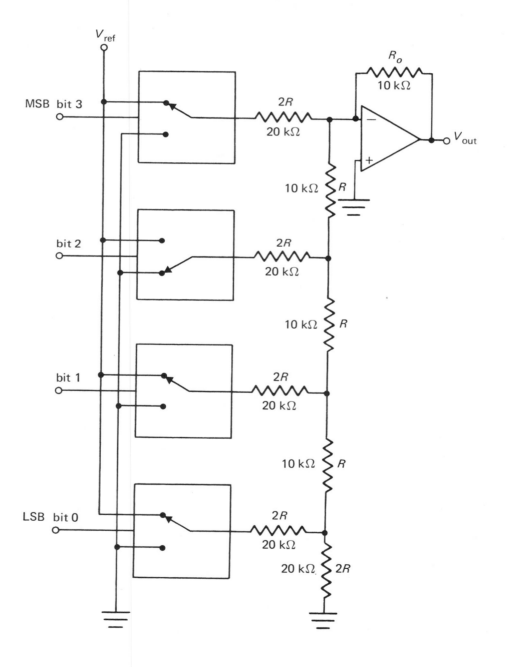

FIGURE 15-5.
R–2R-Ladder DAC

equivalence with the 20-kΩ resistor on bit 0 equal to 10 kΩ. That equivalent resistor is added to the series 10-kΩ resistor between bits 0 and 1; then the process repeats. The most straightforward way of finding the output voltage is to use Equation 15-1.

□ EXAMPLE 15-7

If the input to Figure 15-5 is 6_{16} and the reference voltage is 10 V, what is the output?

Solution   From Equation 15-1, we have

$$V_{out} = (0.0110_2)(10)$$
$$= (0.375_{10})(10)$$
$$= 3.75 \text{ V}$$

But one additional factor must be examined, because Equation 15-1 is correct only if the scale factor is unity. From Equation 15-5,

$$F = \frac{10 \times 10^3}{10 \times 10^3} = 1$$

So the output is 3.75 V.

For comparison purposes, suppose the output resistor for Example 15-7 had been 5 kΩ. Then

$$F = \frac{5 \times 10^3}{10 \times 10^3} = 0.5$$

In that case, we just multiply the output voltage by the scale factor.

$$V'_{out} = (3.75)(0.5) = 1.875 \text{ V}$$

□ ANALOG-TO-DIGITAL CONVERTERS

Now let us examine converters that allow us to change an analog measurement into digital signals. There are a variety of ADCs, each with characteristics suitable for solving a particular problem. Some of these devices are quite low in price but perform the conversion very slowly. Others offer high-speed conversion but are expensive. The discussions that follow identify the features of each type of ADC that make it unique.

Counter ADC

The **counter ADC** is based on a DAC, as Figure 15-6 shows. The analog voltage is applied to the comparator. As long as the analog voltage is larger than the input from the DAC, the comparator has a high output.

The sequence for measuring an analog voltage begins with a reset signal that nulls the counter. This input to the DAC is converted to a 0-V output. Any positive analog voltage will cause the comparator to produce a high output. As a result, the control circuitry passes the first clock pulse through to the counter. Each successive clock pulse is allowed to pass through until the comparator output goes low (meaning that the DAC output exceeds the analog voltage). At that time, the clock input to the counter is blocked by the $\overline{\text{STOP}}$ signal, and the output lines maintain steady levels. The counter output is proportional to the input voltage.

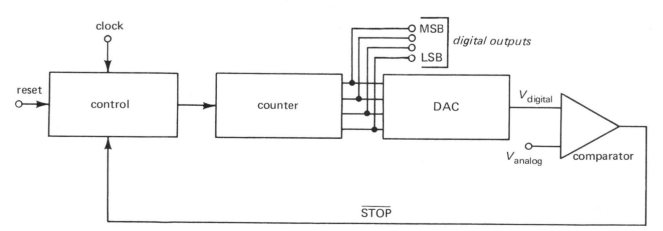

FIGURE 15-6. Counter ADC

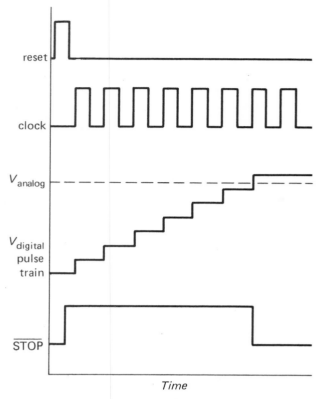

FIGURE 15-7. Counter ADC Timing Diagram

Figure 15-7 shows a timing diagram of important signals in a counter ADC. On each clock pulse, the digital voltage input to the comparator increases by one step. When the $V_{digital}$ voltage exceeds the V_{analog} input, the $\overline{STOP}$ line falls to the low level, halting the count. From this diagram, it is obvious that the output will always be greater than the input by the amount of one LSB of the DAC. Furthermore, overall accuracy of the counter ADC is limited to that of the DAC. Advantages of the counter ADC include its simplicity and low cost. On the other hand, conversion is slow. A full-scale analog input requires 2^n clock periods for conversion, where n is the number of bits of the output.

Tracking ADC

The **tracking**, or **servo**, ADC is a derivative of the counter ADC. The tracking ADC uses an *up-down counter* in place of the simple incremental counter of the previous converter. This modification permits the converter to follow, or *track*, a varying input. The tracking ADC is slow also, so it takes a long time to "lock on" the signal. If the analog input is varying in large jumps, the tracking ADC will not be able to follow it. The maximum variation in input that can be successfully followed is the **tracking rate limit** of the ADC.

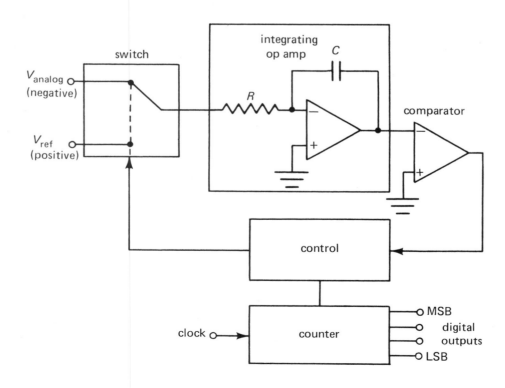

**FIGURE 15-8.
Integrating ADC**

Integrating ADC

As its name implies, this converter uses an integrating op amp in its construction (see Figure 15-8). The two inputs to the device are the analog voltage (which must be negative) and the reference voltage (which is positive). Alternatively, both voltages could have opposite polarities. Only one of these voltages is switched to the integrator at one time.

The integrator output is applied to a comparator, which detects when that voltage reaches ground potential. The control circuitry is used to send incremental signals to a counter, which measures a voltage proportional to the analog input.

The timing diagram in Figure 15-9 shows how the proportional voltage is generated. At the start the analog voltage is switched to the integrator. The switch is left in that position for a fixed amount of time. Then the switch is thrown in the other direction by the control circuit. Because the reference voltage is of opposite polarity, the integrator output will be driven back to ground by the positive input. (The sign reversal on the output is a consequence of using the inverting terminal of the op amp.) The amount of time necessary for the signal to return to 0 V is variable. The relationship between the voltages and times is

$$V_{analog} = -V_{ref}\left(\frac{t_V}{t_F}\right) \qquad (15\text{-}6)$$

where

V_{ref} = reference voltage
t_V = variable time interval
t_F = fixed time interval

The only unknown in the equation is t_V, which can be measured. Then the analog voltage can be found.

☐ EXAMPLE 15-8

The reference voltage for an integrating ADC is 5 V. If the fixed time period is 5 ms and the variable time is 3 ms, what is the analog voltage?

Solution From Equation 15-6, we have

$$V_{analog} = \frac{-5(3 \times 10^{-3})}{5 \times 10^{-3}} = -3 \text{ V}$$

Interestingly enough, the accuracy of this converter does not depend on the resistor and

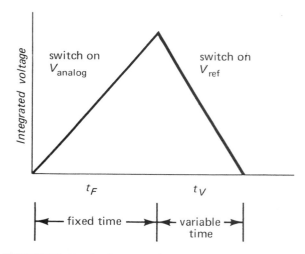

FIGURE 15-9. Integrating ADC Timing Diagram

capacitor, because they are used to make both time measurements. The voltage reference, however, does affect accuracy. Because the counter uses an integrator, noise spikes on the input are canceled out, so the converter offers good noise rejection. This characteristic is especially useful in eliminating 60-Hz noise, if the clock is synchronized to reject noise signals at that frequency. Conversion is relatively slow, however, taking on the order of 10 ms for a full-scale input.

Successive-Approximation ADC

The **successive-approximation ADC** also uses a DAC, as shown in Figure 15-10. The comparator will have a high output until the digital input exceeds the analog voltage, much like the counter ADC. In this case, the input of the DAC comes not from a counter but from a register.

The measuring sequence begins with setting the MSB in the register and then comparing that voltage to the analog input. If the resulting digital voltage is less, that bit remains set (see Figure 15-11). Then the next higher bit is set and compared, and the process repeats until the LSB is reached. The figure gives an example for a four-bit converter, where the MSB and bit 2 produce a voltage less than the analog input. When bit 1 is set, it causes the digital voltage to exceed the analog voltage, so that bit is reset in the register.

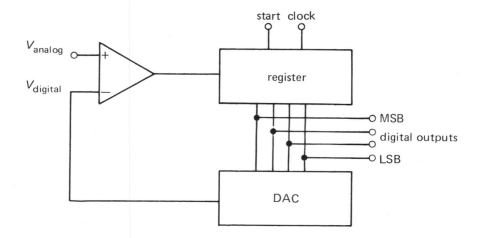

FIGURE 15–10.
Successive-
Approximation ADC

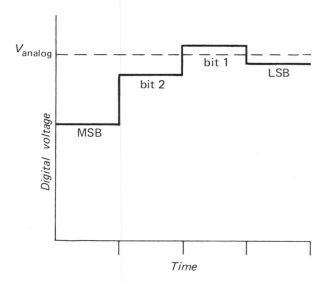

FIGURE 15–11. Successive-Approximation
ADC Timing Diagram

Finally, the LSB is set and the digital output is less than the input. The digitized result is obtained by reading the final contents of the register.

With a good voltage reference and DAC, the successive-approximation ADC is highly accurate. Conversion is swift also. Typical times for full-scale input are 10 to 20 μs.

Parallel ADC

The **parallel**, or **flash**, **ADC** is the most expensive of these components, but it offers the highest speed. Consequently, parallel ADCs are reason- ably priced only for converters with six-bit resolution or less. The number of comparators needed in this converter depends on the number of bits, according to the equation

$$C = 2^{n-1} \tag{15–7}$$

where
  C = number of comparators
  n = number of bits of resolution

Conversion takes place in real time. Processing signals with frequencies in excess of 10 MHz is practical, so these converters are suitable for video waveforms.

The principle of operation for this converter is evident from Figure 15–12. The inputs for each comparator are the analog voltage and a fraction of the reference voltage. The fraction is determined by the resistor ladder. If the analog voltage exceeds the reference, the comparator has a high output. The decoder produces a parallel binary output from the comparator signals.

□ EXAMPLE 15–9

Suppose the reference voltage in Figure 15–12 is 10 V and the input is 6 V. Which comparators have high outputs?

Solution The total resistance of the ladder is $5R$. Comparator A has a reference input of

$$V_A = \left(\frac{R/2}{5R}\right)(10) = 1 \text{ V}$$

The other comparator reference inputs are found in the same manner.

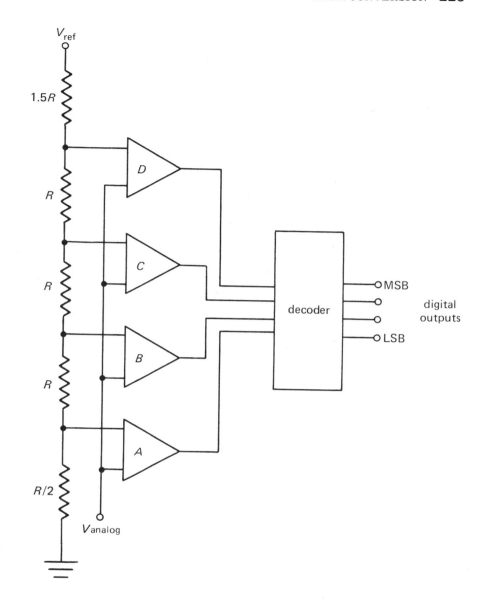

FIGURE 15–12.
Parallel ADC

$$V_B = \left[\frac{3(R/2)}{5R}\right](10) = 3\text{ V}$$

$$V_C = \left[\frac{5(R/2)}{5R}\right](10) = 5\text{ V}$$

$$V_D = \left[\frac{7(R/2)}{5R}\right](10) = 7\text{ V}$$

Hence, all comparators except D will have high outputs.

Example 15–9 shows that for high resolution, many comparators are needed. Here the quanta are 2 V and the output resolution is three

bits. This resolution can be found by using Equation 15–7. If $C = 4$, then we can find n.

$$4 = 2^{n-1}$$

So $n = 3$

☐ CONVERTER SPECIFICATIONS

The performance of any converter is described on its data sheet. Several important parameters are

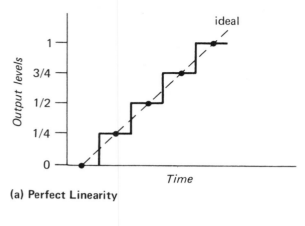

(a) Perfect Linearity

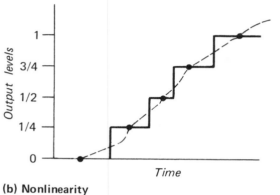

(b) Nonlinearity

FIGURE 15-13. Linearity Characteristics

used by manufacturers in specifying the devices. We will examine these parameters in this section.

You already know about *resolution*, which is the smallest increment (of the input or output). The resolution r is

$$r = \frac{FS}{2^n} \qquad (15\text{-}8)$$

where

$\quad$ FS $=$ full-scale voltage

$\quad n =$ number of bits

The **absolute accuracy** of a converter is limited by any deviation from the ideal full-scale output. Error sources that degrade this accuracy are offset and gain errors, nonlinearity, and drift.

The **relative accuracy** of a converter is the deviation from an ideal transfer function. This deviation is produced by nonlinearity. The relative accuracy is specified in terms of "$\pm(1/2)$ LSB in n bits" or "± 1 LSB in $n + 1$ bits." For example, in 12 bits, a relative accuracy of $\pm(1/2)$ LSB is 0.012%, which is the same as ± 1 LSB in 13 bits.

Linearity is the most important specification for a converter. It measures the deviation of the transfer function from a straight line, as shown in Figure 15-13 a and b. The deviation is measured from zero to full-scale output.

A converter has **monotonicity** if the output always increases or remains the same with increasing input values. This parameter is of special interest in successive-approximation and counter ADCs. Monotonicity is essential in any closed-loop system in order to avoid oscillation.

The **offset error** is a shift in the transfer function by a fixed dc level. It may be positive or negative, as shown in Figure 15-14. A converter has no offset error if a 0-V input produces a zero output. Offset errors can be removed by calibration. (When bipolar codes are used, the offset adjustment is usually made at the negative full-scale level instead of at the zero level.)

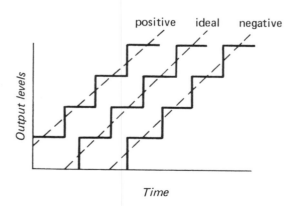

FIGURE 15-14. Offset Errors

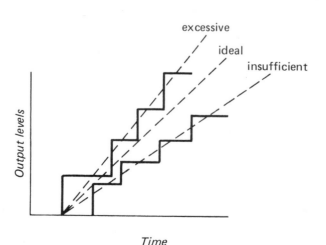

FIGURE 15-15. Gain Errors

The gain of a converter can be either excessive or insufficient, as Figure 15–15 shows. The **gain error** is the deviation from the ideal full-scale value. This error can be removed by adjustment for any given temperature, but it will drift at other temperatures. Gain error is quantified by temperature coefficients, which specify how much error a thermal variation will produce in the gain. These coefficients are specified in parts per million of full-scale value per degree Celsius.

Other performance parameters are also changed by temperature change. The summation of these errors is called **drift**. Drift affects linearity, gain, and offset, and temperature coefficients are established for each parameter. The net drift D is found from the equation

$$D = (\text{TC}_L + \text{TC}_O + \text{TC}_G) \times \Delta T \quad (15\text{–}9)$$

where

$\text{TC}_L = $ linearity temperature coefficient
$\text{TC}_O = $ offset temperature coefficient
$\text{TC}_G = $ gain temperature coefficient
$\Delta T = $ change in temperature (°C)

Several parameters apply only to DACs or to ADCs. The **DAC slew rate** is the large-signal rate of change that the converter can follow. Figure 15–16 shows a change from zero to full-scale output. The slew rate is

$$\text{SR} = \frac{\Delta V}{\Delta t} \quad (15\text{–}10)$$

where

$\Delta V = $ voltage change
$\Delta t = $ time interval

Typical values for slew rates of regular DACs are 2 V/μs, while high-speed DACs can slew at rates of 20 V/μs.

The **settling time** for a DAC is also shown in Figure 15–16. This time is the period required for the output to reach the bounds of the rated accuracy band. It is the most useful of all DAC speed measurements in comparing one model of a converter to another.

The **aperture error of an ADC** is the output deviation caused by the input changing during the conversion process. For a sine wave, the maximum sampling rate R_t is

$$R_t = 2\pi V_p f \quad (15\text{–}11)$$

where

$V_p = $ peak voltage
$f = $ frequency

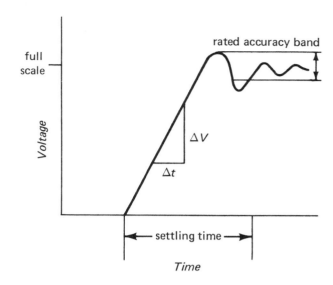

FIGURE 15–16. Slew Rate and Settling Time

For an aperture error of (1/2) LSB or less, the maximum conversion time must be equal to (or less than)

$$t = \frac{1}{2^{n+1}\pi f}$$

where

$n = $ number of bits of resolution

Usually this time is beyond the capabilities of the ADC, so the sample-and-hold circuit described in the following section must be used together with the ADC.

□ SAMPLE-AND-HOLD CIRCUIT

The **sample-and-hold (S/H)** circuit maintains the analog input at a constant value while an ADC is sampling the signal. In this way, the aperture error of the ADC is eliminated. Figure 15–17a shows the components of the S/H circuit. The switch is closed and the capacitor is charged during the *sampling* time. The switch is then opened by the control signal and the sampled voltage remains on the capacitor during the *hold* period (see Figure 15–17b). The unity-gain op amp offers a high resistance to the stored voltage on the capacitor, so the RC time constant of the S/H circuit is large. The output of the op amp is connected to the converter.

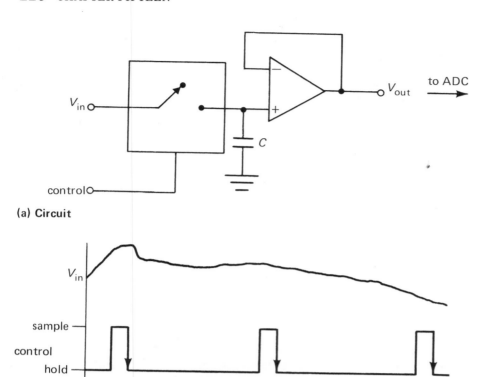

(a) Circuit

(b) Timing

FIGURE 15–17.
Sample-and-Hold
Circuit

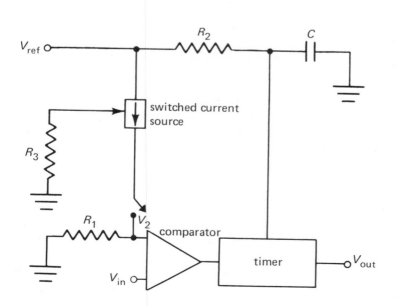

FIGURE 15–18.
Voltage-to-Frequency
Converter

☐ VOLTAGE-TO-FREQUENCY CONVERTER

The **voltage-to-frequency converter (V/F)** changes an analog input to a square wave with a frequency proportional to the input. The components of the V/F converter include a switched current source, an input comparator, and a timer, as shown in Figure 15–18. The resistors R_1 and R_2 are equal in value.

In operation of the V/F converter, the switch is initially open. The input voltage is compared to ground. If the analog voltage is greater, the timer produces an output pulse for a period of

$$T = 1.1R_2C \qquad (15\text{–}12)$$

which charges the capacitor. The switch is then closed, and the capacitor voltage on the V_2 terminal of the comparator is larger than the analog input, causing its output level to reverse. The change in the comparator output level turns the timer off. The capacitor can then discharge, causing the input voltage to exceed V_2. Then the cycle repeats.

The average current flowing into C is

$$I_{\text{in}} = (1.1R_2)(C)(i)(f) \qquad (15\text{–}13)$$

where

$i =$ instantaneous current
$f =$ frequency of the switching cycle

The current flowing out of C is

$$I_{\text{out}} = \frac{V_2}{R_2} \qquad (15\text{–}14)$$

Because I_{in} must equal I_{out}, the comparator will cause V_2 to become equal to the analog input. Then from the equality of the two voltages and from Equation 15–13, we have

$$\frac{V_2}{R_2} = \frac{V_A}{R_1} = (1.1R_2)(C)(i)(f) \qquad (15\text{–}15)$$

because $R_1 = R_2$. According to Equation 15–15, doubling of V_A will double the frequency in order to maintain the balance, because all the other variables on the right side of the equation are fixed.

Chapter Summary

☐ The resolution of the converter code sets a lower bound on the size of its quanta. The largest number a converter can hold is limited by its dynamic range.

☐ The coding of converters represents a fraction of the reference voltage. The full-scale output of a converter is always one quantum (the value of the LSB) less than the reference voltage.

☐ Unipolar codes permit only positive or only negative output values. Bipolar codes allow for an output with both positive and negative voltages.

☐ Converters, whether DAC or ADC, perform transfer functions between voltages and numbers.

☐ In general, a DAC consists of a series of latches, a switching matrix, a resistor network, and an op amp. Common forms are the weighted-ladder and R–$2R$-ladder converters.

☐ Analog-to-digital converters exist in many forms, which vary in speed, cost, and accuracy. Among the converters available are counter ADCs, tracking (servo) ADCs, integrating ADCs, successive-approximation ADCs, and parallel (flash) ADCs.

☐ Converter specifications provide the range of accuracy, speed, and performance of these components. The most important measure of performance of any converter is the linearity. The best parameter for rating DAC speed is the settling time.

☐ A sample-and-hold circuit maintains an input signal at a constant level. It is used to correct for the aperture error of an ADC, which usually exceeds the required measurement accuracy.

☐ Voltage-to-frequency converters permit one to measure analog signals by generating a series of output pulses. The frequency of the output is proportional to the input voltage.

Problems

15-1. The reference voltage for a four-bit DAC is 6 V. Determine the output voltage for the following binary inputs:

    a. 0101_2

    b. 1010_2

    c. 1100_2

    d. 1111_2

15-2. Find the output voltages of a BCD digital-to-analog converter with the following four-bit inputs:

    a. 0011

    b. 0101

    c. 0111

    d. 1001

15-3. What 2's complement codes are equivalent to the offset binary codes listed below?

    a. $0101\ 1111_2$

    b. $1001\ 0001_2$

    c. $1110\ 0101_2$

    d. $0011\ 0110_2$

15-4. If the resistor of the MSB of a five-bit, weighted-resistor-ladder DAC is 5 kΩ, what is the resistance required on each of the other bits?

15-5. If the input to the converter in Problem 15-4 is 10100_2, what is the output voltage? The reference voltage is 7 V.

15-6. What value would you recommend for the scaling resistor of the converter of Figure 15-5 if the output is to vary between 0 and 20 V? V_{ref} is 10 V.

15-7. Find the output voltage produced by the ADC in Figure 15-8. The reference voltage is −5 V. The fixed time interval is 6 ms and the variable time interval is measured to be 4.5 ms.

15-8. How many comparators are required in a four-bit flash ADC? If the reference voltage is 5 V and the input is 3.5 V, which converters have high outputs? What is the voltage generated by each comparator with a high output?

15-9. What is the resolution of a 12-bit converter if its full-scale voltage is 10 V?

15-10. A digital-to-analog converter has a slew rate of 2 V/μs. Is this converter fast enough to sample a 5-V peak-to-peak sine wave? The sine wave frequency is 500 kHz.

Chapter Sixteen
Timers, Oscillators, and Triggers

Throughout the discussion of digital circuits, clocks have appeared as synchronizing signals. The clock waveform is usually a train of rectangular pulses. These pulses serve as the time base for an entire piece of equipment. Time-generation circuits are used in electronic watches, microcomputers, frequency counters, and sequential circuits. Modern integrated circuits use clocks with frequencies as high as 10 MHz. The two most often used ways of producing the timing pulses are crystal oscillators and IC timers. In this chapter, we will examine both of these components and look into some typical applications of them.

Another circuit, closely related to the timer, is the trigger. Triggers are used to stretch pulse duration, restore the shape of distorted pulses, or react only to signals above a certain level. In this chapter, we will also investigate two families of triggers. The first is the *one-shot* (also called single-shot), which produces one output pulse for each input level change. The second is the *Schmitt trigger*, named for the inventor of the vacuum tube version of the circuit. Both triggers are used in a variety of configurations in equipment.

Chapter Objectives

Upon completion of this chapter, you should be able to:

- ☐ Draw a block diagram of a crystal-controlled clock.
- ☐ Compare the relative advantages and disadvantages of crystals and IC timers.
- ☐ Distinguish among the various types of IC timers.
- ☐ Show how the 555 timer can be used as an astable multivibrator.
- ☐ Construct the block diagram and explain the operation of a timer-counter.
- ☐ Explain how the 555 timer can be used as a frequency generator and triangular wave generator.
- ☐ Draw the block diagram of a one-shot based on the integrating op amp.
- ☐ Select component values to produce a specified trigger duration.
- ☐ Design a one-shot by using the 555 timer as a time delay.
- ☐ Sketch the key signals for the one-shot built from the 555.
- ☐ Describe the hysteresis property of a Schmitt trigger.
- ☐ Show how a Schmitt trigger can be constructed by using an op amp.
- ☐ Demonstrate the use of integrated circuit Schmitt triggers.

☐ OSCILLATORS

Oscillators are devices used to generate high-frequency sine waves. Other types of timers are not suitable for high-frequency clocks because they rely on some form of a resistor-capacitor network, and their *RC* time constant is too slow.

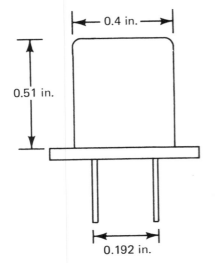

(a) HC18 Case

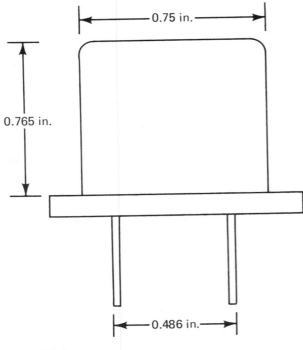

(b) HC33 Case

FIGURE 16-1. Crystal Packaging

Both inductor-capacitor (*LC*) and crystal oscillators can serve in high-frequency applications. However, the accuracy and low cost of crystals make them the most common form of oscillator encountered today.

A **crystal** consists of a piece of quartz constrained between two parallel conducting plates. When a voltage is applied between the plates, mechanical stress is created in the crystal. This stress is caused by the **piezoelectric effect**. As a result of the piezoelectric stresses, the quartz begins to vibrate.

The size and cut of a crystal determine its vibrating frequency. The thickness is the most important dimension in controlling the frequency. The upper limit for crystal oscillation is around 20 MHz; the crystal becomes so thin at these frequencies that it is too fragile for reliable operation. Higher clock frequencies are developed by using *harmonics* (overtone mode) of the fundamental frequency or by using *frequency multipliers*.

The crystal is packaged in a flattened metal case, as shown in Figure 16-1. The figure gives the sizes of two of the most common cases, the HC18 (Figure 16-1a) and the HC33 (Figure 16-1b).

A crystal can be considered from the point of view of its equivalent electrical circuit (see Figure 16-2). The capacitors and inductor in the figure form a **tank circuit**. The capacitor labeled C_p represents the parallel metal plates. The other capacitive component, C_x, is the equivalent electrical value for the quartz crystal itself.

A typical crystal clock requires a *frequency divider* and a *wave shaper*. A block diagram for the configuration is shown in Figure 16-3. A

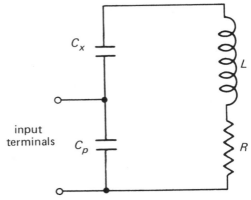

FIGURE 16-2. Equivalent Circuit of a Crystal

FIGURE 16-3.
Crystal-Controlled
Clock

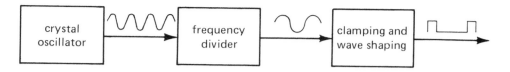

widely used circuit for clamping and wave shaping is the Schmitt trigger, which will be discussed later in the chapter. You already know about frequency dividers from your study of counters in Chapter 12.

□ EXAMPLE 16-1

The fundamental frequency of a crystal oscillator is 5 MHz. What is the frequency of the third harmonic?

Solution The third harmonic h_3 is defined as

$$h_3 = 3f_0 \qquad (16\text{-}1)$$

where

f_0 = fundamental frequency

so $h_3 = 3(5 \times 10^6) = 15$ MHz

□ IC TIMERS

There are many types of IC timers. The relationships of the various types are displayed in Figure 16-4. **Single-cycle timers** charge an external capacitor through a resistor network. The RC time constant controls the clock period. **Timer/ counters** have an internal oscillator and binary counter, which can be used to produce very long time delays.

Each of the main categories can be subdivided into specific types of timers. General-purpose, single-cycle timers are built with one (single), two (dual), or four (quad) of these devices within a single DIP case. If low power consumption or high noise immunity are important, special-purpose, single-cycle timers can be specified. Programmable timer/counters allow the user to change the time delay between pulses by controlling a programmable input. Fixed timer/counters are manufactured with only a single delay. The figure lists some specific examples of each type.

555 Timer

The 555, the first timer to be developed, is the most popular of the single-cycle timers. As Figure 16-5 shows, the timer is packaged in an 8-pin DIP. The 555 can produce an output with a frequency ranging from 0.1 Hz up to 100 kHz. Accuracy is within 1 percent, which is usually far in excess of the accuracy of the external capacitors and resistor. These external components serve to limit the overall timing accuracy to their tolerances.

The 555 is best understood by examining its internal circuitry, which is shown in Figure 16-6. The main components are the two comparators. One accepts the *threshold input* and the other the *trigger input*. The internal resistors control the *reference inputs* to both comparators. Because the three internal resistors are of equal value, the relationships of the reference voltages to the power supply voltage are as listed in Table 16-1. These ratios can be altered by an input on the *control voltage pin*, if desired.

In operation, when the trigger input is less than $1/3 V_{CC}$, that comparator has a high output, setting the RS flip-flop. The $\bar{Q}$ output from the flip-flop is, therefore, low. The inverter produces a high output signal from the 555. When the threshold voltage exceeds $2/3 V_{CC}$, the flip-flop is reset by a high comparator output, resulting in a high $\bar{Q}$ level and a low output signal. Anytime the $\bar{Q}$ level is high, transistor Q_1 is turned on. This transistor provides a low-impedance path between the *discharge* input and ground, when the transistor is on. When the transistor is off, there is an equivalent open circuit.

The reset input overrides all others. It forces the $\bar{Q}$ signal of the flip-flop to go high,

TABLE 16-1. Reference Voltages in the 555 Timer

Comparator	Reference Voltage
Threshold	$2/3 V_{CC}$
Trigger	$1/3 V_{CC}$

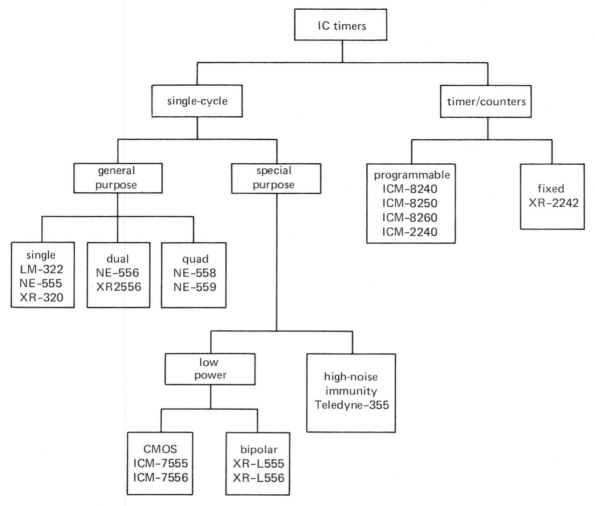

FIGURE 16-4. IC Timer Families

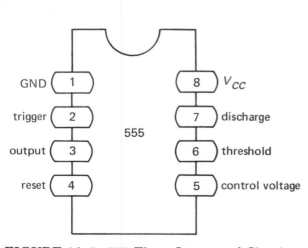

FIGURE 16-5. 555 Timer Integrated Circuit

which produces a low output (after inversion). The discharge transistor is also turned off.

To further your understanding of the 555, we will use it as a clock generator. The schematic, shown in Figure 16-7, uses two external resistors and a capacitor. When connected in this fashion, the 555 becomes an **astable multivibrator**, which produces a series of rectangular output pulses. The control voltage input (pin 5) is usually left open, but connecting a decoupling capacitor between that pin and ground may improve operation. (This connection is a "try it and see" situation.)

Let us follow the operation in Figures 16-7 and 16-8. Assume that the output signal is initially high, which means that the discharge transistor is off. The capacitor charges toward V_{CC}

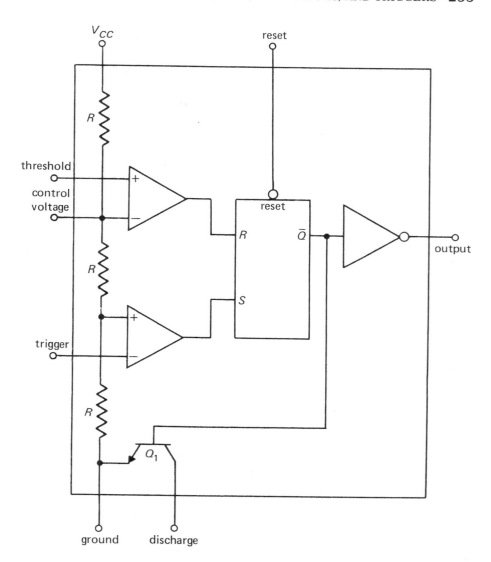

FIGURE 16–6.
Internal Components
of the 555

through the resistors; and the current is limited by R_A and R_B. When the voltage V_C on the capacitor reaches $2/3 V_{CC}$, the threshold comparator switches its output to the high level. The 555 flip-flop is reset, so $\overline{Q}$ becomes high and the output becomes low. The discharge transistor is also turned on, essentially creating a ground at pin 7 of the timer.

The capacitor will then discharge to the ground through R_B until the voltage falls to that of the reference on the trigger comparator. The trigger comparator then produces a high, setting the flip-flop. This level change causes the 555 output to go high and Q_1 to be turned off. The capacitor can once again charge through the two resistors, and the cycle repeats.

The two most important voltages are traced in Figure 16–8. The capacitor voltage is clamped between $1/3 V_{CC}$ and $2/3 V_{CC}$. When the capacitor voltage reaches the upper extreme, V_{out} falls to 0 V. When the capacitor discharges to the lower limit, the output voltage again becomes high. If a power supply voltage of 5 V is used, all inputs and outputs of the timer are TTL-compatible, as the figure shows.

Not only does the 555 offer a readily available clock generator, but it also makes it possible to vary the output frequency. The rela-

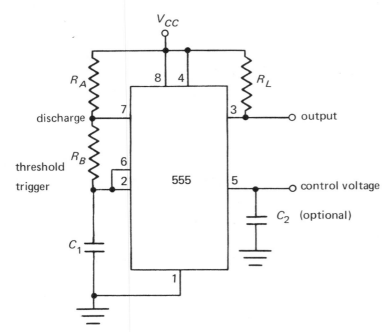

FIGURE 16-7.
Astable
Multivibrator

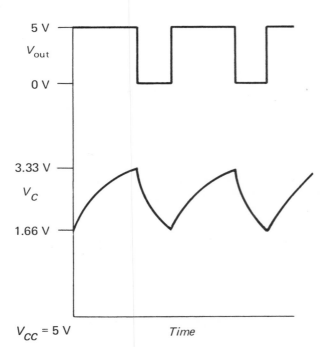

FIGURE 16-8. Timing Diagram of the Astable
Multivibrator

tionships of components and time intervals are
given in the following list:

$$t_H = 0.693(R_A + R_B)C \qquad \textbf{(16-2)}$$

$$t_L = 0.693R_BC \qquad \textbf{(16-3)}$$

$$T = t_H + t_L$$
$$= 0.693(R_A + 2R_B)C \qquad \textbf{(16-4)}$$

$$f = \frac{1}{T}$$
$$= \frac{1.44}{(R_A + 2R_B)C} \qquad \textbf{(16-5)}$$

$$D = \frac{t_L}{t_H + t_L}$$
$$= \frac{R_B}{R_A + 2R_B} \qquad \textbf{(16-6)}$$

where

t_H = duration of high-level output
t_L = duration of low-level output
T = period of one output cycle
f = frequency of the output
D = output driver duty cycle

□ **EXAMPLE 16-2**

Compute all the output signal characteristics if
the external components connected to the 555 in
Figure 16-7 are as listed below.

$R_A = 4 \text{ k}\Omega$ $C = 0.15 \text{ }\mu\text{F}$
$R_B = 3 \text{ k}\Omega$ $R_L = 1 \text{ k}\Omega$

Note that R_L has no effect on timing.

TABLE 16-2. Some 555 Families

Specification	Designation				
	NE-555	NE-556	ICM-7555	NE-559	XR-L555
V_{CC} (V)	4.5–16	4.5–16	2–18	4.5–16	2.7–15
Timing accuracy (%)	1	1	2	2	1
Package	8-pin	14-pin	8-pin	16-pin	8-pin
Technology	Bipolar	Bipolar	CMOS	Bipolar	Bipolar
Manufacturers	Signetics, AMD, EXAR, Fairchild, Intersil, Motorola, National, RCA, TI	Signetics, AMD, EXAR, Fairchild, Intersil, Motorola, National, Raytheon	Intersil	Signetics, EXAR	EXAR, Signetics

Solution We use Equations 16–2 through 16–6.

$$t_H = 0.693(4 \times 10^3 + 3 \times 10^3)(0.15 \times 10^{-6})$$
$$= (0.693)(7 \times 10^3)(0.15 \times 10^{-6})$$
$$= 727.7 \ \mu s$$

$$t_L = 0.693(3 \times 10^3)(0.15 \times 10^{-6})$$
$$= 311.9 \ \mu s$$

$$T = (727.7 + 311.9) \times 10^{-6}$$
$$= 1.04 \ ms$$

$$f = \frac{1}{1.04 \times 10^{-3}}$$
$$= 961.5 \ Hz$$

$$D = \frac{311.9 \times 10^{-6}}{1.04 \times 10^{-3}} = 0.3$$

□ **EXAMPLE 16–3**

Compute the values of R_A and C for a 555 timer with a frequency of 2 kHz and a duty cycle of 30 percent if R_B is 2 kΩ.

Solution From Equation 16–6, we have

$$D = \frac{R_B}{R_A + 2R_B}$$

Then solving for R_A, we obtain

$$R_A = \frac{R_B(1 - 2D)}{D}$$
$$= \frac{(2 \times 10^3)(1 - 2 \times 0.30)}{0.30}$$
$$= 2.67 \ k\Omega$$

From Equation 16–5, we have

$$f = \frac{1.44}{(R_A + 2R_B)C}$$

Then solving for C, we obtain

$$C = \frac{1.44}{(R_A + 2R_B)f}$$
$$= \frac{1.44}{(2.67 \times 10^3 + 2 \times 2 \times 10^3)(2 \times 10^3)}$$
$$= 0.11 \ \mu F$$

The 555 is available in bipolar and CMOS technology. Table 16-2 lists the characteristics of representative examples of the family of single-cycle timers. The 556 is a dual timer and the 559 is a quad timer package.

Timer/Counters

Recall that a **timer/counter** is a multiple-cycle device. Figure 16-9 shows its key components. The *external RC network* selects the *oscillator* frequency. The *binary counter* acts as a frequency divider to create the time delay; it holds the signal until the specified number of oscillator pulses has been accumulated.

The maximum count of the timer (*n*) is programmable. The trigger input starts the process, at which time the output goes high. The process stops when the terminating count is reached. The binary counter causes the output signal to go low

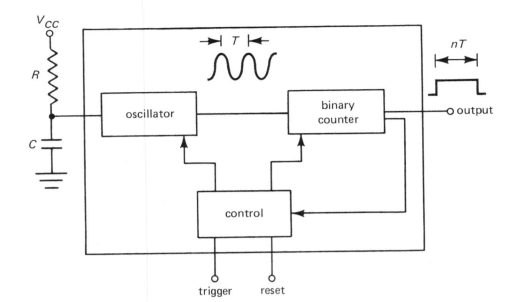

FIGURE 16-9.
Timer/Counter
Internal Components

and signal the control logic. A control signal stops the oscillator and consequently the timing cycle, until the next trigger signal is applied. The output period is nT, where T is the period of the oscillator.

Applications

Because of its universal applicability, the 555 appears in many pieces of equipment. Here we will consider how the timer can be used as a music generator and as a triangular wave generator.

The first circuit, shown in Figure 16-10, varies the output frequency by the use of a bank of capacitors. Each capacitor will produce a different tone at the speaker when its push button is depressed. All other components in the circuit are standard for the astable multivibrator. The setting of R_1 controls the frequency range. In Figure 16-10, the values for the components are $R_1 = 100$ kΩ, $R_2 = 1$ kΩ, $C = 4.7$ μF, $C_1 = 0.1$ μF, $C_2 = 0.05$ μF, and $C_3 = 0.01$ μF.

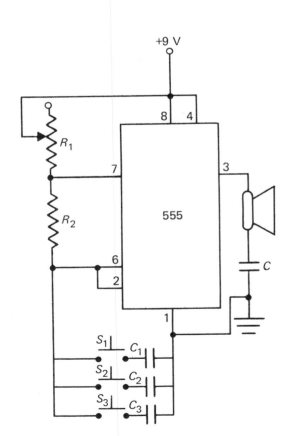

FIGURE 16-10. Music Maker

☐ **EXAMPLE 16-4**

What frequency tone does the music maker produce when button S_1 is pressed?

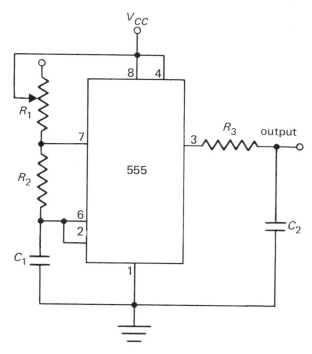

FIGURE 16-11. Triangular Wave Generator

Solution Assume R_1 is set to 100 kΩ. From Equation 16-5, we have

$$f = \frac{1.44}{(100 \times 10^3 + 2 \times 10^3)(0.1 \times 10^{-6})}$$
$$= 141 \text{ Hz}$$

The triangular wave generator, shown in Figure 16-11, simply integrates the output with an RC network. Compare this circuit to the integrating amplifier of Chapter 13. The frequency of the triangular output signal is the same as that of the 555. The triangular wave varies between 0 and -2 V. Maximum frequency is 10 kHz. The adjustment of R_1 controls the frequency up to this limit. The values for the components given in the figure are $R_1 = 100$ kΩ, $R_2 = 1$ kΩ, $R_3 = 10$ kΩ, $C_1 = 0.1$ μF, and $C_2 = 0.01$ μF.

☐ ONE-SHOTS AND MONOSTABLE MULTIVIBRATORS

A problem not unusual in digital circuits is that of a pulse too narrow to properly trigger a gate.

Another and similar problem is a pulse that arrives too soon. For example, consider a two-input AND gate. Both inputs must be applied at the same time. However, should one of the signals arrive much ahead of the other, some type of time compensation is required.

An appropriate solution to such problems is the **one-shot**, or **monostable**, **multivibrator**. This circuit acts as a "pulse stretcher." A very narrow input is expanded into an output pulse with a longer duration.

The use of an integrating op amp in this manner is shown in Figure 16–12a. The signal is applied to the inverting input, so the output signal exhibits a phase reversal. More important, observe in Figure 16–12b that the output pulse is low for a considerably longer time than is the input, or *trigger*, pulse. By choosing the proper values of the resistor and capacitor, one can adjust the duration of the output pulse.

The output pulse of the one-shot is low as

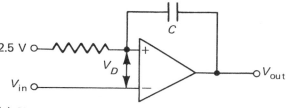

(a) Circuit Diagram

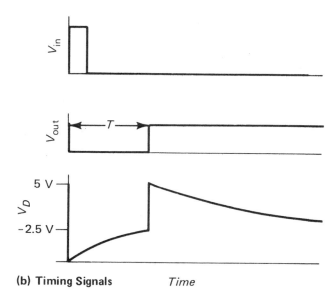

(b) Timing Signals   *Time*

FIGURE 16–12. One-Shot Multivibrator

long as the differential voltage V_D is negative. The formula for V_D in this circuit is

$$V_D = -2.5 + 5(1 - e^{-t/RC}) \qquad (16\text{-}7)$$

where

$e =$ base of natural logarithms
$R =$ resistor value
$C =$ capacitor value
$t =$ time

Solving for t when the differential voltage is 0 V, we have, for this circuit,

$$0 = -2.5 + 5(1 - e^{-t/RC})$$
$$\frac{2.5}{5} = 1 - e^{-t/RC}$$
$$e^{-t/RC} = 0.5$$
$$t = -RC \ln(0.5) = 0.693RC$$

Rounding the decimal number, we have

$$t = 0.7RC \text{ seconds} \qquad (16\text{-}8)$$

From Equation 16-8, we see that we can select any time duration by choosing the appropriate resistor-capacitor combination.

□ **EXAMPLE 16-5**

Find the resistor value that will produce a 100-μs pulse from the one-shot if the capacitor is 0.1 μF.

Solution   From Equation 16-8, we have

$$R = \frac{t}{0.7C}$$
$$= \frac{100 \times 10^{-6}}{(0.7)(0.1 \times 10^{-6})}$$
$$= 1.4 \text{ k}\Omega$$

The 555 timer can also function as a one-shot. The schematic diagram for this device is shown in Figure 16-13. In this circuit, only one external resistor, together with a capacitor, is used. The duration of the output pulse is

$$t = 1.1RC \qquad (16\text{-}9)$$

□ **EXAMPLE 16-6**

Using the same capacitor value and time delay given in Example 16-5, find the resistor value.

Solution   Using Equation 16-9, we have

$$R = \frac{t}{1.1C}$$
$$= \frac{100 \times 10^{-6}}{(1.1)(0.1 \times 10^{-6})}$$
$$= 909 \ \Omega$$

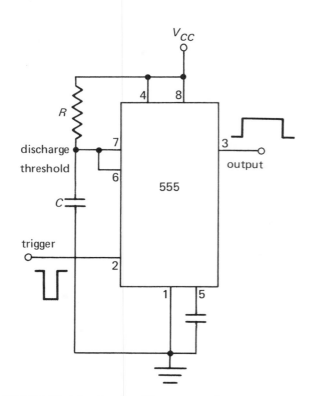

FIGURE 16-13. 555 Timer as a One-Shot

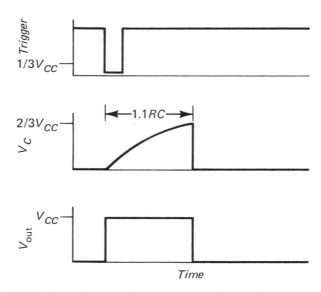

FIGURE 16-14. 555 One-Shot Timing Diagram

The operation of the 555 one-shot can be analyzed by using Figure 16–6. The trigger input must be negative going and also be less than $1/3\,V_{CC}$. This input causes the trigger comparator to set the flip-flop. The low output of the $\overline{Q}$ terminal turns the discharge transistor off and produces a high output (after inversion). Figure 16–14 shows the timing diagram. The capacitor can then begin to charge through the resistor. When the capacitor voltage reaches $2/3\,V_{CC}$, it causes the threshold comparator to reset the flip-flop. The discharge transistor is turned on, and the output level falls to 0 V. With the discharge transistor saturated, the capacitor rapidly loses its charge. All signals then remain at their present levels until the next trigger input.

☐ SCHMITT TRIGGERS

Another widely used triggering circuit, the **Schmitt trigger**, generates a train of square waves. The circuit is shown in Figure 16–15. The inverting terminal of the comparator receives the input signal.

Characteristics of the Schmitt trigger can be analyzed by using the voltage plots of Figure 16–16. In Figure 16–16a, the input voltage begins at a level of 0 V and steadily increases. When the input voltage reaches 6 V, the output voltage reverses. The effect of applying a steadily decreasing input is shown in Figure 16–16b. A similar reversal in the output takes place when the input decreases to 5 V. If we combine these two graphs, we arrive at Figure 16–16c, which shows on a single plot how the circuit reacts to either type of input signal.

Note that the switching points are not the same for the increasing and decreasing input signals. This difference is called the **hysteresis voltage** V_{hys}. It is computed from

$$V_{\text{hys}} = V_H - V_L \qquad (16\text{–}10)$$

where

V_H = high-voltage switching point
V_L = low-voltage switching point

An example of the way the Schmitt trigger converts a sine wave to a square wave is shown in Figure 16–17. When the sine wave reaches the **upper threshold**, the output falls. (The upper threshold corresponds to point a in Figure 16–16c.) The sine wave continues to rise to its

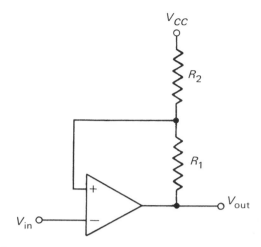

FIGURE 16–15. Schmitt Trigger

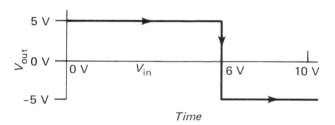

(a) Increasing V_{in}

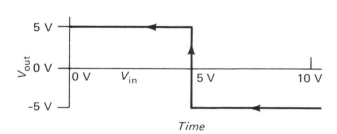

(b) Decreasing V_{in}

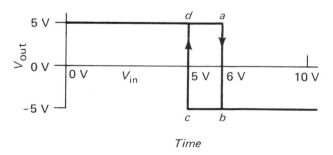

(c) Composite Curve

FIGURE 16–16. Voltage Plots for the Schmitt Trigger

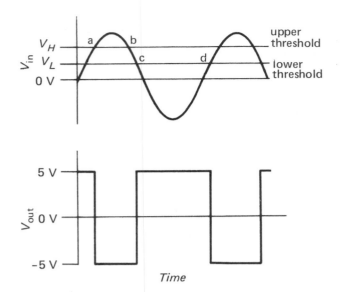

FIGURE 16-17. Schmitt Trigger Operation

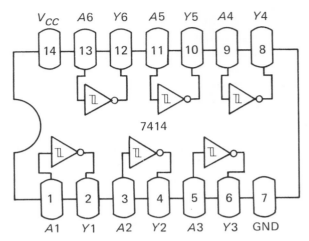

FIGURE 16-18. 7414 Schmitt Trigger Hex Inverter

peak value; then it begins to descend. Although the input passes below the upper threshold (point *b* in Figure 16-16c), the output remains low. It is not until the sine wave decreases to the lower threshold (point *c* in Figure 16-16c) that the output level rises. For the remainder of the sine wave cycle, the output remains high (point *d* and beyond on Figure 16-16c). The process repeats when the input again reaches the upper threshold.

IC Schmitt Triggers

As you probably expected, Schmitt triggers are packaged as integrated circuits. The 7414 of Figure 16-18 contains six Schmitt trigger inverters. These inverters perform the normal inversion function; that is

$$Y = \overline{A} \qquad (16\text{-}11)$$

They also exhibit hysteresis voltage switching characteristics. The symbol inside each inverter represents the hysteresis curve of Figure 16-16c.

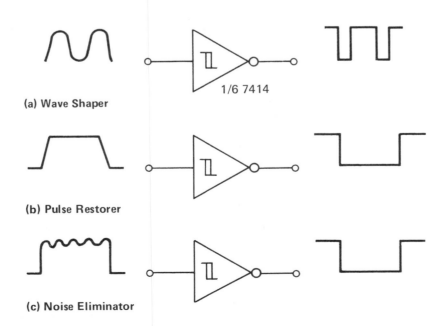

(a) Wave Shaper

1/6 7414

(b) Pulse Restorer

(c) Noise Eliminator

FIGURE 16-19.
7414 Applications

A few of the useful applications of the 7414 are illustrated in Figure 16-19. The first circuit, Figure 16-19a, is a **wave shaper**. In this circuit, the input is a slowly varying sine wave that is not suitable for input to digital circuits. The 7414 Schmitt trigger converts it to a crisp, inverted series of pulses, which give reliable results when used as inputs.

The **pulse restorer** of Figure 16-19b is useful in "sharpening" the rise and fall times of a changing signal. The input is a trapezoidal wave, but the trigger converts it to a sharp square wave.

A final example is the **noise eliminator** of Figure 16-19c. Here the undesirable ripple on the input is removed. The small amount of distortion on the signal is not large enough to reach the lower threshold, so the output signal remains low. None of the noise is passed through to the output.

NAND Schmitt Triggers

The 74132 is a quad NAND Schmitt trigger package. Each of the NAND gate outputs can be written as

$$Y = \overline{AB} \qquad (16\text{-}12)$$

Figure 16-20a shows the pin assignments of the 74132.

The NAND gates act as Schmitt triggers since the output falls to 0.8 when *both* inputs are above 1.7 V. The output rises to the high level when *either* input falls below 0.9 V. These voltage relationships are shown in Figure 16-20b. Again we see the hysteresis voltage effect.

The NAND Schmitt trigger is widely used. A few representative circuits are shown in Figure 16-21. The **threshold detector** of Figure 16-21a responds only to input pulses that are above the threshold level. All other input pulses are ignored. In the figure, there are five input pulses; only three are higher than the threshold. The output consists of three pulses, corresponding to those inputs.

Another use, the **debounced switch**, is shown in Figure 16-21b. Here the capacitor must charge to the threshold level before an output pulse is generated. The *RC* time constant is long enough for all transients to die out, so only a single pulse is produced.

The same principle that is used for the debounced switch is applied to design the **pulse stretcher** of Figure 16-21c. In this circuit, the

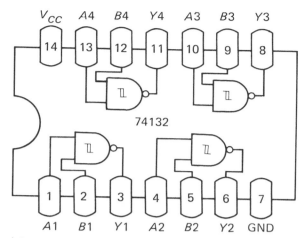

(a) Pin Assignments

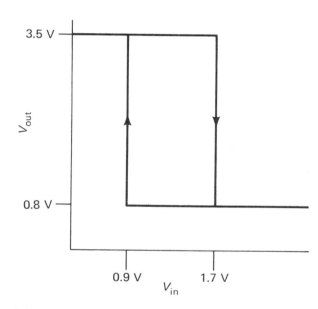

(b) Voltage Characteristics

FIGURE 16-20. 74132 Quad NAND Schmitt Trigger

output pulse from the open-collector gate is increased in time. The *RC* time constant of *R* and *C* makes this expansion possible.

A final example is the **phototransistor receiver** of Figure 16-21d. Without the Schmitt trigger gate the rise and fall times of the pulse would be more gradual. Furthermore, a great deal of noise would be present in the signal.

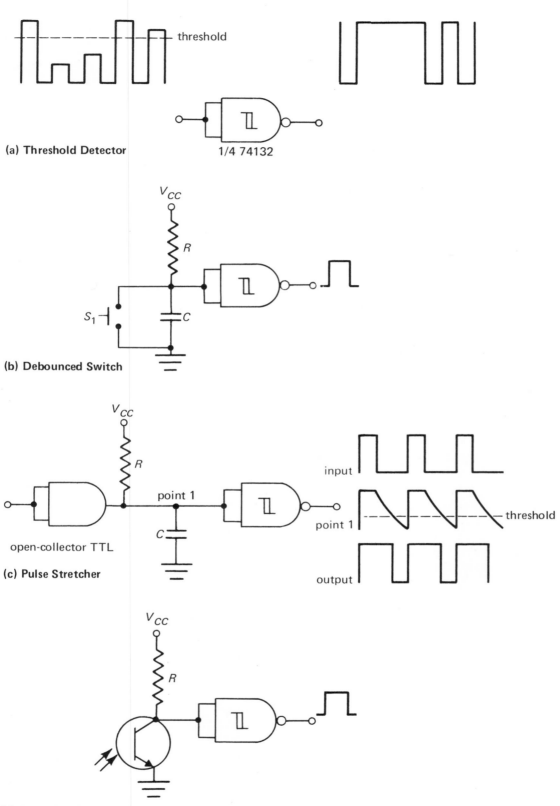

(a) Threshold Detector

1/4 74132

(b) Debounced Switch

(c) Pulse Stretcher

open-collector TTL

(d) Phototransistor Receiver

FIGURE 16–21. 74132 Applications

Chapter Summary

☐ Oscillators produce a continuous sine wave output. Because they use either an LC circuit or a crystal, oscillators can run at much higher frequencies than timers based on RC networks.

☐ The size and cut of a crystal determine its vibrating frequency. The width becomes the limiting factor for the highest-frequency crystal oscillator. For yet higher frequencies, harmonics of the fundamental are selected.

☐ A crystal oscillator together with a frequency divider and wave shaper comprise a crystal clock.

☐ Both single-cycle timers and timer/counters are available as integrated circuits. Single-cycle timers are available in single, dual, and quad configurations. Programmable timer/counters generate variable delays that depend on the input value.

☐ The 555 timer is the most widely used single-cycle timer. With two resistors and a capacitor, an astable multivibrator can be built. Changing the values of the passive elements adjusts the signal timing.

☐ Timer/counters contain an oscillator, a binary counter, and control circuitry.

☐ With the addition of only a few other components, the 555 can be made into a music maker or a triangular wave generator.

☐ The one-shot can expand or delay pulses.

☐ The integrating op amp and the 555 timer can both be adapted to work as one-shots. The selection of appropriate resistor and capacitor values permits an adjustment of the pulse duration. Each trigger input generates a single output pulse.

☐ The Schmitt trigger generates a series of square waves. Its characteristics result from a difference in the upper and lower thresholds, called the hysteresis voltage.

☐ Schmitt trigger inverters and NAND gates are provided as standard TTL circuits. With these ICs, several pulse-shaping circuits can be built.

Problems

16–1. If a crystal oscillator has a frequency of 7.5 kHz, what is its third harmonic? What harmonic would be used to produce a signal of 37.5 kHz?

16–2. What is the period of an astable multivibrator built from the 555 circuit for the resistor and capacitor values given below? Sketch the output wave.

$$R_A = 5\ \text{k}\Omega \qquad R_B = 1\ \text{k}\Omega \qquad C = 0.1\ \mu\text{F}$$

16–3. What is the frequency of the output signal of Problem 16–2? What is its duty cycle?

16–4. What values would you select for a 555–based astable multivibrator in order to produce an output frequency of 2 kHz, if $D = 0.25$ and $R_B = 2\ \text{k}\Omega$?

16–5. Find t_H, t_L, the period, and the duty cycle of a 555 astable multivibrator, using the components below.

$$R_A = 8\ \text{k}\Omega \qquad R_B = 5\ \text{k}\Omega \qquad C = 1\ \mu\text{F}$$

16–6. Suppose you want a 555 clock with a duty cycle of exactly 1/2. What size would R_A be if R_B is 1 kΩ? If the capacitor is 0.2 μF, what is the frequency?

16–7. What is the frequency of the output from the music maker (Figure 16–10) when button S_2 is pressed? When S_3 is pressed? R_1 is set to maximum in both cases.

16–8. Suppose R_1 is set at 50 kΩ in Figure 16–10. What is the frequency of the tone if S_1 and S_2 are pressed simultaneously? Remember that parallel capacitors are combined by *adding* their values.

16–9. Sketch the output of Figure 16–11 when R_1 is set to maximum.

16–10. Repeat Problem 16–9 but use $R_1 = 1 \text{ k}\Omega$.

16–11. If the bias voltage on the integrating op amp in Figure 16–12a is changed to 2 V, the equation for V_D becomes

$$V_D = -2 + 5(1 - e^{-t/RC})$$

Solve for the time delay in terms of the RC time constant for this modified circuit.

16–12. If the circuit in Figure 16–12a is to produce a pulse with a 500-μs duration, what capacitor value would you use? The resistor is 2 kΩ.

16–13. Repeat problem 16–12 but use the 555 timer in place of the integrating op amp.

16–14. What is the hysteresis voltage for the 74132 NAND Schmitt trigger?

16–15. Sketch the input and output voltage timing diagrams for the circuit in Figure 16–19b. Your diagrams should be similar to those in Figure 16–17.

16–16. Suppose that the switching characteristics of the 7414 are identical to the 74132. If the high level of the input to Figure 16–19c is 3.5 V, how large a ripple voltage can be tolerated and still guarantee proper operation?

16–17. If the threshold level for the circuit in Figure 16–21c is 0.9 V, what is the duration of the expanded pulse? The load resistor is 2 kΩ and the capacitor is 1 μF. The high-level voltage at point 1 is 3.5 V, and the low level is 0 V.

16–18. Determine the duration of the pulse for the debounced switch of Figure 16–21b if circuit values are

$$R = 5 \text{ k}\Omega \qquad C = 0.1 \text{ μF}$$

16–19. What is the minimum voltage needed for input pulses to be detected by the circuit in Figure 16–21a?

16–20. The output of the phototransistor of Figure 16–21d is given in Figure 16–22. Sketch the output pulse of the circuit. Label all important voltages.

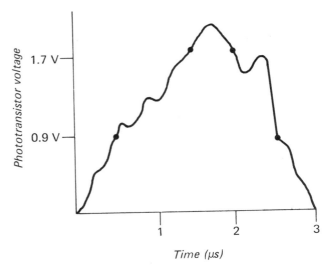

FIGURE 16–22.

Chapter Seventeen
Phase-Locked Loops

A combination of the circuits you have already studied together with a special type of oscillator form a new circuit element called the **phase-locked loop (PLL)**. The PLL has wide applications in electronic equipment used to generate audio or radio frequency signals in response to a digital input, such as in a citizen's band (CB) transceiver or an FM radio. Alternatively, the PLL can convert an oscillating signal to digital outputs, as in a Touch-Tone decoder used in telephone systems.

In this chapter, we will analyze the basic principles of phase-locked loops; then we will examine several applications. Of particular interest are frequency synthesizers, detectors, demodulators, and decoders. These applications will demonstrate how PLL integrated circuits are readily adapted to a variety of functions.

Chapter Objectives

Upon completion of this chapter, you should be able to:

- [ ] Draw a block diagram of a phase-locked loop.
- [ ] Describe how the feedback of a PLL keeps it locked on a frequency.
- [ ] List the states of a phase-locked loop.
- [ ] Compute the phase error between two signals, in degrees and radians.
- [ ] Discuss the use of an exclusive OR gate as a phase comparator.
- [ ] Compute the duty cycle of a phase comparator and convert that value to an output voltage.
- [ ] Describe the operation of a voltage-controlled oscillator.
- [ ] Explain the operation of a PLL-based circuit.

☐ GENERALIZED PHASE-LOCKED LOOP

The phase-locked loop consists of three elements, as shown in Figure 17–1. The component at the right, the **voltage-controlled oscillator (VCO)**, produces an output frequency proportional to its input voltage. When the circuit is initially powered, the VCO is in the **free-running condition**. The output frequency, f_o, depends on the external RC or LC network attached to the oscillator.

Immediately after the input frequency f_i is applied, the **phase comparator** causes a change to occur. The phase comparator subtracts the output frequency from the input frequency and generates a voltage proportional to the error. This error is a combination of the frequency and the phase difference between f_i and f_o:

$$\Delta f = f_i - f_o \qquad (17\text{–}1)$$

where
  Δf = frequency difference

The phase difference is discussed further in a later section.

The error voltage is passed through the low-pass filter to remove any high-frequency noise. After filtering, the error voltage controls the VCO frequency. The size of the frequency difference is thus reduced. Since this process of error reduction is continuous, the PLL is always attempting to produce an output frequency that is the same as the input frequency.

As the PLL operates, it passes through three distinct states. In the free-running state, as explained above, the output frequency depends only on the external RC or LC components connected to the voltage-controlled oscillator. When the VCO begins to change frequency in response to the error voltage, the loop enters the **capture state**. Finally, the loop is **phase-locked** when f_o

becomes equal to f_i. (An important note about the phase-locked condition is that although the two frequencies are equal, there is a difference in phase between the input and output at all times.)

The frequency of the VCO will continue to track the input over a range of values. The frequency range over which the PLL can follow the incoming frequency is called the **lock range**. The bandwidth over which capture is possible is the **capture range**. The capture range can never exceed the lock range.

The low-pass filter reduces the capture range because the filter is limited in the size of error it will allow through. Another limitation that the filter imposes on PLL performance is only apparent after phase lock. At that time, the filter limits the tracking speed, because of the maximum rate at which it can slew as frequencies change. This effect in the PLL is analogous to the settling time that we observed in the sample-and-hold circuit in an earlier chapter.

Phase Comparator

The phase comparator, also called a *phase detector*, generates an average voltage that indicates the phase difference between the input signal and the output of the VCO. Before we examine the phase comparator, we must first understand the factors involved in measuring phase differences.

Consider the two sine waves of equal frequency shown in Figure 17–2. Signal 1 begins at 0 V at the start of the timing cycle, but signal 2 does not reach that point until approximately a quarter cycle later. Signal 1 is said to *lead* signal 2 in phase. Conversely, we can also express the relative phases by saying that signal 2 *lags* signal 1.

The amount of phase difference is found by measuring the time between the equivalent points on the two signals. In this case, we will

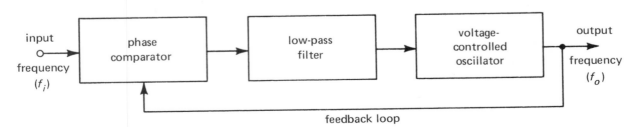

FIGURE 17–1. Phase-locked Loop Components

measure the time difference between the two peaks (indicated by points t_1 and t_2). We must also measure the period of the waves, time T. The phase difference, $\Delta\phi$, is then computed as

$$\Delta\phi = 2\pi \left(\frac{t_2 - t_1}{T}\right) \qquad \text{(17-2)}$$

Note that phase difference is computed in radians. To convert to degrees, recall that

$$1 \text{ radian} = \frac{180°}{\pi} = 57.3°$$

So we can convert $\Delta\phi$ from radians to degrees by multiplying by $57.3°$.

☐ EXAMPLE 17-1

The times in Figure 17-2 are measured and found to be

$$t_1 = 350 \text{ ms}$$
$$t_2 = 750 \text{ ms}$$
$$\text{period} = 1.5 \text{ s}$$

Find the phase difference in radians and degrees.

Solution From Equation 17-2, we have

$$\Delta\phi = 2\pi \left(\frac{750 - 350}{1500}\right) = 1.68 \text{ radians}$$

Converting to degrees, we obtain

$$\Delta\phi = (1.68 \text{ radians}) \left(57.3 \frac{\text{radians}}{\text{degree}}\right) = 96°$$

The output voltage of the phase comparator can be interpreted as the phase difference between the input frequency and the VCO output. This error voltage is

$$v_e = k_c \Delta\phi \qquad \text{(17-3)}$$

where

$\quad \Delta\phi = $ phase difference (in radians)
$\quad k_c = $ phase comparator conversion gain (in volts per radian)

A circuit that you are already familiar with provides a good example of a phase comparator. The exclusive OR shown in Figure 17-3a has the input signal and the VCO feedback voltage applied to its terminals. In Figure 17-3b, square waves are shown in order to clearly indicate the

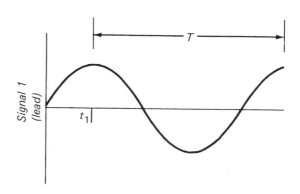

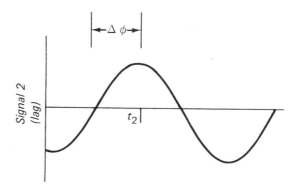

FIGURE 17-2. Phase Difference

concept, but the same effect results with sine wave inputs. Both signals have the same frequency, but the VCO feedback lags by $\pi/4$ radians (45°). The exclusive OR has a high output only when the input signals are unequal, such as between times of 0 and $\pi/4$ radians and π and $5\pi/4$ radians.

The average output voltage can be found if we know the **duty cycle** of the output. The duty cycle DC is defined as

$$\text{DC} = \frac{t_H}{T} \qquad \text{(17-4)}$$

where

$\quad t_H = $ interval duration when the signal is high during one period
$\quad T = $ length of one period

The duty cycle of the exclusive OR can range from 0 to 1, as Figure 17-4 indicates. The phase difference between the two signals is the only factor that affects the duty cycle.

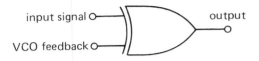

(a) Exclusive OR Gate

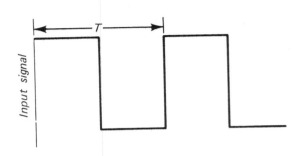

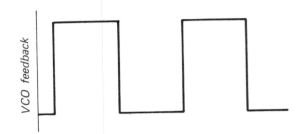

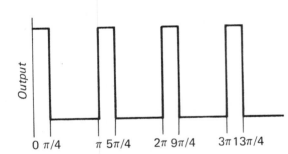

(b) Timing of Signals

FIGURE 17-3. Phase Comparator

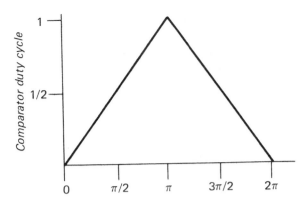

Phase difference

FIGURE 17-4. Duty Cycle of the Phase Comparator

□ **EXAMPLE 17-2**

For the situation shown in Figure 17-3, compute the duty cycle of the output.

Solution From the figure, we observe that the output is high between 0 and $\pi/4$ and between π and $5\pi/4$ for the first period. Using Equation 17-4, we obtain

$$\text{DC} = \frac{(\pi/4) + (\pi/4)}{2\pi} = 0.25$$

Expressed as a percentage, the duty cycle is 25%.

□ **EXAMPLE 17-3**

Show that the duty cycle value shown on the graph in Figure 17-4 is correct for a phase difference of π radians.

Solution The two inputs with this phase difference must appear as shown in Figure 17-5. Again applying Equation 17-4, we have

$$\text{DC} = \frac{\pi + \pi}{2\pi} = 1.0$$

which is the same as the value obtained from the graph.

If we know how to compute the duty cycle, we can find the average output voltage of the exclusive OR gate. The average voltage is

$$V_{\text{avg}} = V_H(\text{DC}) \tag{17-5}$$

where
V_H = high logic level voltage

□ **EXAMPLE 17-4**

Using the duty cycle of Example 17-2, find the average output voltage of the exclusive OR gate. The gate is a TTL gate with a high logic level of 3.4 V.

Solution From Equation 17-5, we have

$$V_{\text{avg}} = (3.4)(0.25) = 0.85 \text{ V}$$

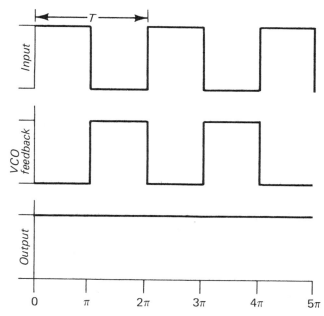

FIGURE 17-5. Duty Cycle for a Phase Difference of π radians

In addition to exclusive OR gates, **edge-triggered flip-flops** are frequently used as digital phase comparators of PLLs. More common are monolithic PLL integrated circuits, which use analog phase comparators. The analog comparator uses a *double-balanced mixer*. The specific implementation of the phase comparator is not particularly important, because the PLL is a self-contained IC. As a technician, you should be more concerned with the function the phase comparator performs than with the way it is built.

Voltage-controlled Oscillator

The voltage-controlled oscillator is the source of the output frequency. This frequency (in degrees) is

$$f_o = \frac{K_v V_{\text{in}}}{2\pi} \qquad (17\text{-}6)$$

where

V_{in} = input voltage (in volts)
K_v = VCO conversion gain (in radians per second per volt)

The output of the VCO is usually expressed in ra-

dian frequency, ω_o. The radian frequency can be found from f_o:

$$\omega_o = 2\pi f_o \qquad (17\text{-}7)$$

Or it can be found directly from the circuit parameters:

$$\omega_o = K_v V_{\text{in}} \qquad (17\text{-}8)$$

☐ EXAMPLE 17-5

Find the output frequency from the voltage-controlled oscillator if the input voltage is 0.35 V. The VCO conversion gain is 10^7 radians/s/V. Express the answer in degrees and in radian frequency.

Solution From Equation 17-6, we have

$$f_o = \frac{(10^7)(0.35)}{2\pi} = 557 \text{ kHz}$$

The radian frequency, from Equation 17-8, is

$$\omega_o = (10^7)(0.35) = 3.5 \times 10^6 \text{ radians/s}$$

To verify our answers, we can use Equation 17-7 as a check:

$$\omega_o = 2\pi(557 \times 10^3) = 3.5 \times 10^6 \text{ radians/s}$$

which is the same as the result in the step above.

Now let us examine a specific example of a voltage-controlled oscillator. The MC4024 integrated circuit shown in Figure 17-6 is called a *voltage-controlled multivibrator* by the manufacturer. It contains two independent multivibrators (which produce square waves proportional to the input voltage) and two output buffers. As the figure shows, three voltage supply pins and grounds are provided. For isolation of the two multivibrators, each has its own power supply and ground terminals. The output buffers share the third common supply voltage and ground pins.

The schematic for using the MC4024 as a voltage-controlled oscillator in a phase-locked loop is shown in Figure 17-7. The supply voltage is provided for voltage-controlled multivibrator 1 and the output buffers. The approximate capacitor value can be found from the manufacturer's formula

$$C = \frac{300}{f_o} \text{ pF} \qquad (17\text{-}9)$$

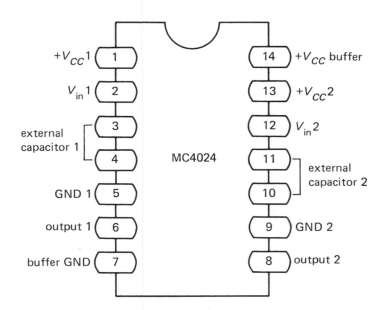

FIGURE 17-6.
MC4024 Pin
Assignments

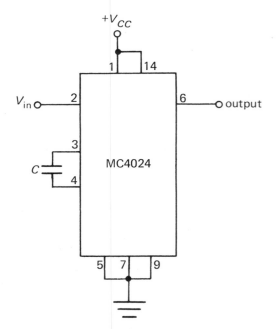

FIGURE 17-7. Voltage-controlled
Oscillator for a Phase-Locked Loop

where

f_o = free-running output frequency
(in MHz)

(The formula is most accurate for capacitor values above 100 pF). The maximum frequency for this circuit is 25 MHz.

Low-Pass Filter

This circuit will be thoroughly covered in the discussion on low-pass filters in Chapter 19. You may wish to refer to that material at this time. As mentioned earlier, this filter does not affect the tracking range of the phase-locked loop. It does, however, influence how rapidly locking can occur and the frequency range of the PLL output.

□ TONE DETECTOR

A **tone detector** is often found in telephones and in control units. Using a phase-locked loop, we will develop a tone detector that will respond with an output frequency of up to 500 kHz. The frequency depends only on the external components attached to the PLL.

The 567 phase-locked loop integrated circuit is shown in Figure 17-8. It is an 8-pin DIP capable of providing up to 100 mA in output current. When the input frequency matches the IC's center frequency, f_0, the level on pin 8 goes low. Otherwise, the level is high. This feature will be used in our tone decoder application.

The center frequency for the PLL depends on the timing capacitor and the timing resistor connected to pins 6 and 5, respectively. It is

$$f_0 = \frac{1.10}{R_T C_T} \qquad (17\text{-}10)$$

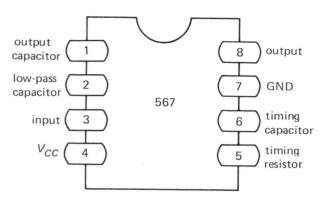

FIGURE 17–8. 567 Phase-Locked Loop and Tone Decoder

where

R_T = timing resistor
C_T = timing capacitor

The value for R_T should be within the range of 2 kΩ to 20 kΩ. The range of f_0 is from 0.01 Hz to 500 kHz.

The low-pass capacitor is selected according to the bandwidth desired. The 567 data sheet provides full details, but typical values can be chosen by using the equation:

$$C_L = \frac{n}{f_0} \,\mu\text{F} \qquad (17\text{–}11)$$

where

f_0 = center frequency
n = 1,300 for a detection bandwidth of 14 percent of f_o
n = 62,000 for a detection bandwidth of 2 percent of f_o

The output capacitor is not critical and is typically twice that of C_L:

$$C_o = 2C_L \qquad (17\text{–}12)$$

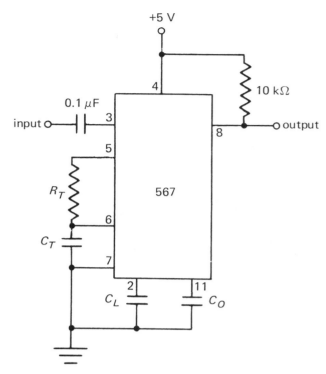

FIGURE 17–9. Basic 567 Circuit

Solution We find R_T from Equation 17–10.

$$
\begin{aligned}
R_T &= \frac{1.10}{f_0 C_T} \\
&= \frac{1.10}{(700)(0.1 \times 10^{-6})} \\
&= 14.3 \text{ kHz}
\end{aligned}
$$

Using Equation 17–11 for a 14 percent bandwidth, we obtain

$$C_L = \frac{1300}{770} = 1.7 \,\mu\text{F}$$

And, finally, the output capacitor is found with Equation 17–12.

$$C_o = 2(1.7) = 3.4 \,\mu\text{F}$$

□ EXAMPLE 17-6

Select the components for the circuit based on the 567 and shown in Figure 17–9. The device is to have a center frequency of 770 Hz. The bandwidth should be 14 percent of f_0. Use a value of 0.1 μF for C_T.

□ TOUCH-TONE DECODER

The telephone system is converting from rotary-dial instruments to those using Touch-Tone inputs. The digits 0 through 9 and two symbols (# and *) are encoded as a composite of two frequencies. The code is listed in Table 17–1. Reading from that list, we see that the digit 1 is a combination of 697- and 1209-Hz tones, the digit 2 is 697 and 1336 Hz, and so on.

Referring to Example 17–6, we note that we have already designed a decoder for the 770-Hz tone. In a similar manner, we could decode each of the other six tones as well. With these basic decoders, we can convert the tone combinations to their digital values.

A decoder for the digit 4 is shown in Figure 17–10. It is simply a combination of our previously designed 770-Hz decoder and a new 1209-Hz decoder. The outputs of each decoder are then NORed together. If the tones for the digit 4 are received at the input, both decoders have a low output, producing a high output after passing through the NOR gate. For an input of any other tone combination, either or both of the 770-Hz or 1209-Hz decoders will have a high output. Consequently, the NOR gate output will be low.

A complete 12-digit decoding circuit is shown in Figure 17–11. In addition to the seven tone decoders, 12 NOR gates are required. By tracing the lines, we find that the inputs for the NOR gate that signify that the digit 1 has been received are from the 697-Hz and 1209-Hz decoders. That NOR gate output will be high when those two tones are the inputs to this circuit. All other NOR gates will then have low outputs. A corresponding set of levels is generated for each of the other digits when the proper tone combination is present at the input.

TABLE 17–1. Touch-Tone Frequency Code

Digit/Symbol	Frequency 1 (Hz)	Frequency 2 (Hz)
1	697	1209
2	697	1336
3	697	1477
4	770	1209
5	770	1336
6	770	1477
7	852	1209
8	852	1336
9	852	1477
0	941	1209
*	941	1336
#	941	1477

□ FREQUENCY SYNTHESIZER

The 562 phase-locked loop can be used to synthesize several frequencies. The output frequency for the circuit shown in Figure 17–12b is

$$f_o = Nf_i \qquad (17\text{–}13)$$

where

f_i = input frequency
N = divider value in the divide-by-N counter

The 562 makes the VCO outputs and phase comparator inputs available at pins (there are two of

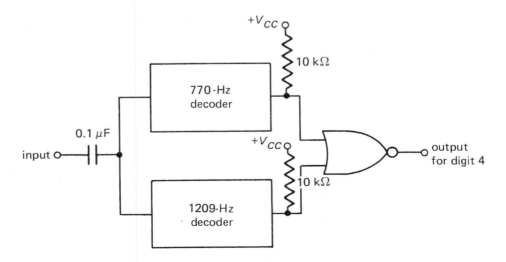

FIGURE 17–10.
Touch-Tone Decoder
for the Digit 4

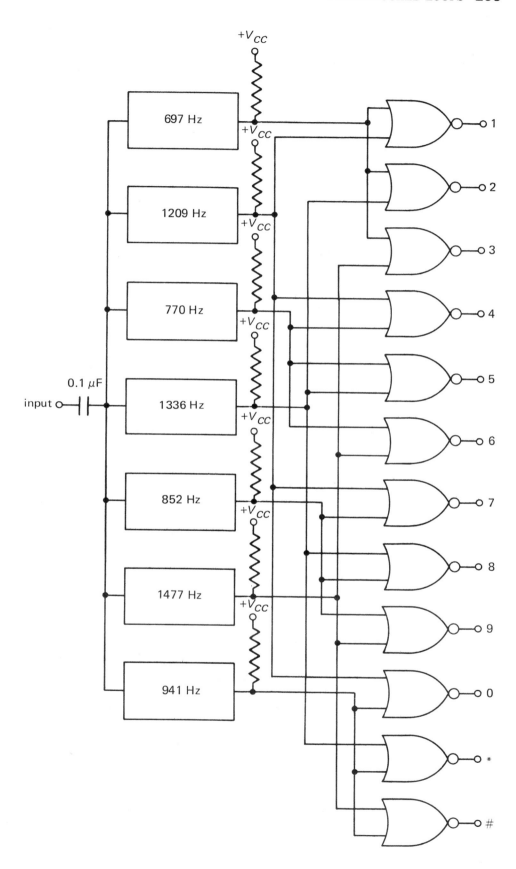

FIGURE 17–11.
Complete Touch-Tone
Decoder

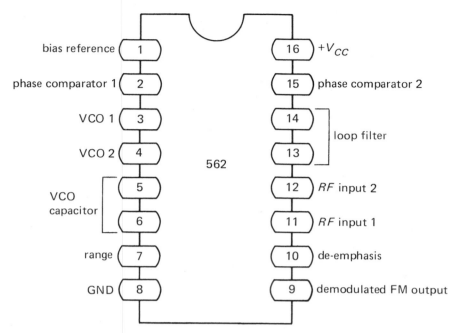

(a) Pin Assignments

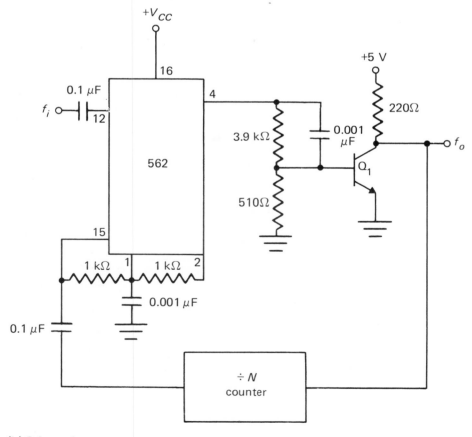

(b) Schematic

FIGURE 17–12.
Frequency
Synthesizer

each; see Figure 17–12a), so another circuit (here we want to use a divider) can be inserted. A programmable divider is an excellent choice for use in the synthesizer.

☐ EXAMPLE 17–7

If the input frequency to the synthesizer in Figure 17–12 is 1.3 MHz, what will the output be for the following divider values: 2, 14, 267?

Solution From Equation 17–12, the respective output frequencies will be

$$f_o = 2(1.3 \times 10^6) = 2.6 \text{ MHz}$$
$$f_o = 14(1.3 \times 10^6) = 18.2 \text{ MHz}$$
$$f_o = 267(1.3 \times 10^6) = 347 \text{ MHz}$$

Chapter Summary

☐ A voltage-controlled oscillator, a phase comparator, and a low-pass filter comprise a phase-locked loop. The oscillator generates the output frequency in response to an error voltage produced by the comparator. The filter eliminates unwanted high-frequency noise.

☐ The PLL will be in one of three states: free-running, capture, and phase-locked. The frequency range over which the phase-locked loop can follow incoming signals is called the lock range. Capture is possible over a bandwidth known as the capture range. The capture range is never wider than the lock range.

☐ Both analog and digital phase comparators are used in PLLs. The average voltage output of the comparator is a measure of the phase difference between the two input signals.

☐ Phase difference can be expressed in degrees or radians.

☐ The duty cycle of the comparator is the ratio of the time during which the signal is high to the duration of one cycle.

☐ The voltage-controlled oscillator frequency depends on the input voltage and the VCO conversion gain factor.

☐ A tone detector provides a digital output that is low when the input signal matches the center frequency. Otherwise, the output is high.

☐ A Touch-Tone decoder combines the outputs of pairs of tone detectors with center frequencies equal to the seven tones used. NOR gate outputs indicate which digit was received last.

☐ Frequency synthesizers can generate several different frequencies by simply changing the divider count.

Problems

17–1. Convert the radian values listed below to their equivalent in degrees.

   a. 0.6   c. $7\pi/8$
   b. 1.2   d. 3π

17–2. Find the phase difference between the two signals shown in Figure 17–13. Express your answer in degrees and radians.

17–3. Find the output of a phase comparator if the phase difference of the two signals is 90°. The phase comparator conversion gain is 2.86 V/radian.

17–4. Compute the average output voltage of an exclusive OR phase comparator with inputs as shown in Figure 17–14. The TTL exclusive OR gate has a high logic level of 3.2 V.

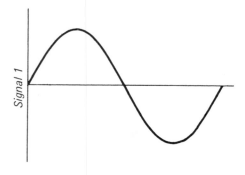

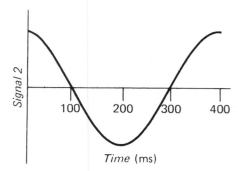

FIGURE 17–13.

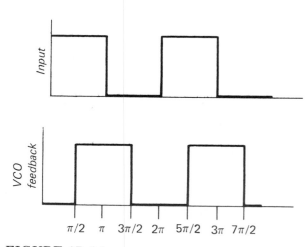

FIGURE 17–14.

17–5. Change the vertical scale of Figure 17–4 so that it provides a direct reading of the phase comparator output voltage; the high logic level of the gate is 3.4 V. Using your diagram, find the output voltages for the phase differences listed below.

    a. $\pi/3$

    b. $\pi/4$

    c. $3\pi/5$

17–6. What frequency is produced by a VCO with an input voltage of 0.5 V if the conversion gain is 10^7 radians/s/V?

17–7. Design a tone detector suitable for the lower Touch-Tone frequency of the digit 9. Use a 0.1-μF timing capacitor and a 14 percent bandwidth.

17–8. What frequency would be produced by the 562 used as a synthesizer if the divider were set to 23? The input frequency is 3.5 MHz. What divider value would you select to produce a 430.5-MHz output?

17–9. A voltage-controlled oscillator is to produce a free-running output of 250 kHz. If the MC4024 IC is to be used, what capacitor value would you recommend?

17–10. The error voltage generated by a phase comparator is 2.9 V. If the conversion gain is 1.7 V/radian, draw the input waveforms when the VCO feedback signal is lagging.

Chapter Eighteen

Optoelectronics

The field of **optoelectronics** is a diverse one that requires a knowledge of optical properties of materials as well as a knowledge of electronics. In the optical realm, the physiology of the human eye and how it responds to light must be appreciated. The method of focusing and conducting light with lenses and fibers must also be understood. In electronics, we must know how the light is controlled, modulated, displayed, or recorded.

Optoelectronic components are being used increasingly in displays, measuring equipment, sensors, sources, and receivers, and hence you will inevitably encounter them in your work. In this chapter, we will discuss the relationship of visible light to other forms of electromagnetic radiation. In addition, we will describe several optoelectronic components, such as sensors, displays using light-emitting diodes and liquid crystals, optoisolators, and fiber optic systems.

Chapter Objectives

Upon completion of this chapter, you should be able to:

- ☐ Relate various types of electromagnetic radiation to their wavelengths.
- ☐ Explain why the human eye is sensitive only to visible light.
- ☐ Describe the operation of photodiodes and phototransistor sensors.
- ☐ Draw light-emitting diode schematic diagrams.
- ☐ Explain why different types of light-emitting diodes produce various colors.
- ☐ Show how the light-emitting diode can be used to indicate states of logic gates.
- ☐ Discuss the use of optoisolators for voltage isolation.
- ☐ Distinguish between common-anode and common-cathode displays.
- ☐ Show how to connect a light-emitting diode decoder/driver IC.
- ☐ Explain how liquid-crystal display decoder/drivers must be used.
- ☐ Connect multiple-digit displays.
- ☐ Describe the operation of fiber optic transmitters and receivers.

☐ ELECTROMAGNETIC SPECTRUM

Electromagnetic radiation, such as radio waves, cosmic rays, and light, can be distinguished by its wavelength. For example, radio waves have the longest wavelengths, and gamma and cosmic rays have the shortest wavelengths. Figure 18-1 shows the range.

The Greek letter λ (lambda) is a common symbol for wavelength. Observe that radio waves extend above 10^8 μm in wavelength, while cosmic rays are extremely short, around 10^{-7} μm. Visible light is near the center of the spectrum, from about 0.4 to 0.8 μm. Just shorter than light waves are ultraviolet (UV) waves. On the other side of visible light is infrared radiation (IR).

Within the range of visible light, we see colors depending on the wavelength of the light. Table 18-1 lists the wavelengths of the colors, beginning with violet at the shortest extreme to red at the longest. The way in which we perceive colors, therefore, depends only on the wavelength of the light. Figure 18-2 makes this point even more clearly. Plotted on the figure is the relative sensitivity of the eye as compared to emission or

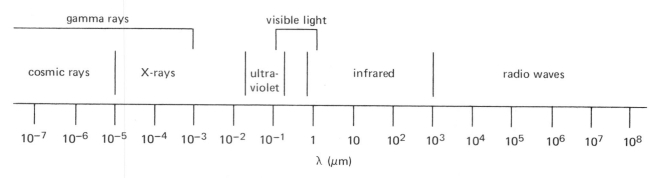

FIGURE 18-1. Electromagnetic Radiation Spectrum

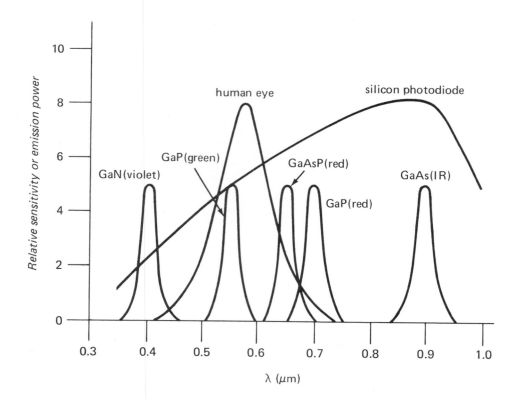

FIGURE 18-2. Sensitivity of the Human Eye and of Semiconductors

TABLE 18-1. Visible Radiation

Color	Wavelength (nm)
Violet	380–440
Blue	440–495
Green	495–580
Yellow	580–640
Red	640–750

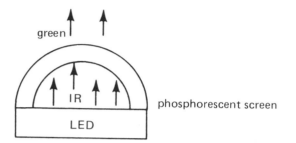

FIGURE 18-3. Converting IR to Green Light

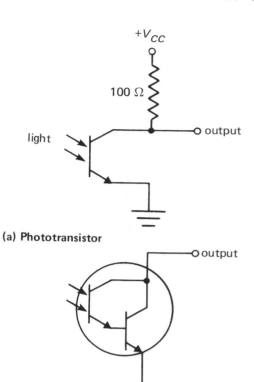

(a) Phototransistor

(b) Photo Darlington

FIGURE 18-4. Photodetectors

detection characteristics of semiconductors (to be more fully described in following sections). For example, compare the sensitivity of a silicon photodetector, with a detection range of 0.3 to 1.0 μm, to the eye, which is limited to a much narrower range of 0.4 to 0.7 μm.

The eye is just barely able to detect the radiation of the GaAsP (gallium, arsenic, and phosphorus) light-emitting diode (LED), which appears red. The GaAs infrared emission is undetectable. Realizing this limitation on our sight, manufacturers convert the wavelength of radiation from IR to visible light by using a screen, as shown in Figure 18-3. As the IR radiation from the light-emitting diode strikes it, the phosphorescent screen looks green to our eyes. The conversion in wavelength results from the IR waves exciting the atoms in the screen and causing them to emit radiation in the green portion of the spectrum.

☐ PHOTODETECTORS

Both diodes and transistors are used as **photodetectors**. Light falling on the silicon semiconductor changes the internal potentials, so the device switches from a nonconducting to a conducting state. This phenomenon is known as the **photoelectric effect**.

Consider the **phototransistor** in Figure 18-4a. When light strikes it, the transistor saturates, pulling the output down to the collector-emitter saturation voltage. Switching time is on the order of a microsecond. When the detector is in the dark, its equivalent resistance is several hundred megohms. Thus no current flows from the supply, and the output voltage is V_{CC}.

A typical phototransistor will have a window in its case through which light may enter. Both flat and lense-shaped windows are available. These devices are used in "electric eyes," intrusion alarms, paper tape and punched card readers, photographic light meters, and optical character readers.

Frequently, a phototransistor is packaged with an amplifying transistor as a **photo Darlington combination** (see Figure 18-4b). The phototransistor operates as explained above, while the amplifying transistor makes it possible

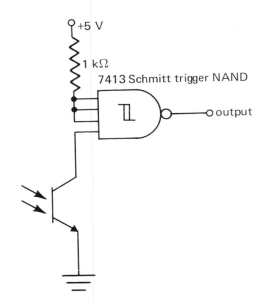

FIGURE 18-5. Light Pulse Detector

FIGURE 18-6. Photodiode

potential is applied, and the latter is named for the semiconductor materials comprising the diode. Applications for photodiodes include detectors, laser measurement systems, character recognition, and fiber optic receivers.

Another way in which photodetectors are used increasingly is in **bar code readers** or **wands**. Figure 18-7 shows a block diagram for the wand. The optical sensor distinguishes the dark and light areas of the bar code pattern. This signal is amplified and applied to a digitizing circuit, such as that shown in Figure 18-5. The digital signal level indicates whether the wand is scanning a black or a white stripe, so the wand output can be directly applied to a logic circuit or microprocessor.

to detect very faint signals. Therefore, photo Darlingtons are capable of highly sensitive operation.

An example of a **pulse detector**, such as found in a paper tape reader, is shown in Figure 18-5. Here the output of the phototransistor is the only changing input to a Schmitt trigger NAND gate. The light pulses are converted to TTL-compatible voltage levels. When light strikes the photodetector, that input to the gate becomes low. The gate output switches from the previous low level to the high state. With a Schmitt trigger, a crisp switching signal is produced.

Another photosensitive device is the **photodiode**, shown in Figure 18-6. The photodiode will conduct only when light is falling on it. Two types of these components that you may encounter are the *avalanche photodiode (APD)* and the *PIN diode*. The former is named for the voltage that flows when a large reverse

☐ LIGHT-EMITTING DIODES

The **light-emitting diode**, or **LED**, has become a common element in many electronic units. LEDs are used in games, indicator panels, automobile dashboards, home appliances, and industrial equipment. Their principle of operation is quite simple. The LED emits radiation and conducts when it is forward-biased. Reverse-biasing a LED produces much the same effect as occurs in an ordinary diode—no current flows and no light is emitted. Figure 18-8a shows the LED symbol and Figure 18-8b shows a typical LED lamp.

Use as Transmitters

As Figure 18-2 showed, the color emitted by a LED depends on its composition (unless a screen

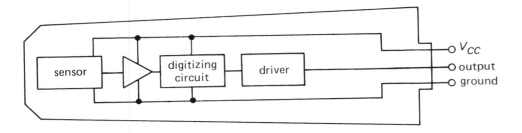

FIGURE 18-7. Bar Code Wand

(a) Symbol

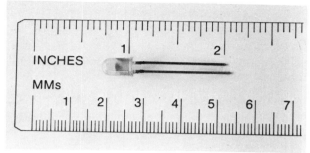

(b) LED Lamp

FIGURE 18-8. Light-Emitting Diode Lamp

TABLE 18-2. LED Materials

Material	Wavelength (nm)	Color
Si	1140	IR
GaAs	900	IR
$GaAs_{60}P_{40}$	650	Red
$GaAs_{35}P_{65}$	625	Orange
$GaAs_{15}P_{85}$	590	Yellow
GaP	555	Green
SiC	540 to 400	Blue to violet

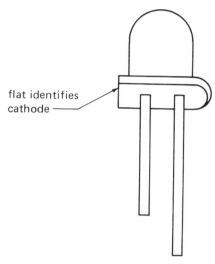

flat identifies cathode

Part number	Color
5082-4550	yellow
5082-4555	bright yellow
5082-4650	red
5082-4655	bright red
5082-4950	green
5082-4955	bright green

FIGURE 18-9. 5082 LEDs

is used). Table 18-2 lists formulas for several LED compositions. At this time, blue LEDs are experimental; the silicon carbide (SiC) from which they are made is extremely hard, difficult to work with, and requires high temperature in processing.

Table 18-2 also shows another method that is used to shift the wavelength of the emitted light. There are three mixtures listed for the GaAsP diode. [Subscripts indicate the ratio of phosphorus (P) to arsenic (As).] As the phosphorus percentage increases, the radiation wavelength becomes shorter. Consequently, light is red for a 40-60 phosphorus-to-arsenic ratio, but it is yellow when the mixture is changed to an 85-15 ratio.

A LED will often have a flat spot indicating the cathode, as shown in Figure 18-9. All lamps in the 5082 series have this configuration. The last four digits indicate the color of the emission. In addition to the usual yellow, red, and green colors, this series offers an option for a brighter display in each color.

It is often necessary to vary the brightness of LEDs. Another way of controlling the brightness is to select the proper size for the load resistor. (The load resistor protects the LED from high currents that can shorten the expected lamp life or even permanently damage it. In general, the brighter the lamp is run, the shorter its lifetime will be.) For example, Figure 18-2 showed that our eyes are less sensitive to red light than to green light. If two LEDs (one red and the other green) are to appear to have the same intensity, the red lamp must be brighter than the green one.

The red lamp can be made brighter by selecting an appropriate load resistor. The formula for the load resistor is

$$R_L = \frac{V_{CC} - V_F}{I_F} \qquad (18\text{-}1)$$

where

V_{CC} = supply voltage
V_F = forward bias from manufacturer's data sheet
I_F = forward current from manufacturer's data sheet

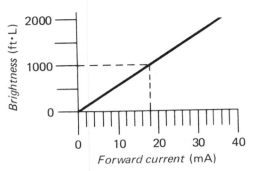

(a) Current

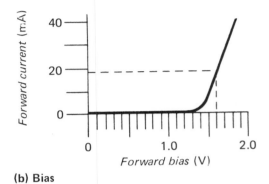

(b) Bias

FIGURE 18-10. LED Forward Current and Bias

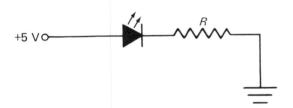

FIGURE 18-11. LED Circuit

Figure 18-10 are sample forward current (Figure 18-10a) and forward bias (Figure 18-10b) curves.

□ **EXAMPLE 18-1**

Find the load resistor to be used in the circuit of Figure 18-11. The LED is to have a brightness of 1000 ft·L.

Solution From Figure 18-10a, we see that the forward current must be 19 mA. Then according to Figure 18-10b, the forward bias must be 1.6 V. Using Equation 18-1, we obtain

$$R_L = \frac{5 - 1.6}{19 \times 10^{-3}} = 179\ \Omega$$

The resistor power rating required in the LED circuit is also readily calculated because we know the resistance and current. The power is

$$P = I_F^2 R \qquad (18\text{-}2)$$

□ **EXAMPLE 18-2**

What power rating should the resistor of Example 18-1 have?

Solution From Equation 18-2, we have

$$P = (19 \times 10^{-3})^2 (179) = 64.6\ \text{mW}$$

So a 1/8-W resistor can safely be used.

Use as Indicators

There are many times when we would like to have an indication of a gate's output level on a circuit board. LEDs can be used for this purpose as an aid in troubleshooting. For example, one computer manufacturer supplies boards that turn a LED on when a hardware malfunction is detected.

A LED can be used to illuminate either logic level, high or low. Refer to the circuit in Figure 18-12a. Tracing the signals in that schematic, we see that when the NAND gate output is low, the cathode of the LED is almost at ground potential. The power supply will forward-bias the light-emitting diode, so the device is illuminated. If the gate output switches to high, the LED is no longer forward-biased and is off.

The opposite conditions are true for the indicator in Figure 18-12b. Here a high gate output produces the potential to forward-bias the LED. A low level turns the LED off.

Yet another useful way to employ LEDs is in the two-color indicator of Figure 18-12c. If current flows from terminal 1 to terminal 2, the green LED is forward-biased. Hence it is turned on. Reversing the current direction turns off the green LED and turns on the red one.

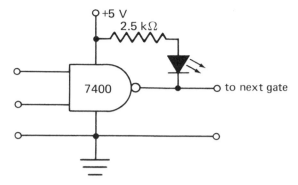

(a) On When Output Low

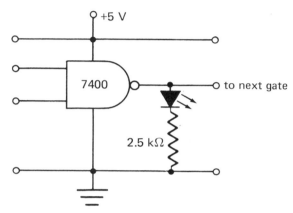

(b) On When Output High

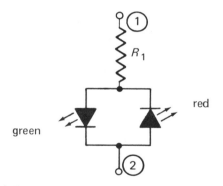

(c) Two-Color LED

FIGURE 18-12. LED Fault Indicators

☐ OPTOISOLATORS

Place a LED inside the same package with a phototransistor and you have an **optoisolator**. Optoisolators, also called **optocouplers**, offer high-voltage electrical isolation. Such isolation is vital for protecting low-voltage circuitry like TTL.

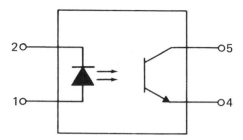

FIGURE 18-13. Optoisolator Principle of Operation

Figure 18-13 shows the principle of operation for the optoisolator. When the LED is forward-biased, the light emitted strikes the phototransistor. The transistor saturates, so the collector-to-emitter voltage drops to a low value. When the LED does not light, the transistor is cut off. The high speed and small size of the optoisolator make it a practical component in many areas. Isolation of 2.5 kV with a low-cost plastic DIP is quite easily accomplished.

Figure 18-14a is a photograph of an optoisolator, and Figure 18-14b gives the pin assignment for a 4N25 component. Pins 1 and 2 are the anode and cathode of the diode, respectively. All three transistor leads are made available at pins, but the base is not normally used.

To demonstrate how an optoisolator can be used to protect digital logic, we will examine the **20-mA current loop**. This current loop is a standard technique used to communicate with teletypes. The teletype channel consists of a twisted-pair cable that carries a 20-mA current to signify a 1 and no current for a 0. The problem is that this current may be excessive for TTL inputs, and voltages of 12 V or more are typically employed. As you know, TTL is limited to 5 V.

The teletype current loop-to-TTL converter shown in Figure 18-15 uses the 4N25 optoisolator. The only connection between the high current and the TTL gates is a light beam. Hence damaging overvoltages are avoided. The highest voltage on the TTL output is the 5-V source, no matter what the voltages and currents are in the teletype loop.

When the 20-mA current flows to represent the 1 level, the diode illuminates. The 5-V source is grounded through the saturated transistor. The inverter then produces a high-level output. On the other hand, when no current is flowing, the transistor is cut off. The input to the Schmitt

(a) Typical Optoisolator

(b) 4N25

FIGURE 18-14. Optoisolator

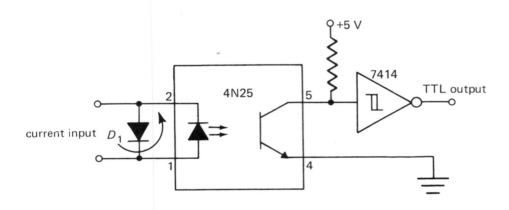

FIGURE 18-15.
Teletype Current
Loop-to-TTL
Converter

trigger inverter is 5 V, which becomes a low signal after inversion.

The diode on the input to the optoisolator offers the LED protection against current flowing in the wrong direction. Too much reverse bias could damage the LED. In the case of the 4N25, the maximum reverse bias is 3 V. The circuit in Figure 18-15 is properly protected because D_1 will conduct at 0.7 V.

☐ LED DISPLAYS

The **7-segment LED display** is found everywhere. Figure 18-16a shows this type of display on the left and a **dot-matrix display** on the right.

Segmented Displays

First we will discuss the segmented displays. Figure 18-16b shows how letters are used to identify each segment. A similar scheme is used with the newer **16-segment displays**, as Figure 18-16c indicates. Because this system of designation is so common, you should become familiar with it.

The 7-segment display is manufactured with either a *common anode* (see Figure 18-17a) or a *common cathode* (Figure 18-17b). Seven separate LEDs are used to form the segments. (Another LED is required to supply the decimal point, DP.) In the common-anode version, all anodes are tied to a common pin, while the seven cathodes are routed to individual pins. The converse is true with the common cathode, in which

(a) Seven-Segment and Dot Matrix LED Displays

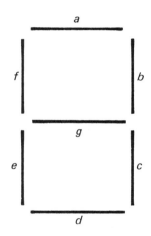

(b) Nomenclature for 7-Segment LED

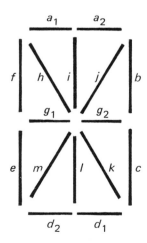

(c) Nomenclature for 16-Segment LED

FIGURE 18–16. Multisegment LED Displays

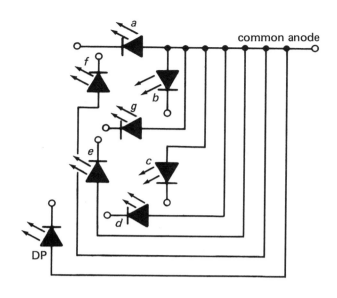

(a) Common-Anode Display

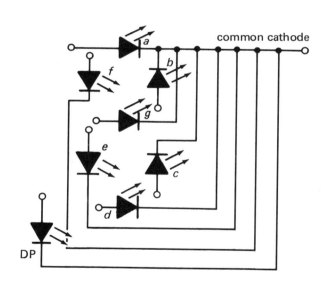

(b) Common-Cathode Display

FIGURE 18–17. Comparison of Common-Anode and Common-Cathode Displays

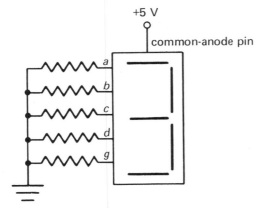

(a) Common-Anode Display

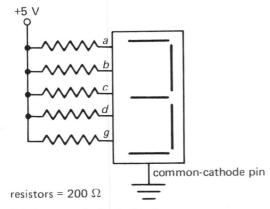

resistors = 200 Ω

(b) Common-Cathode Display

FIGURE 18-18. Lighting the Digit 3

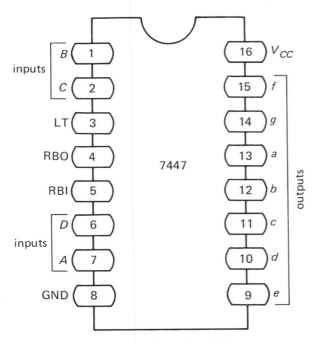

FIGURE 18-19. LED Decoder/Driver

there will be only one cathode pin. You must know which type of display you have in order to operate it.

Suppose we wish to light the segments corresponding to the digit 3 with a common-anode LED display. The connections shown in Figure 18-18a would be used. Five current-limiting resistors are connected from the ground to the appropriate pins. (Segments *a* through *d* and *g* form a 3.) The source voltage is tied to the common anode. Compare this circuit to the equivalent one for the common-cathode display in Figure 18-18b.

Obviously, it is not practical to physically connect or disconnect resistors to change the digit displayed. Instead, we use a **LED decoder/driver**. This integrated circuit is a standard TTL component. The 7447 decoder/driver is used with common-anode displays and the 7448 decoder/driver with common-cathode displays.

The functions of the 7447 are listed in Table 18-3. Observe that the segments turned on correspond to the decimal digits for inputs of 0000_2 to 1001_2. Binary inputs above 1001_2 produce unique, though not very useful, displays, also. The pin assignments for the 7447 are illustrated in Figure 18-19. (The 7448 IC has identical pin assignments.) For our purposes, the lamp test (LT), the ripple-blanking-in (RBI), and the ripple-blanking-out (RBO) can all be connected to +5 V. (These inputs are used only in testing or chaining of displays.)

In use, the output pins of the IC are connected to the corresponding segments of the common-anode display through current-limiting resistors. Figure 18-20 shows the schematic. By comparing Figures 18-18a and 18-20, we conclude that the 7447 must ground the segments needed to form the digit matching the binary input. (That is, the outputs of the 7447 are *active-low*.)

Only minor rearrangements are needed to use the common-cathode display with the 7448. The pin assignments for this IC are identical to those of the 7447. Figure 18-21 shows how the connections are to be made. In the case of the 7448, the outputs are *active-high*, supplying the voltage necessary to turn on the common-cathode display segments. Table 18-4 lists the functions of this decoder/driver.

Decade Counter Revisited

Combining this knowledge of LED displays with what you learned in Chapter 12, you should read-

TABLE 18–3. 7447 Functions

Inputs				Outputs[a]							Display
D	C	B	A	a	b	c	d	e	f	g	
0	0	0	0	L	L	L	L	L	L	H	
0	0	0	1	H	L	L	H	H	H	H	
0	0	1	0	L	L	H	L	L	H	L	
0	0	1	1	L	L	L	L	H	H	L	
0	1	0	0	H	L	L	H	H	L	L	
0	1	0	1	L	H	L	L	H	L	L	
0	1	1	0	H	H	L	L	L	L	L	
0	1	1	1	L	L	L	H	H	H	H	
1	0	0	0	L	L	L	L	L	L	L	
1	0	0	1	L	L	L	H	H	L	L	
1	0	1	0	H	H	H	L	L	H	L	
1	0	1	1	H	H	L	L	H	H	L	
1	1	0	0	H	L	H	H	H	L	L	
1	1	0	1	L	H	H	L	H	L	L	
1	1	1	0	H	H	H	L	L	L	L	
1	1	1	1	H	H	H	H	H	H	H	blank

[a]LT is high, RBI is high, and RBO is high.

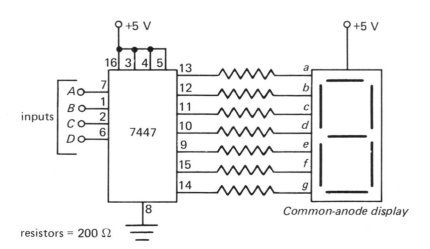

FIGURE 18–20.
Common-Anode
Decoder/Driver

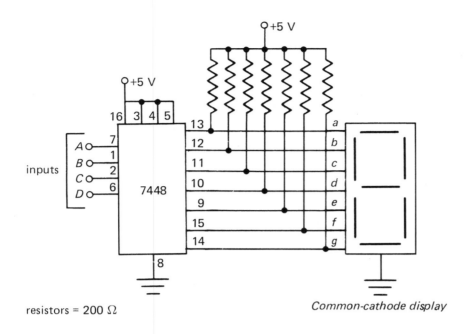

resistors = 200 Ω

Common-cathode display

FIGURE 18-21.
Common-Cathode
Decoder/Driver

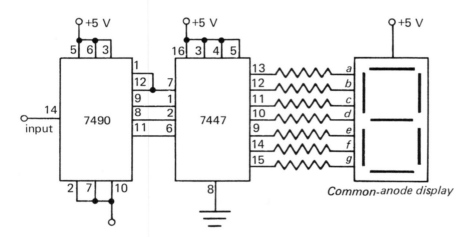

Common-anode display

FIGURE 18-22.
Decade Counter with
Display

ily understand the operation of the decade counter of Figure 18-22. As each input pulse is received, the count increments and the accumulated total is displayed. After ten input pulses, the display cycles back to the original digit.

Dot-Matrix Displays

While the 16-segment display can handle both letters and numbers (referred to as **alphanumeric characters**), the dot-matrix display offers much more flexibility. A 5 × 7 LED matrix is shown in Figure 18-23. Alphanumeric characters as well as punctuation marks and letters in foreign alphabets can be formed on this display.

Because there are 36 LEDs involved, the dot matrix is more expensive than the 7-segment display. Furthermore, a more sophisticated decoder/driver IC is needed. If space is restricted, the integrated display shown in the photograph of Figure 18-16a may be the answer. The 5082-7340 displays all decimal digits and the letters A through F as programmed by the 4-bit input. Table 18-5 lists the functions of this circuit, and Figure 18-24 provides pin assignments. (Note: The figure shows a bottom view, so pin numbers are reversed.)

From the function table, it is clear that this display is also suitable for representing hexadecimal digits, too. When space is at a premium, one could hardly wish for a simpler solution to the display problem.

TABLE 18-4. 7448 Functions

Inputs				Outputs[a]							Display
D	C	B	A	a	b	c	d	e	f	g	
0	0	0	0	H	H	H	H	H	H	L	
0	0	0	1	L	H	H	L	L	L	L	
0	0	1	0	H	H	L	H	H	L	H	
0	0	1	1	H	H	H	H	L	L	H	
0	1	0	0	L	H	H	L	L	H	H	
0	1	0	1	H	L	H	H	L	H	H	
0	1	1	0	L	L	H	H	H	H	H	
0	1	1	1	H	H	H	L	L	L	L	
1	0	0	0	H	H	H	H	H	H	H	
1	0	0	1	H	H	L	L	L	H	H	
1	0	1	0	L	L	L	H	H	L	H	
1	0	1	1	L	L	H	H	L	L	H	
1	1	0	0	L	H	L	L	L	H	H	
1	1	0	1	H	L	L	H	L	H	H	
1	1	1	0	L	L	L	H	H	H	H	
1	1	1	1	L	L	L	L	L	L	L	blank

[a]LT is high, RBI is high, and RBO is high.

TABLE 18-5. 5082-7340 Functions

Input				Display		Input				Display
D	C	B	A			D	C	B	A	
0	0	0	0	0		1	0	0	0	8
0	0	0	1	1		1	0	0	1	9
0	0	1	0	2		1	0	1	0	A
0	0	1	1	3		1	0	1	1	B
0	1	0	0	4		1	1	0	0	C
0	1	0	1	5		1	1	0	1	D
0	1	1	0	6		1	1	1	0	E
0	1	1	1	7		1	1	1	1	F

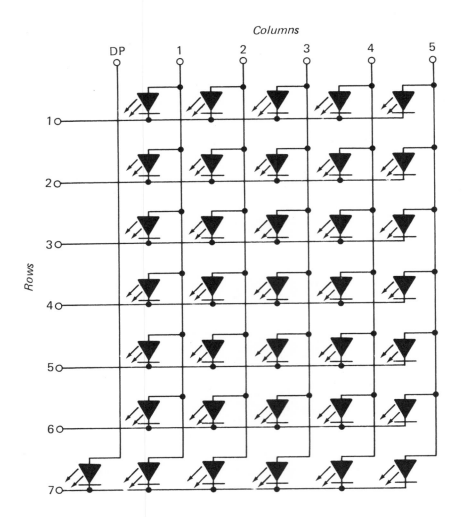

FIGURE 18–23.
5 × 7 Alphanumeric
Display

Dot-matrix displays are also available in multicharacter formats, with four or more characters in a single display. Such display systems can provide all 128 characters of the American Standard Code for Information Interchange, which includes upper- and lowercase letters, numbers, and punctuation marks.

Bar Graph Display

Many times alphanumeric characters are not the best way to convey information. For example, water levels and automobile speeds may be better displayed in the form of a bar graph. Displays such as the one in Figure 18–25 are commercially available to fill this need also. This display consists of ten separate LEDs, each with its anode and cathode available at pins. (The chamfer indicates pin 1.) As each segment lights in se-

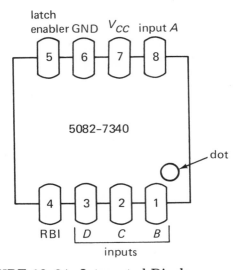

FIGURE 18–24. Integrated Display

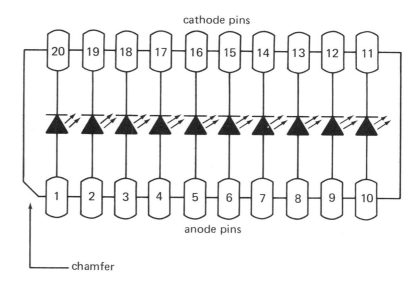

FIGURE 18-25. Bar
Graph Display

quence, the bar graph length increases. Should ten segments not be enough, additional display units can be stacked end to end to create any length.

☐ LIQUID-CRYSTAL DISPLAYS

Unlike LEDs, **liquid-crystal displays (LCD)** generate no light. Instead, the display controls transmission or reflection of light from an external source. The most common LCD relies on the *twisted-nematic field effect*. The display holds twisted liquid-crystal molecules in an orderly arrangement.

The display is always viewed between polarizers, as shown in Figure 18-26. When no electric field is applied, light passes through the LCD unchanged. The external light source behind the display can be seen, so the surface looks blank. (Alternatively, the display can be backed by a mirror. With no electric field, the external light coming from the front of the LCD is not affected. Again, the display appears to be blank.) Applying a field causes the liquid-crystal molecules to align parallel to it. The parallel matrix of molecules rotates the polarized light by 90°, so you see a dark area. By arranging the liquid crystals in segments, as in Figure 18-16, numbers or characters can be formed.

The LCD operates on alternating current. If a single-polarity power supply (+5 V, for ex-

ample) is used, a bridge circuit is required. The bridge is built into the LCD driver integrated circuit, so you need not be concerned about it.

A typical driver is shown in Figure 18-27. The 4511 is a BCD-to-seven-segment LCD decoder/driver. In addition to the 4511 drive for each segment, the LCD requires **backplane drive**, that is, current drive to the backplane of the LCD. The combined dc component of all drive

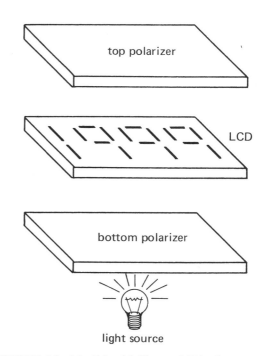

FIGURE 18-26. Liquid-Crystal Display

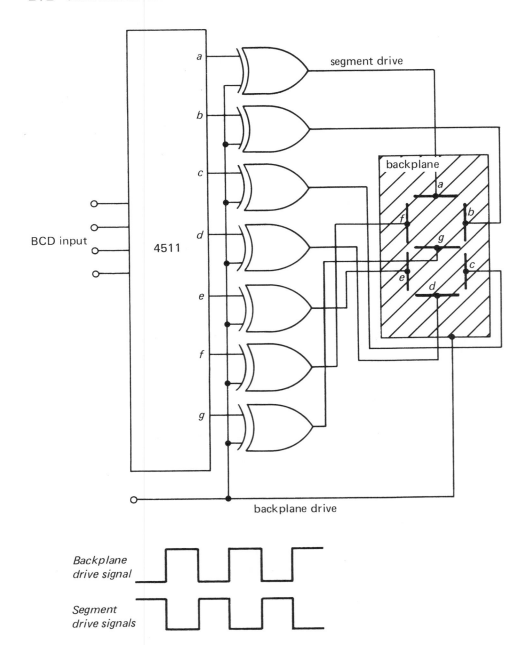

FIGURE 18-27. Relationship of Segment and Backplane Drive of an LCD

voltages must be limited to 50 mV. Otherwise, electrochemical changes in the liquid crystal will shorten the life of the display. The figure shows how exclusive OR gates produce segment drive voltages that are 180° out of phase with the backplane drive. This technique minimizes the average dc voltage.

Multiple-digit LCDs can also be used. The example shown in Figure 18-28 would be suitable for use in a digital multimeter. Here, CD4054 and CD4056 decoder/drivers are chosen. The dc voltage is minimized by the decoder/driver, so separate gating is not necessary to produce out-of-phase segment and backplane drive.

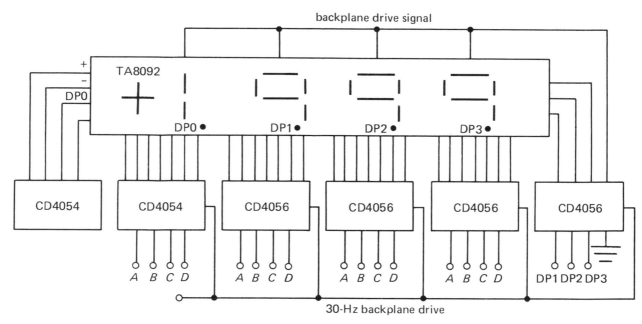

FIGURE 18-28. 3 1/2-Digit LCD

☐ **FIBER OPTICS**

A digital signal can be sent over long distances by simply turning lights on and off instead of by placing one of two voltage levels on a copper wire. The principle of fiber optics (FO) is that simple. Various forms of glass have traditionally been used as the fibers, but plastic fibers are appearing now also.

Regardless of the construction of the optical cable, the digital link requires a transmitter and receiver. You can purchase a complete fiber optic system with a transmitter and a receiver. But as a test of how well you have understood the material so far, we will investigate a simple system built from individual optoelectronic com-ponents. Figure 18-29 shows the transmitter and receiver.

The transmitter combines a data pulse with an enable signal. (The enable signal would usually be a clock pulse train.) A high output from the gate saturates the transistor, providing a ground to the LED. The light emitted is channeled into the fiber optic assembly. A low level from the gate cuts off the transistor, so current cannot flow through the LED. Thus no light is generated.

The receiver is a photodiode that conducts only when a flash of light arrives. The photodiode connects either a high or low voltage to the output terminal, depending on whether or not light shines on it.

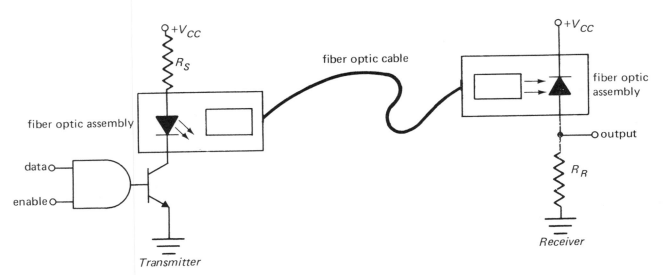

FIGURE 18-29. Fiber Optic Transmitter and Receiver

Chapter Summary

☐ The electromagnetic spectrum includes radio waves with long wavelengths at one extreme and cosmic rays with very short wavelengths at the other. Visible light is near the center of the spectrum, with wavelengths of 0.4 to 0.8 μm. Infrared radiation has a longer wavelength than light, and ultraviolet radiation has a shorter wavelength.

☐ Both transistors and diodes are used as photodetectors. A photo Darlington includes an amplifier in the same case as the detector.

☐ LEDs are used as indicators and transmitters. The spectrum of energy generated depends on the materials used to build the diode.

☐ Optoisolators combine an emitter and a detector in one IC. The device is used to protect low-voltage circuitry from excessive voltages or currents.

☐ Segmented LEDs provide alphanumeric displays, which include numbers, letters, and bar graph indicators. A decoder/driver IC is usually selected to provide inputs to the display. A dot-matrix display offers even more flexibility in the format of information. Segmented displays are available with common-anode or common-cathode configurations.

☐ Liquid-crystal displays generate no light. Instead, they darken portions of the display surface containing the liquid crystals to form characters.

☐ Fiber optic systems require a light transmitter, a sensor, and the light-conducting cables.

Problems

18-1. Select the load resistor for a LED that must have a brightness of 1500 ft·L. Use the curves in Figure 18-10.

18-2. Would a 1/4-W resistor be suitable for the application in Problem 18-1? Justify your answer.

18–3. A 1/8-W, 300-Ω resistor is used as the load for the LED circuit shown in Figure 18–11. How brightly does the LED glow? Use the bias curves for current and voltage from this chapter.

18–4. Determine the color of a GaAsP LED with a ratio of 45 percent phosphorus and 55 percent arsenic.

18–5. Both LEDs in the two-color display are to appear to have the same brightness. To compensate for the human eye's difference in sensitivity to red and green, you must insert another resistor in the green LED leg (to decrease its intensity). Find the value of both resistors if the red LED must have a brightness of 1500 ft·L and the green one a brightness of 1000 ft·L. Use the bias voltage and current curves given in this chapter.

18–6. Draw a diagram, similar to Figure 18–18a, showing the resistor connections necessary to display the digit 6 on a common-anode display.

18–7. Resistors are connected between the pins of a common-cathode display and the power supply as in Figure 18–18b. If pins a, c, d, f, and g are attached to resistors, what appears on the display?

18–8. Draw a circuit diagram for a counter circuit that displays numbers from 00_{10} to 99_{10} using a common-anode display. (Refer to Chapter 12.)

18–9. Repeat Problem 18–8 for a common-cathode display.

18–10. What connections to the power supply and ground would be required to illuminate the decimal point and all LEDs in column 3 of the dot-matrix display shown in Figure 18–23?

Chapter Nineteen

Power Supply and Control

Every electronic circuit that has been described in this book has required a source of power. Moreover, the power had to be provided at a specific voltage level that can vary only within a very limited range. As you will see, the power supplies for modern electronic equipment have benefited from integrated circuitry as much as logic or linear components have. In this chapter, we will examine how alternating current can be converted to direct current, how voltage levels can be maintained, and how modular power supplies function.

Chapter Objectives

Upon completion of this chapter, you should be able to:

☐ Explain how zener diodes act as voltage references.

☐ Distinguish between half- and full-wave rectifiers, and explain the advantages and disadvantages of each.

☐ Select capacitor filters to reduce ripple in a power supply.

☐ Discuss the operation and use of voltage regulators.

☐ Describe the operation of series, shunt, and switching regulators.

☐ Select modular power supplies tailored for a special application.

☐ VOLTAGE REFERENCES

In the discussion of diodes in earlier chapters, we noted that the device conducted in the forward-bias direction only. While most diodes operate in exactly this way, specialized construction can produce a unique feature, the zener diode.

Zener Diode

As Figure 19-1 shows, when a **zener diode** is reverse-biased sufficiently, a large current abruptly begins to flow. The point at which the current increases in this fashion is called the **knee**, and that voltage is called the **zener voltage**. Even before the zener voltage is reached, a small leakage current flows. This current is normally specified as the flow at a voltage equal to 80 percent of the zener voltage.

Another observation that we can make from the figure is that the slope of the curve, from the knee, can be interpreted as the reciprocal of an equivalent resistance. That is,

$$\frac{1}{R_Z} = \frac{I_T - I_Z}{V_T - V_Z} \qquad (19\text{-}1)$$

where

R_Z = equivalent resistance of the zener diode

I_T, V_T = current and voltage at operating point

I_Z, V_Z = current and voltage at the knee

☐ EXAMPLE 19-1

Suppose the zener voltage is -20 V and current at that point is -5 mA. If current at the operating point is -25 mA, with a voltage of -20.5 V, what is the equivalent diode resistance?

Solution

$$\frac{1}{R_Z} = \frac{(-25 + 5) \times 10^{-3}}{-20.5 + 20}$$
$$= 0.04$$
$$R_Z = 25 \ \Omega$$

All zener diodes must be protected against excessive current with a series load resistor. Otherwise, the large current will destroy the diode. Manufacturers will specify a maximum reverse current for the device.

The properties of the zener diode suit it for use as a *voltage reference*. As the reverse bias on the diode increases, so does the current flow. The equivalent resistance of the diode tends to restore the voltage to that at the knee.

☐ EXAMPLE 19-2

Examine the voltage difference between the knee and the operating point for the zener diode in Example 19-1.

Solution At the knee, the voltage at the anode is

$$V = V_Z - R_Z I_Z$$
$$= -20 - (25)(-5 \times 10^{-3})$$
$$= -19.88 \text{ V}$$

At the operating point, the voltage is

$$V = V_Z + R_Z(I_T - I_Z)$$
$$= -20 + 25(-25 \times 10^{-3} + 5 \times 10^{-3})$$
$$= -20.5 \text{ V}$$

Although current has increased by a factor of 5, the voltage increase is only 0.62 V.

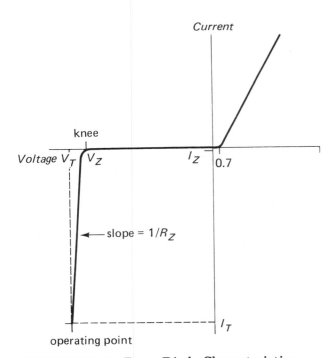

FIGURE 19-1. Zener Diode Characteristics

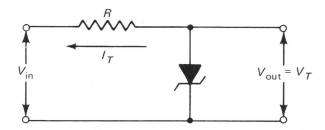

FIGURE 19-2. Voltage Reference

Voltage Reference Circuit

A practical circuit for using the zener diode as a voltage reference is shown in Figure 19-2 (do not confuse the zener diode symbol with the Schottky diode symbol). Perhaps you recall the reference voltage necessary for data converters. This example is typical of the circuit required.

One point remains to be clarified, and that is how to select the current-limiting resistor. We normally want the operating point to be about half the maximum-rated reverse current for the diode. From the figure, we can see that the output voltage is

$$V_{\text{out}} = V_{\text{in}} - RI_T \qquad \text{(19-2)}$$

where
R = value of current-limiting resistor
I_T = current at operating point

Also, the output voltage is the operating-point voltage, V_T. From Example 19-2, we know that V_T is approximately equal to the zener voltage. Using the approximation $V_T = V_Z$ in Equation 19-2, we have

$$V_Z = V_{\text{in}} - RI_T$$

Rearranging, we obtain

$$R = \frac{V_{\text{in}} - V_Z}{I_T} \qquad \text{(19-3)}$$

Now the load resistor can be found from the diode specifications and the known input voltage.

□ EXAMPLE 19-3

Select an appropriate current-limiting resistor for a 50-V zener diode with a maximum reverse current rating of 10 mA. The input voltage will be 70 V.

Solution Using an operating current of half the maximum rating and using Equation 19-3, we obtain

$$R = \frac{70 - 50}{5 \times 10^{-3}} = 4 \text{ k}\Omega$$

□ RECTIFIERS

Now we will turn our attention to the use of a diode in converting ac to dc. Such converters are called **rectifiers**. In this section we will examine three types: half-wave, full-wave, and bridge rectifiers.

Half-Wave Rectifier

Consider the circuit in Figure 19-3. An alternating current source supplies the load through a diode. Because the diode only conducts when forward-biased, all the negative portions of the input

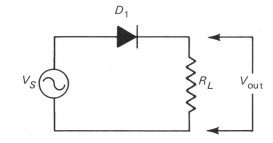

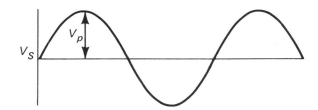

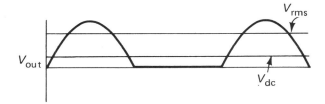

FIGURE 19-3. Half-Wave Rectifier

signal are removed. The load only receives the current flowing in the forward, or positive, direction. Hence this circuit is a **half-wave rectifier**.

Because a full sine wave is not delivered to the load, the expected reading will not be obtained when one is measuring the voltage on a meter. Two types of meters are available: direct current (dc) and **root mean square (rms)**. From the input signal, you can predict the reading on either type of meter, as well as convert from one voltage to the other.

$$V_{rms} = \frac{V_p}{\sqrt{2}} = 0.707 V_p \qquad (19\text{-}4)$$

$$V_{dc} = \frac{V_p}{\pi} = 0.318 V_p \qquad (19\text{-}5)$$

$$V_{dc} = \frac{\sqrt{2} \, V_{rms}}{\pi} = 0.45 V_{rms} \qquad (19\text{-}6)$$

where

V_p = peak voltage of input signal
V_{dc} = dc voltmeter reading
V_{rms} = rms voltmeter reading

☐ EXAMPLE 19-4

The peak input voltage is 25 V. What would rms and dc voltmeters read on the output of the half-wave rectifier?

Solution

$$V_{rms} = (0.707)(25) = 17.7 \text{ V}$$
$$V_{dc} = (0.318)(25) = 80 \text{ V}$$

As a check, we apply Equation 19-6 to convert the rms reading to dc.

$$8.0 = (0.45)(17.7)$$
$$8.0 = 8.0$$

The quality of a rectifier output voltage is often expressed in terms of the amount of **ripple**, or unevenness, on the output. By definition, the percent ripple is

$$R_p = \frac{V_R}{V_{dc}} \qquad (19\text{-}7)$$

where

V_R = rms ripple voltage
V_{dc} = dc output voltage

(The rms ripple voltage for a half-wave rectifier with a sine wave input is 0.386 V_p.)

☐ EXAMPLE 19-5

Find the percent ripple for a half-wave rectifier.

Solution From Equation 19-7, we have

$$R_p = \frac{0.386 V_p}{0.318 V_p} = 121\%$$

The percent ripple, in this case, is independent of the input voltage. We can conclude that although the half-wave rectifier is simple and inexpensive, its ripple is high.

In most cases, a transformer is used with the rectifier in place of a voltage source. As you have learned in your ac circuit course, a transformer has an output voltage of

$$V_{sec} = \left(\frac{N_s}{N_p}\right)(V_{pri}) \qquad (19\text{-}8)$$

where

V_{sec} = secondary voltage
V_{pri} = primary voltage
N_p = number of turns on primary
N_s = number of turns on secondary

Where there are more secondary than primary turns, we have a **step-down transformer**.

☐ EXAMPLE 19-6

What is the secondary voltage of a transformer with 1000 secondary and 10,000 primary turns? The input voltage is 120 V.

Solution

$$V_{sec} = \left(\frac{10^3}{10^4}\right)(120) = 12 \text{ V}$$

☐ EXAMPLE 19-7

A half-wave rectifier with an input transformer is shown in Figure 19-4. The operation of this circuit is identical to that of Figure 19-3, except that the voltage is stepped down as well as rectified. Find the dc and rms output voltages.

Solution

$$V_{rms} = 0.707(12) = 8.5 \text{ V}$$
$$V_{dc} = 0.318(12) = 3.8 \text{ V}$$

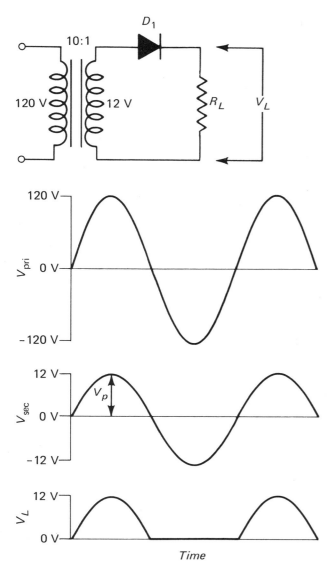

FIGURE 19-4. Half-Wave Rectifier with Transformer Input

Full-Wave Rectifier

If we connect a center-tapped transformer to two diodes, we have constructed a **full-wave rectifier**. The circuit appears in Figure 19-5. As the figure indicates, D_1 conducts on the positive half cycle. The other diode conducts the remainder of the time. The load receives current on both halves of the alternating current waveform.

In a full-wave rectifier, the voltages of interest are as follows:

$$V_{dc} = \left(\frac{2}{\pi}\right)(V_p) = 0.636V_p \qquad \textbf{(19-9)}$$

$$V_{rms} = \frac{V_p}{\sqrt{2}} = 0.707V_p \qquad \textbf{(19-10)}$$

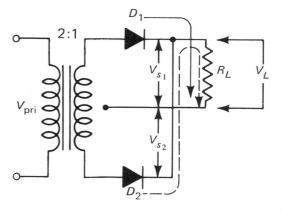

Key

—— current flow on positive half cycle

– – – current flow on negative half cycle

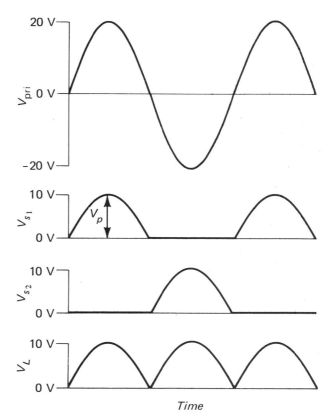

FIGURE 19-5. Full-Wave Rectifier

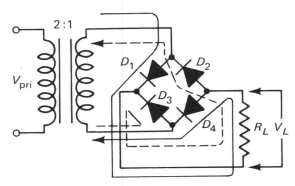

Key

—— current flow on positive half cycle

‐ ‐ ‐ current flow on negative half cycle

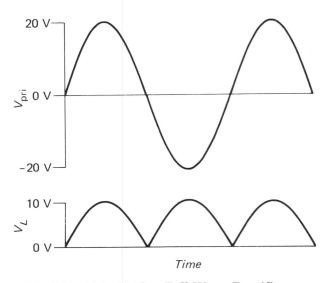

Time

FIGURE 19–6. Bridge Full-Wave Rectifier

The rms ripple voltage is

$$V_R = 0.307 V_p$$

So the percent ripple for a full-wave rectifier is

$$R_p = \frac{0.307 V_p}{0.636 V_p} = 48\%$$

which is less than half that of the half-wave rectifier.

Bridge Rectifier

Often, the input to a rectifier must come from a two-lead source; that is, a center-tapped transformer is not available. In such cases, the bridge rectifier of Figure 19–6 can be used.

As the current flow arrows indicate, D_1 and D_4 conduct on the positive part of the cycle. Diodes D_2 and D_3 conduct during the negative portion. The dc and rms voltages of the bridge rectifier are the same as those of the full-wave rectifier. Furthermore, the percent ripple is the same for both rectifiers as well.

Table 19–1 compares the three rectifier designs. The simplest approach is the half-wave rectifier with a high percent ripple. The full-wave and bridge rectifiers offer improved performance at the cost of higher complexity.

☐ POWER SUPPLY FILTERS

The output from any of the rectifiers discussed above is not acceptable for use in electronic circuits. High-quality power supplies must limit the ripple to less than 1 percent. One means of "smoothing out" the peaks in the output is to use a low-pass filter, as shown in Figure 19–7. The filter passes the dc while blocking the ripple frequencies.

TABLE 19–1. Rectifier Comparison

	Type		
Parameter	Half-Wave	Full-Wave	Bridge
Number of diodes	1	2	4
dc voltage	$0.318 V_p$	$0.636 V_p$	$0.636 V_p$
rms voltage	$0.707 V_p$	$0.707 V_p$	$0.707 V_p$
Ripple percent	121	48	48

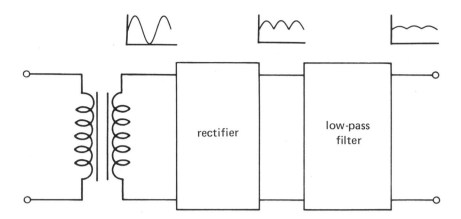

FIGURE 19-7.
Low-Pass Filter to
Smooth the Output
Voltage

The design of such filters is well understood, so many low-pass designs exist. Figure 19–8 illustrates five filters of varying complexity. As the number of circuit elements increases, the ripple can be limited to any desired level. However, reducing the ripple in this manner can require large (and expensive) capacitors or inductors (called *chokes*). The output voltage is also reduced by the voltage dropped in the filter.

Table 19–2 lists the output voltage and ripple percent for each filter shown in Figure 19–8 for 60-Hz operation. These values can be calculated from the known circuit elements. The table can also be used to design a filter with specified performance. In the table,

$$I_{\text{dc}} = \frac{V_{\text{dc}}}{R_L}$$

where
  V_{dc} = dc voltage
  R_L = load resistance

For all equations given, capacitance is measured in microfarads and inductance in henrys.

☐ **EXAMPLE 19–8**

If the capacitor of the low-pass filter of Figure 19–8c is 1 mF and the choke is 1 mH, what is the output voltage and ripple of a full-wave rectifier? The peak voltage is 10 V.

Solution Using Table 19–2, we obtain

$$V_{\text{out}} = (0.63)(10) = 6.3 \text{ V}$$
$$R_p = \frac{0.83}{(1000)(0.001)}$$

Note the use of capacitance in microfarads and inductance in henrys in this equation. So

$$R_p = 0.83 \text{ percent}$$

TABLE 19-2. Low-Pass Filter Performance

| Filter | Half-Wave Rectifier | | Full-Wave Rectifier | |
	V_{out} (V)	Ripple (%)	V_{out} (V)	Ripple (%)
a	$V_p - \left(\dfrac{8350}{C}\right) I_{\text{dc}}$	$\dfrac{4760}{CR_L}$	$V_p - \left(\dfrac{4170}{C}\right) I_{\text{dc}}$	$\dfrac{2380}{CR_L}$
b	NA	NA	$0.63 V_p$	$\dfrac{RL}{1600L}$
c	NA	NA	$0.63 V_p$	$\dfrac{0.83}{CL}$
d	$V_p - \left(\dfrac{8350}{C}\right) I_{\text{dc}}$	$\dfrac{2.6 \times 10^4}{C^2 L R_L}$	$V_p - \left(\dfrac{4170}{C}\right) I_{\text{dc}}$	$\dfrac{3300}{C^2 L R_L}$
e	$V_p - \left(\dfrac{8350}{C} + R\right) I_{\text{dc}}$	$\dfrac{2.5 \times 10^6}{C^2 R R_L}$	$V_p - \left(\dfrac{4170}{C} + R\right) I_{\text{dc}}$	$\dfrac{10^7}{C^2 R R_L}$

Note: NA indicates not applicable.

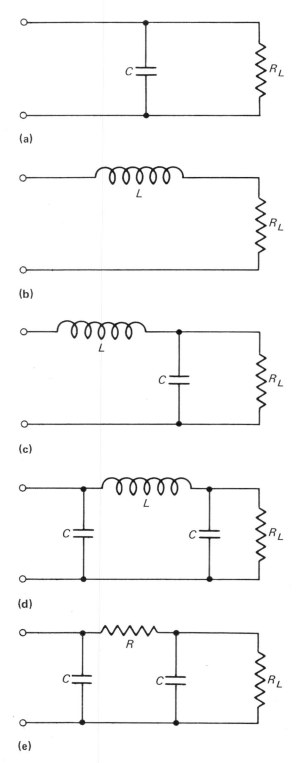

FIGURE 19-8. Low-Pass Filter Designs

□ VOLTAGE REGULATORS

The purpose of a **voltage regulator** is to convert varying ac or dc voltage to a stable dc voltage. The regulator is used in a power supply following the low-pass filter. The output voltage of the regulator remains constant under changing load conditions. The widespread application of these components is a consequence of their ease of use. No additional external components are needed. Regulators are quite reliable, partly because of the internal thermal protection (which prevents overheating) and built-in short-circuit protection.

A block diagram for a regulator is shown in Figure 19-9. The voltage reference must be quite stable, of course. The output voltage will always be equal to the reference voltage or a multiple of it. The sampling element monitors the output voltage and feeds it back to the comparator. (If the output is a multiple of the reference voltage, the sampling element also translates the output to approximately that of the reference level by voltage dividing.) The sampling element is the most critical component, because it is the largest source of error, typically ± 5 percent. The comparator produces an error signal, which causes the control circuitry to either increase or reduce the output voltage. All these elements are packaged within one integrated circuit.

Regulators are classified by the type of control element used. Figure 19-10 shows a **series regulator.** The transistor connected in series with the input controls the output voltage by varying the current. The error signal on the base can increase or decrease the current, thus controlling the voltage dropped across the load. The series regulator is inexpensive, but it is not satisfactory in high-current circuits. Large currents produce unacceptable power losses in the transistor.

The **shunt regulator** of Figure 19-11 places the transistor in parallel with the sampling voltage divider formed by R_1 and R_2. As the current of the transistor decreases, more current is delivered to the output. This effect is just the opposite of the effect of the series regulator, so the inverting input to the comparator must be reversed. (The sampling element voltage for the series regulator is inverted as compared to the reference voltage in the shunt regulator.) The shunt regulator is less efficient than the series regulator, but the shunt is also less sensitive to transient voltages.

In the **switching regulator** of Figure 19-12,

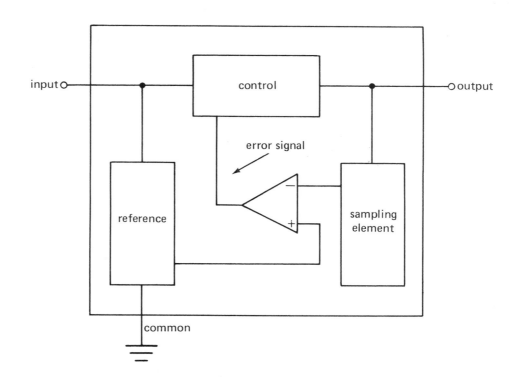

FIGURE 19–9.
Voltage Regulator
Components

the output voltage depends on the transistor duty cycle:

$$V_{\text{out}} = V_{\text{in}} \left(\frac{t_{\text{on}}}{t_{\text{on}} + t_{\text{off}}} \right) \qquad \textbf{(19–11)}$$

where

t_{on} = period the transistor is switched on
t_{off} = period the transistor is switched off

If the duty cycle is changed, the output voltage can be controlled. The *RC* filter averages the voltage to produce a constant level with little ripple. The power consumed in the transistor of a switching regulator is low. Either the transistor is saturated and the voltage drop is a minimum, or the transistor is cut off and no current flows. Therefore, the switching regulator is inherently a low-power component. The switching regulator is the best choice for high-load currents and for circuits in which the input voltage is considerably different from the desired output voltage.

When using a voltage regulator, circuit layout is quite important. Stray capacitance and line inductance must be minimized, so short leads are necessary. For that reason, the regulator should

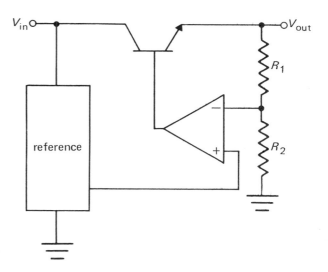

FIGURE 19–10. Series Voltage Regulator

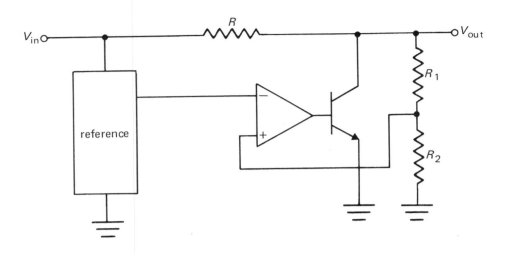

FIGURE 19-11.
Shunt Voltage
Regulator

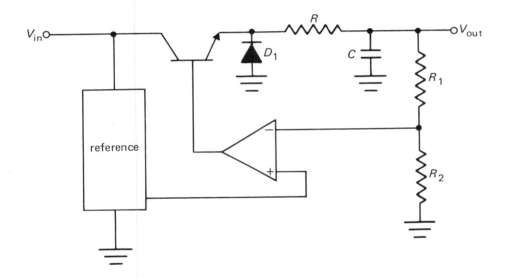

FIGURE 19-12.
Switching Voltage
Regulator

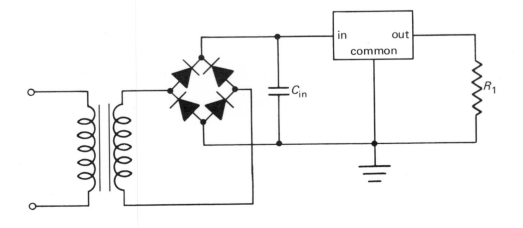

FIGURE 19-13.
Regulated Power
Supply

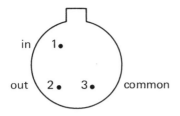

FIGURE 19–14. Bottom View of the LM109 Voltage Regulator

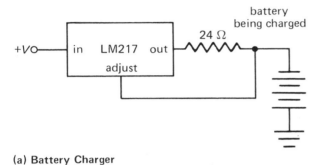

(a) Battery Charger

heat sink tab

(b) LM217 Package

FIGURE 19–15. Application of an Adjustable Voltage Regulator

be located near the load. A complete regulated power supply is shown in Figure 19–13. The capacitor should be mounted close to the regulator for best performance.

The power supply of Figure 19–13 is capable of driving TTL circuits. For example, the LM109 regulator in Figure 19–14 could be used in this circuit. This regulator is designed to produce a steady 5-V output.

A second regulated supply is shown in Figure 19–15a. Here the LM217 regulator is connected as a battery charger. The LM217 is an adjustable regulator that can run with an input of 1.2–37 V; it has a maximum current capacity of 1.5 A. The battery charger shown will provide a constant source of 50-mA current. Figure 19–15b shows the LM217 package configuration.

☐ MODULAR POWER SUPPLIES

When manufacturers investigate the economic factors for power supplies, they often select an off-the-shelf unit rather than build their own. Such **modular power supplies** offer reliable operation with internal thermal and short-circuit protection.

The most frequently used model is the **linear supply**, characterized by the use of a series voltage regulator. The linear supply generates more heat and is larger than other types.

Ferroresonant supplies feature a resonant secondary circuit on the transformer. They are economical because they have a low parts count, but they are quite sensitive to line frequency changes. Their regulation and ripple are not as good as in other types of supplies, either.

The **switching supply**, named for the regulator used, is a medium-cost unit. This supply is, unfortunately, vulnerable to heat damage and can produce large-voltage spikes. It also has a tendency to permit 60-Hz noise to pass through.

A fourth version of modular power supply is the **hybrid**. A hybrid supply is a switching supply with one or more series-regulated outputs.

A summary of the type of performance that can be expected from all the modular supplies is listed in Table 19–3.

TABLE 19–3. Comparison of Modular Power Supplies

Type	Cost	Reliability	Heat Produced	Weight	Size	Typical Regulation (%)
Ferroresonant	Low	High	Low	Heavy	Large	±15
Linear	Medium to high	Medium	High	Heavy	Large	±0.1
Hybrid	Medium	Medium	Medium	Medium	Large	±3
Switching	Medium	Medium	Low	Light	Small	±3

Chapter Summary

☐ Zener diodes provide a very stable voltage reference when reverse-biased beyond their zener voltage point. The slope of the voltage from the knee to the operating point can be represented as an equivalent resistance. A current-limiting resistor must be used in conjunction with the diode to protect it against excessive current flow.

☐ Rectifiers convert alternating current to direct current. The most common rectifiers are half-wave, full-wave, and bridge. The output voltage of a rectifier is expressed in either direct current or root mean square form.

☐ The half-wave rectifier is simple and inexpensive to construct, but it produces a high ripple output.

☐ Full-wave rectifiers require a center-tapped transformer. Their output voltage has less than half the ripple of a half-wave rectifier.

☐ A bridge rectifier eliminates the requirement for a center-tapped transformer, but four diodes are required in its construction. In other ways, the bridge rectifier is quite similar to the full-wave rectifier.

☐ Ripple can be reduced by using a low-pass filter on the power supply output. Often, this filter is just a capacitor of the proper size.

☐ Voltage regulators are simple, low-cost components that improve power supply stability. The regulator may have a series, shunt, or switching control element.

☐ Purchasing a modular power supply is sometimes more economical than developing a new design. Linear, ferroresonant, switching, and hybrid supplies may be purchased from commercial manufacturers.

Problems

19–1. A zener diode has a voltage rating of −30 V. Current at the knee is −7 mA. If the operating point is −31 V and −35 mA, what is the equivalent resistance of the diode?

19–2. Determine how much the voltage changes between the knee and the operating point for a −25-V zener diode with the following parameters:

equivalent resistance: 30 Ω

zener current: −3 mA

operating point current: −30 mA

19–3. Find the required current-limiting resistance for a −20-V zener diode with a reverse-current rating of 1 A. The input voltage is −25 V.

19–4. The peak input voltage to a half-wave rectifier is 40 V. What are the dc and rms output voltages?

19-5. Repeat Problem 19–4 for a full-wave rectifier.

19-6. Compare the percent ripple of a half-wave rectifier with that of a bridge rectifier if the rectifiers are connected to the secondary of a transformer. The peak input voltage to the 1:10 step-down transformer is 100 V. If the primary of the transformer has 500 turns, how many turns are on the secondary? What is the secondary voltage?

19-7. Find the output voltage of a half-wave rectifier using the low-pass filter shown in Figure 19–8d. The circuit components and voltages are

$$V_p = 20 \text{ V} \qquad R_L = 100 \text{ }\Omega$$
$$C = 1 \text{ mF} \qquad L = 0.5 \text{ mH}$$

What is the ripple percent?

19-8. What is the output voltage and ripple for the full-wave rectifier of Figure 19–8a? R_L is 250 Ω, V_p is 30 V, and C is 0.5 mF.

19-9. Find the output of a switching regulator with an "on" time of 250 μs and an "off" time of 400 μs. The input voltage is 15 V.

19-10. A -10-V zener diode has an equivalent resistance of 50 Ω. If current at the knee is -6 mA and if the operating point voltage is -18 V, what is the operating current?

Chapter Twenty

Construction and Troubleshooting

Working with microelectronics in the lab and on the job means that you must develop new skills and apply the correct handling techniques. While these components are reliable and rugged, improper maintenance can damage them. In this chapter, we will discuss some of the methods currently used by the electronics industry to test prototype circuits, build circuit boards, and troubleshoot faulty equipment.

An important tool in troubleshooting is the data book, which describes the integrated circuits. A detailed example of reading a data sheet for an IC is provided in the following discussion. The use of test equipment such as logic probes, pulsers, digital multimeters, and breadboards is discussed next. Then an examination of some unique problems associated with fault localization in analog circuits is provided.

Chapter Objectives

Upon completion of this chapter, you should be able to:

- ☐ Interpret a manufacturer's data sheet.
- ☐ Show how logic probes and pulsers can be used in circuit testing and troubleshooting.
- ☐ Describe the use of current tracers and digital multimeters.
- ☐ Apply the techniques of breadboarding for prototype circuits.
- ☐ Explain effective ways for connecting liquid-crystal displays into circuits.
- ☐ Discuss step-by-step analog circuit troubleshooting.

☐ DATA SHEETS

Every circuit component that we have studied is described by the manufacturer on a data sheet. Figure 20-1 is the first page of the data sheet for the 74LS47 LED decoder/driver that we studied in Chapter 18. Suppose we want to use the low-powered Schottky version of this IC in our circuit. We must identify pin assignments, find out what function the device performs, and verify voltage compatibility as well.

Starting with the top line of Figure 20-1, we note that this sheet applies not only to the 74LS47 but to many other chips as well. Thus care must be taken to read only those portions of the data sheet that are applicable to the IC of interest. Below the identification is a brief description of the functions that the 74LS47 performs.

The next section of the data sheet is a summary of the electrical characteristics. For the SN74LS47 we read that its active level is low (meaning that the decoder/driver should be used with common-anode displays). The outputs are open-collector. The maximum current that the IC can safely sink is 24 mA, and the maximum voltage is 15 V. The typical power dissipation is not as useful a parameter as the maximum, but this information does provide an approximation.

Finally, the packing configurations (such as plastic and ceramic DIP) are identified. Below that table is the pin assignment diagram.

Next the data sheet would provide a function table. You have already examined the 74LS47 functions (Table 18-3). Another way of presenting the functions is in the form of a logic diagram, as shown in Figure 20-2. All these gates are included in the DIP. The numerals in parentheses are pin numbers. The internal connections of input and output pins, as shown in Figure 20-3, are also provided. Of interest are the Schottky-clamped input terminals and the Schottky transistors used on the outputs for faster switching.

Figure 20-4 lists the complete electrical specifications for this circuit. Maximum, minimum, and nominal values are tabulated. The operating temperature range of 0° to 70°C is also specified. As pointed out in an earlier chapter, the minimum or maximum levels are guaranteed performance characteristics. These values are much more useful than typical or nominal levels. Should you wish to test incoming ICs to ensure that they meet switching specifications, the data sheet lists the load resistor and capacitor in the last block.

Note that the temperature and power supply voltage must be at 25°C and 5 V, respectively, before such testing is accomplished.

☐ LOGIC TEST EQUIPMENT

A **logic probe** is a low-cost, versatile item of test equipment that is used in diagnosing problems in all logic families. As Figure 20-5 shows, there is a switch on the probe for either TTL or CMOS timing. Power is obtained by clipping the probe leads to the power supply.

The probe can do much more than just detect high or low levels. It also indicates open circuits and shows approximate pulse frequency. Furthermore, it supplies an indication of whether the pulses are going from low to high levels, or vice versa.

Another test equipment item often used in conjunction with a probe is the **logic pulser**, shown in Figure 20-6. The pulser can also be used with either TTL or CMOS logic. As the name implies, the pulser injects a signal at one of the pins of an IC. Figure 20-7 illustrates how the probe and pulser can be used for "stimulus-response" testing. The inverter complements the input pulse, which is detected by the probe. This technique can be used to verify circuit truth tables.

A **logic clip** is quite similar to the probe. This equipment clamps simultaneously to all inputs and outputs of a 14- or 16-pin DIP. The clip has a LED indicator for each pin. If the LED is on, that pin is at a high level. Otherwise, the pin is low. Logic clips speed up the tracing of logic levels, because the states of all pins are visible simultaneously. Logic clips can be used on both TTL and CMOS integrated circuits.

A new handheld circuit tester is the **current tracer**. It detects problems that cannot be found with a probe. The current tracer is not voltage-sensitive; instead, it senses the magnetic field generated by signals from the circuit or a logic pulser. The tracer is moved along printed circuit board paths, and a light indicates presence or absence of current. Furthermore, the light intensity gives the relative current level. The tracer shows individual pulses that occur as well as pulse trains. The tracer works with any logic family within the range of 1 mA to 1 A. Frequencies up to 10 MHz are acceptable.

TYPES SN5446A, '47A, '48, '49, SN54L46, 'L47, SN54LS47, 'LS48, 'LS49, SN7446A, '47A, '48, SN74L46, 'L47, SN74LS47, 'LS48, 'LS49
BCD-TO-SEVEN-SEGMENT DECODERS/DRIVERS

'46A, '47A, 'L46, 'L47, 'LS47 feature	'48, 'LS48 feature	'49, 'LS49 feature
• Open-Collector Outputs Drive Indicators Directly	• Internal Pull-Ups Eliminate Need for External Resistors	• Open-Collector Outputs
• Lamp-Test Provision	• Lamp-Test Provision	• Blanking Input
• Leading/Trailing Zero Suppression	• Leading/Trailing Zero Suppression	

- All Circuit Types Feature Lamp Intensity Modulation Capability

| TYPE | DRIVER OUTPUTS | | | | TYPICAL POWER DISSIPATION | PACKAGES |
	ACTIVE LEVEL	OUTPUT CONFIGURATION	SINK CURRENT	MAX VOLTAGE		
SN5446A	low	open-collector	40 mA	30 V	320 mW	J, W
SN5447A	low	open-collector	40 mA	15 V	320 mW	J, W
SN5448	high	2-kΩ pull-up	6.4 mA	5.5 V	265 mW	J, W
SN5449	high	open-collector	10 mA	5.5 V	165 mW	W
SN54L46	low	open-collector	20 mA	30 V	160 mW	J
SN54L47	low	open-collector	20 mA	15 V	160 mW	J
SN54LS47	low	open-collector	12 mA	15 V	35 mW	J, W
SN54LS48	high	2-kΩ pull-up	2 mA	5.5 V	125 mW	J, W
SN54LS49	high	open-collector	4 mA	5.5 V	40 mW	J, W
SN7446A	low	open-collector	40 mA	30 V	320 mW	J, N
SN7447A	low	open-collector	40 mA	15 V	320 mW	J, N
SN7448	high	2-kΩ pull-up	6.4 mA	5.5 V	265 mW	J, N
SN74L46	low	open-collector	20 mA	30 V	160 mW	J, N
SN74L47	low	open-collector	20 mA	15 V	160 mW	J, N
SN74LS47	low	open-collector	24 mA	15 V	35 mW	J, N
SN74LS48	high	2-kΩ pull-up	6 mA	5.5 V	125 mW	J, N
SN74LS49	high	open-collector	8 mA	5.5 V	40 mW	J, N

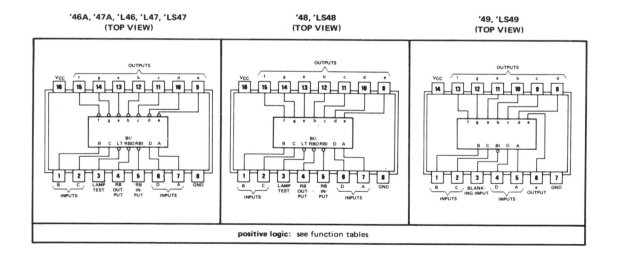

FIGURE 20–1. Data Sheet Showing Pin Assignments (Courtesy Texas Instruments, Inc.)

TYPES SN5446A, '47A, '48, '49, SN54L46, 'L47, SN54LS47, 'LS48, 'LS49, SN7446A, '47A, '48, SN74L46, 'L47, SN74LS47, 'LS48, 'LS49
BCD-TO-SEVEN-SEGMENT DECODERS/DRIVERS

functional block diagrams

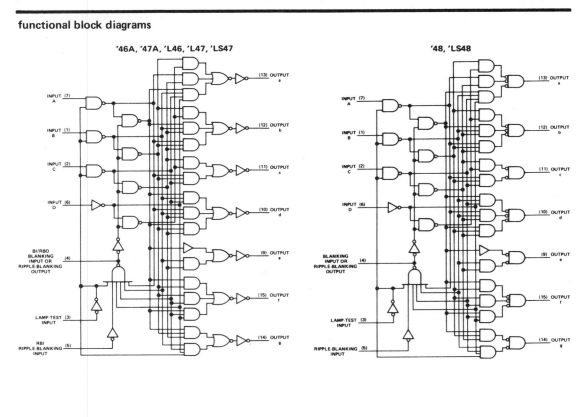

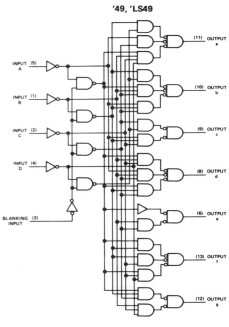

FIGURE 20–2. Logic Diagram Data Sheet (Courtesy Texas Instruments, Inc.)

TYPES .SN54LS47, 'LS48, 'LS49, SN74LS47, 'LS48, 'LS49
BCD-TO-SEVEN-SEGMENT DECODERS/DRIVERS

schematics of inputs and outputs

'LS47, 'LS48, 'LS49

EQUIVALENT OF EACH INPUT
EXCEPT BI/RBO

LT and RBI ('LS47, 'LS48): $R_{eq} = 20\ k\Omega$ NOM
BI ('LS49): $R_{eq} = 20\ k\Omega$ NOM
A, B, C, and D: $R_{eq} = 25\ k\Omega$ NOM

'LS47, 'LS48, 'LS49

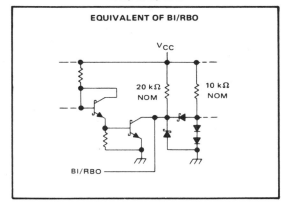

EQUIVALENT OF BI/RBO

'LS47

TYPICAL OF OUTPUTS
a THRU g

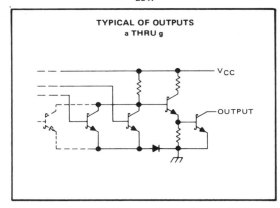

'LS48

TYPICAL OF OUTPUTS
a THRU g

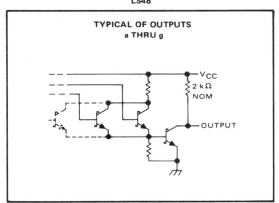

'LS49

TYPICAL OF OUTPUTS
a THRU g

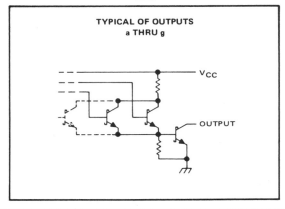

FIGURE 20–3. Input and Output Circuit Data Sheet (Courtesy Texas Instruments, Inc.)

TYPES SN54LS47, SN74LS47
BCD-TO-SEVEN-SEGMENT DECODERS/DRIVERS

absolute maximum ratings over operating free-air temperature range (unless otherwise noted)

Supply voltage, V_{CC} (see Note 1)	7 V
Input voltage	7 V
Peak output current ($t_W \leqslant$ 1 ms, duty cycle $\leqslant$ 10%)	200 mA
Current forced into any output in the off state	1 mA
Operating free-air temperature range: SN54LS47	-55°C to 125°C
SN74LS47	0°C to 70°C
Storage temperature range	-65°C to 150°C

NOTE 1: Voltage values are with respect to network ground terminal.

recommended operating conditions

		SN54LS47			SN74LS47			UNIT
		MIN	NOM	MAX	MIN	NOM	MAX	
Supply voltage, V_{CC}		4.5	5	5.5	4.75	5	5.25	V
Off-state output voltage, $V_{O(off)}$	a thru g			15			15	V
On-state output current, $I_{O(on)}$	a thru g			12			24	mA
High-level output current, I_{OH}	BI/RBO			-50			-50	μA
Low-level output current, I_{OL}	BI/RBO			1.6			3.2	mA
Operating free-air temperature, T_A		-55		125	0		70	$^\circ$C

electrical characteristics over recommended operating free-air temperature range (unless otherwise noted)

PARAMETER		TEST CONDITIONS†		SN54LS47			SN74LS47			UNIT
				MIN	TYP‡	MAX	MIN	TYP‡	MAX	
V_{IH}	High-level input voltage			2			2			V
V_{IL}	Low-level input voltage					0.7			0.8	V
V_{IK}	Input clamp voltage	V_{CC} = MIN,	$I_I = -18$ mA			-1.5			-1.5	V
V_{OH}	High-level output voltage BI/RBO	V_{CC} = MIN, V_{IH} = 2 V,	$V_{IL} = V_{IL}$ max, $I_{OH} = -50\,\mu$A	2.4	4.2		2.4	4.2		V
V_{OL}	Low-level output voltage BI/RBO	V_{CC} = MIN, V_{IH} = 2 V, $V_{IL} = V_{IL}$ max	I_{OL} = 1.6 mA		0.25	0.4		0.25	0.4	V
			I_{OL} = 3.2 mA					0.35	0.5	
$I_{O(off)}$	Off-state output current a thru g	V_{CC} = MAX, V_{IH} = 2 V, $V_{IL} = V_{IL}$ max, $V_{O(off)}$ = 15 V				250			250	μA
$V_{O(on)}$	On-state output voltage a thru g	V_{CC} = MAX, V_{IH} = 2 V, $V_{IL} = V_{IL}$ max	$I_{O(on)}$ = 12 mA		0.25	0.4		0.25	0.4	V
			$I_{O(on)}$ = 24 mA					0.35	0.5	
I_I	Input current at maximum input voltage	V_{CC} = MAX,	V_I = 7 V			0.1			0.1	mA
I_{IH}	High-level input current	V_{CC} = MAX,	V_I = 2.7 V			20			20	μA
I_{IL}	Low-level input current	Any input except BI/RBO V_{CC} = MAX, V_I = 0.4 V				-0.4			-0.4	mA
		BI/RBO				-1.2			-1.2	
I_{OS}	Short-circuit output current BI/RBO	V_{CC} = MAX		-0.3		-2	-0.3		-2	mA
I_{CC}	Supply current	V_{CC} = MAX,	See Note 2		7	13		7	13	mA

†For conditions shown as MIN or MAX, use the appropriate value specified under recommended operating conditions.
‡All typical values are at V_{CC} = 5 V, T_A = 25°C.
NOTE 2: I_{CC} is measured with all outputs open and all inputs at 4.5 V.

switching characteristics, V_{CC} = 5 V, T_A = 25°C

PARAMETER		TEST CONDITIONS	MIN	TYP	MAX	UNIT
t_{off}	Turn-off time from A input	C_L = 15 pF, R_L = 665 Ω, See Note 4			100	ns
t_{on}	Turn-on time from A input				100	
t_{off}	Turn-off time from RBI input				100	ns
t_{on}	Turn-on time from RBI input				100	

NOTE 4: t_{off} corresponds to t_{PLH} and t_{on} corresponds to t_{PHL}.

FIGURE 20–4. Electrical Summary Data Sheet (Courtesy Texas Instruments, Inc.)

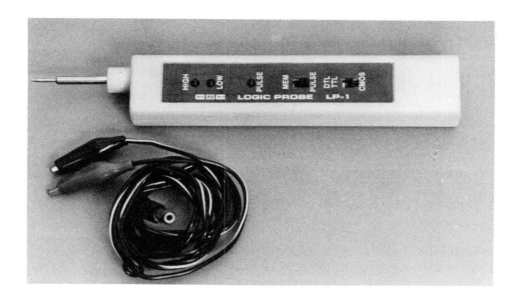

FIGURE 20-5.
Logic Probe

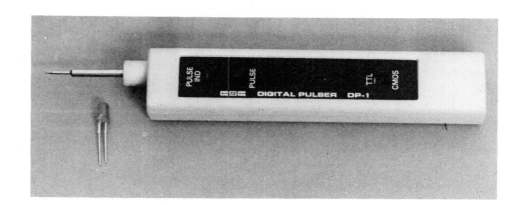

FIGURE 20-6.
Logic Pulser

Digital multimeters (DMM) are replacing analog meters because they are faster, easier to use, and more accurate. Accuracy is specified as a percent of the full-scale plus the offset error. (Compare this specification to that of a data converter.) The resolution depends on the number of digits in the display, as listed in Table 20-1.

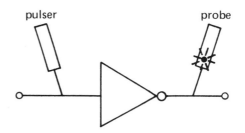

FIGURE 20-7. Verifying a Truth Table

TABLE 20-1. DMM Examples

Number of Digits	Minimum	Maximum	Resolution (%)
3 1/2	0000	1999	±0.05
4 1/2	00000	19999	±0.005

The DMM can measure small incremental changes as well as the total output. It is ideally suited to monitoring small adjustments in power levels.

Another piece of test equipment frequently used by technicians is the oscilloscope, which you have probably encountered in earlier courses.

☐ BREADBOARDING

When a new circuit or a major modification is being tested, you should not use printed circuit or wire-wrapped construction. Instead, you should use a **breadboard**, like the one in Figure 20-8. The breadboard allows components to be readily inserted or removed. In addition, the possibility of heat damage from a soldering iron is eliminated, so the components can be reused.

The contacts in the board accept solid wire ranging from #22 to #30. The wire is prepared for insertion by removing 3/8 in. (1 cm) of insulation from both ends. (Be sure not to nick the wires.) Then the wire is simply pressed into the contact hole.

Almost any component can be mounted on the board. For example, resistors in sizes from 1/8 W to 1/2 W, diodes, transistors, and of course integrated circuit DIPs also fit into the holes. (Note the use of a DIP switch in Figure 20-8.

Four individual switches are available in this particular unit.)

Careful layout and connection are needed for breadboard circuits. One convention that can save a lot of time is to configure the breadboard just like the schematic. Place the power line at the top and the ground at the bottom. (Color-coded wires will help in tracing connections as the circuit grows in complexity.) Orient all ICs with pin 1 to the left. Make 90° bends in the wires, and keep all leads short. (Long leads are a source of inductance and stray capacitance.)

The use of decoupling capacitors is especially important with TTL devices. The guidelines for determining the number of capacitors required are listed in Table 20-2. The disk capacitors should be of a good quality, and leads

TABLE 20-2. Decoupling Capacitor Usage

IC Type	Number	
Standard TTL	5 to 10	Use one disk
74H or 54H series	5	capacitor
One-shot	1	(0.01 to 0.1 μF)
Line driver	1	for the number
Line receiver	1	of ICs indicated.

FIGURE 20-8. Breadboard

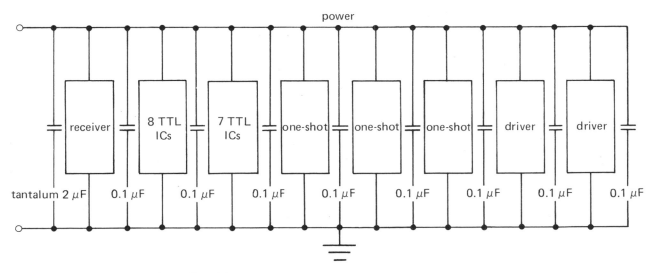

FIGURE 20-9. Decoupling Capacitors

should be clipped short. A tantalum capacitor (2.0 to 20 μF) should be connected at the point where power enters the board. All capacitors are connected between the power and ground lines, as shown in Figure 20-9.

□ EXAMPLE 20-1

Find the number of decoupling capacitors necessary in a breadboard circuit with 1 line receiver, 2 line drivers, 15 7400 series TTL chips, and 3 one-shots.

Solution From Table 20-2, we can determine the number of capacitors needed. The tabulation is given in Table 20-3. Figure 20-9 shows how the capacitors can be connected. The single tantalum capacitor recommended above is also shown.

TABLE 20-3. Capacitors Needed for Example 20-1

Component	Capacitors
1 line receiver	1
2 line drivers	2
15 standard TTLs	2
3 one-shots	3
Total	8

□ CONNECTING LIQUID-CRYSTAL DISPLAYS

Faced with the problem of making electrical contact with an LCD, you will discover that this display has no pins. Usually, there are a row of pads on the glass, and, traditionally, spring finger contacts have been used to make the connection. Unfortunately, the fingers scrape off the pad area, and, eventually, the resistance increases a great deal. Furthermore, insertion is difficult, and the display is susceptible to vibration or shock damage.

Recently, a rubber device called a **zebra** has been used to make the LCD contact (see Figure 20-10). The layers of the zebra are alternately conducting and insulating rubber. The zebra is

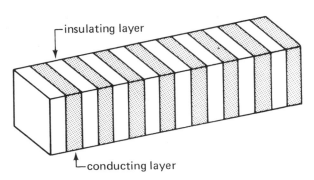

FIGURE 20-10. Conductive Rubber Zebra

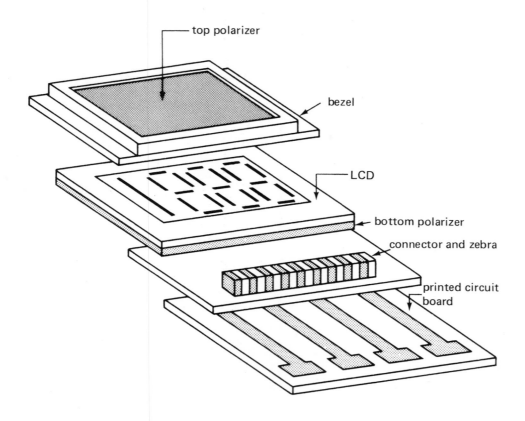

FIGURE 20-11.
Mounting an LCD
with a Zebra

TABLE 20-4. Zebra Connectors

Series	Conductive Layers per Inch	Minimum LCD Pad Width (in.)	Minimum Centerline Spacing of Pads (in.)
1002	240	0.005	0.010
1006	100	0.015	0.030
1010	50	0.025	0.050
1020	25	0.040	0.075

placed between the LCD and the printed circuit board, as shown in Figure 20-11. The circuit board traces are wider than the zebra spacing, so each LCD contact matches only one circuit board trace. The zebra also protects against vibrations and forms a moisture-proof seal. Table 20-4 lists the sizes and spacings for several series of zebra connectors.

□ ANALOG CIRCUIT TROUBLESHOOTING

Analog circuits are more difficult to troubleshoot than are digital circuits. As Figure 20-12 shows, the fault can propagate in both directions throughout the analog circuit. Digital faults propagate only in one direction—from inputs to outputs.

Another difference between analog and digital circuits is that there are fewer pins in the analog circuit, even though there are more discrete components. Most important of all, analog voltages vary over a range of valid inputs, while digital circuits depend only on voltage levels.

The most common approach to analog fault localization is **probe tracing**. A meter and oscilloscope can effectively be used together here. Start with the power supply. If there is no voltage, test the ground and circuit board pins next, looking for a short. If the voltage is incorrect, narrow your search to an excessive load or a faulty component in the supply. If supply voltages are correct, move on to the other circuits. There are two procedures that will rapidly indicate the area of the fault: (1) a check of junction voltage drops in semiconductors and (2) a check of resistance or impedance verification between nodes. (Be sure to disconnect the power before testing the node resistance.) The equipment manual will list the voltage or resistance to be found in normal operation. Manuals also indicate normal oscilloscope waveforms that appear at certain test points.

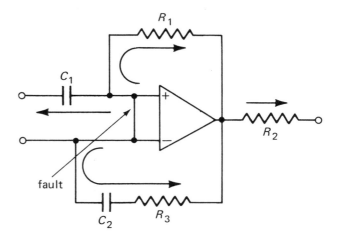

FIGURE 20-12. Analog Circuit Fault Propagation

Chapter Summary

☐ Manufacturers' data sheets specify pin assignments, logic functions, and electrical performance of electronic components.

☐ Logic probes and pulsers can be used in stimulus-response testing to verify truth tables. A logic clip will test all pins of an IC at once. Other useful items of test equipment are the current tracer, the DMM, and the oscilloscope.

☐ Breadboards readily accommodate prototype circuit development. Additions or changes are made by simply inserting or removing components.

☐ A handy new device for connecting LCDs is the zebra. Zebras come in various sizes, which are selected to conform to the LCD pad spacing.

☐ Analog circuits are more difficult to troubleshoot than are digital circuits. A logical sequence that isolates the fault must be applied.

Appendix

Transistors

Throughout this book, transistors have appeared in many of the circuits. The discussion in this appendix is intended to provide a unified discussion of transistor analysis. You may wish to refer to these descriptions to supplement the material in any particular chapter of the text.

We begin with an investigation into semiconductor theory, and then we look at the simplest transistor configurations. The characteristics of these circuits are explained in terms of widely used transistor models. Next, we take up the topic of transistor amplifiers. Finally, we consider various biasing arrangements for transistors.

☐ SEMICONDUCTOR MATERIALS

All matter is composed of atoms, which, as you know, possess a central *nucleus* surrounded by negatively charged *electrons*. No two electrons in a single atom can be at the same energy levels. This splitting of energy levels is called the **Pauli exclusion principle**. Energy levels are important because they determine whether a material is a *conductor* or *insulator* of electricity.

Figure A-1a shows that, at room temperature, the electrons around a conductor are grouped into two adjacent energy levels: the conduction band and the valence band. The **valence band** is the lowest energy level for the electrons. At the temperature of *absolute zero* ($-273.16°C$), all electrons of the material are in the valence band, which is completely filled. At higher temperatures, the **conduction band** begins to fill as the electrons that leave the valence band become *free electrons*.

Figure A-1b illustrates the room temperature energy levels in an insulator. The valence and conduction bands are separated by an **energy gap**.

Another type of material, between an insulator and a conductor, is the *semiconductor* (see Figure A-1c). It is characterized by a relatively small energy gap between the valence and conduction bands at room temperature.

Table A-1 compares the *resistivity* of several materials. Rubber, mica, and glass (all good insulators) have very high resistance. Aluminum, gold, and copper (conductors) have low resistance. Silicon offers more resistance to current flow than the metals, yet its resistance is low enough to class it as a semiconductor.

Let us return for a moment to a consideration of what happens to the electrons as the temperature increases just slightly above absolute zero. As the electrons move from the valence band to the conduction band, they leave a **hole** behind. To visualize what a hole is, consider the two-story parking garage in Figure A-2. Initially (Figure A-2a), all four cars (representing electrons) are parked on the first floor (corresponding to the valence band). All cars are at the lowest energy level; that is, they are on the bottom floor.

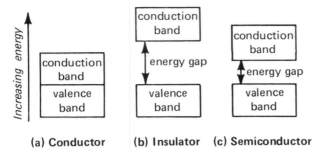

(a) Conductor   (b) Insulator   (c) Semiconductor

FIGURE A-1. Electron Energy Levels

TABLE A-1. Resistance of Materials

Material	Resistivity $(\Omega \cdot cm)^a$
Rubber	10^{18}
Mica	9×10^{15}
Glass	5×10^{13}
Silicon	58×10^{-6}
Brass	7×10^{-6}
Aluminum	2.8×10^{-6}
Gold	2.4×10^{-6}
Copper	1.7×10^{-6}

^{a}At 20°C.

Then someone drives one of the cars to the second floor (Figure A-2b). Energy was needed to raise the car up, and an empty space was left behind (a hole). After the car is moved again (Figure A-2c), the holes have also moved. Thus movement of an electron produces a change in the location of holes.

Of course, the garage is a poor analogy for an atom. The atoms that we are interested in form a very regular crystalline structure in a semiconductor. Each atom of silicon shares two electrons with each adjacent atom. This structure is called a **covalent bond** (see Figure A-3a).

Often, a manufacturer wishes to create a semiconductor with an excess of electrons. These electrons are introduced by **doping** the crystal with impurities. These impurities, called **donor atoms**, have five electrons in their outer shell. Examples of donors include arsenic and antimony.

When donor atoms occupy space in the crystal lattice, they provide an additional electron, as shown in Figure A-3b. (Although there are more electrons in the lattice than in a crystal of pure silicon, the material is still *electrically*

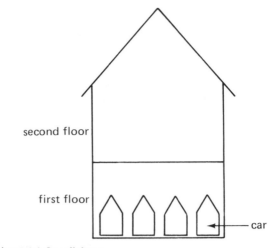

(a) Initial Conditions

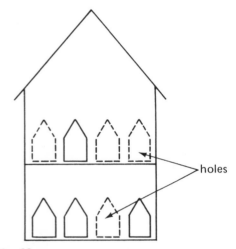

(b) After One Car Moves

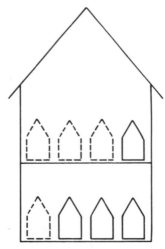

(c) After Second Move

FIGURE A-2. Hole Analogy

neutral. Remember that the electrical charge of electrons is exactly balanced by the positive protons in the nucleus.) This extra electron is loosely bound, so it can move freely in the lattice (leaving a hole behind). Because there are more electrons than holes in material doped with donor atoms, electrons are called *majority carriers of charge*, while the holes are called *minority carriers*. Because of the excess electrons, the doped crystal is referred to as *n*-**type material**.

Contrast *n*-type material with *p*-**type material**. The doping agent here has only three electrons in its outer shell. The lack of one electron in the **acceptor atoms** produces a hole (see Figure A–3c). Gallium and indium are commonly used acceptor doping agents. The holes are the majority carriers in *p*-type material, while electrons are minority carriers.

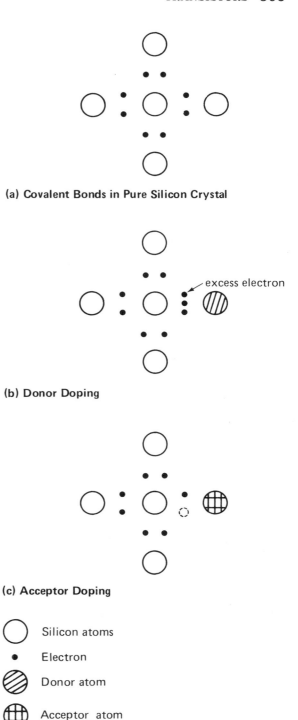

(a) Covalent Bonds in Pure Silicon Crystal

(b) Donor Doping

(c) Acceptor Doping

○ Silicon atoms

• Electron

⬛ Donor atom

⊕ Acceptor atom

○ Hole

FIGURE A–3. Doping and Crystal Lattices

☐ BIPOLAR JUNCTION TRANSISTORS

The bipolar transistor can be formed in two ways. Both *npn* and *pnp* transistors are available. In either case, the biasing arrangement necessary for the transistor to operate in the active region is the same. That is, the emitter is forward-biased with respect to the base, and the collector is reverse-biased with respect to the base. Figure A–4 shows the biasing arrangements for both *npn* (part a) and *pnp* (part b) transistors.

With normal biasing, the majority carrier current can flow from the emitter to the collector. The amount of current flow depends on the base biasing. The emitter current is always greater than the collector current, because

$$I_E = I_B + I_C \qquad \text{(A-1)}$$

where

I_E = emitter current
I_B = base current
I_C = collector current

The base current is small but never zero, so the collector current is decreased by this amount. As Equation A–1 shows, the transistor is a *current-controlled device*.

Current ratios are an important measure of

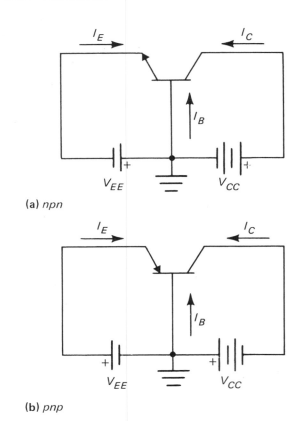

(a) *npn*

(b) *pnp*

FIGURE A–4. Transistor Biasing

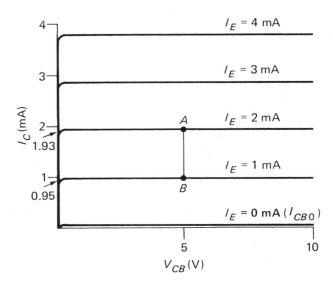

FIGURE A–5. Common-Base Transistor Characteristic Curves

transistor performance. The steady state collector-to-emitter current is designated as

$$\alpha = \frac{I_C}{I_E} \tag{A–2}$$

Obviously, α is always less than one. (If the emitter current ever becomes zero, collector current is also zero, but the condition is a nonoperational case.)

Common-Base Circuit

The circuit that we have been examining so far is called the **common-base configuration**. The characteristic curves for the common-base transistor circuit are shown in Figure A–5. Note that the collector current is always slightly less than that of the emitter at any fixed collector-to-base voltage, because α is less than one. For example, when I_E is 1 mA, I_C is about 0.95 mA.

We will analyze the circuit operation by using the characteristic curves and the schematic in Figure A–6. In addition to the steady state

bias, an alternating signal has been introduced in the emitter leg. Just for the example, suppose we assume that α for the transistor is 0.95. Then, from Equation A–2, we have

$$I_C = 0.95 I_E$$
$$I_B = 0.05 I_E$$

When the alternating signal is positive going, it opposes the emitter bias. Thus the emitter current is reduced. The decrease in the emitter current also decreases the collector current. The voltage drop V_L across the load resistor is

$$V_L = I_C R_L \tag{A–3}$$

So the output voltage

$$V_o = V_{CC} - I_C R_L \tag{A–4}$$

will increase, because the resistor voltage drop is less. The point labeled 1 on the voltage waveforms in Figure A–6 corresponds to this condition. On the other hand, as the emitter current is increasing (such as at point 2), the collector current also increases. The voltage drop across the resistor becomes greater, thus reducing the output voltage.

Just as we were able to compare the steady state currents and voltages with a ratio, we can do the same for the **dynamic**, or ac, **current gain** of the transistor. It is

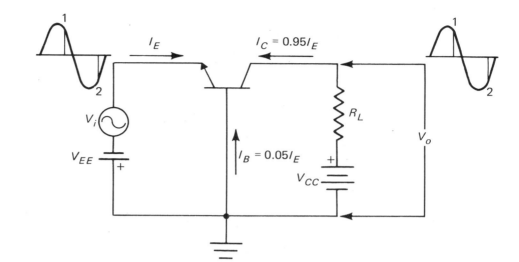

FIGURE A-6.
Common-Base Circuit
with Alternating
Input

$$\alpha_{ac} = \frac{\Delta I_C}{\Delta I_E}\Bigg|_{\Delta V_{CB} = 0} \qquad \textbf{(A-5)}$$

where

ΔI_C = change in collector current
ΔI_E = change in emitter current
ΔV_{CB} = change in collector-to-base voltage

This equation may look somewhat strange because of the vertical line notation. The meaning is really quite simple, though. The notation means that the ratio is computed only for the case in which there is no change in the collector-to-base voltage.

Consider the current changes from point A to point B on Figure A-5. At these points, we have the following values:

Point	Emitter Current (mA)	Collector Current (mA)	V_{CB} (V)
A	1	0.95	5
B	2	1.93	5

Then, we have

$$\alpha_{ac} = \frac{1.93 - 0.95}{2 - 1} = 0.98$$

The dynamic current gain for a common-base circuit is always less than unity.

Common-Emitter Circuit

Another way of arranging the transistor and its input signal is the **common-emitter circuit**, which is shown in Figure A-7. Here, the alternating signal is applied to the base. The characteristic curves for this circuit appear in Figure A-8. Immediately apparent is the fact that these curves are less linear than those of the common-base configuration. The reason for the difference is that, in this case, the base current does not directly control the collector current. (In contrast, the collector current was almost equal to the emitter current in the common-base circuit.)

We can define gain equations for the common-emitter circuit also. However, in this situation, we are most interested in the comparison of base current to collector current. The gain equations are

$$\beta = \frac{I_C}{I_B} \qquad \textbf{(A-6)}$$

$$\beta_{ac} = \frac{\Delta I_C}{\Delta I_B}\Bigg|_{\Delta V_{CE} = 0} \qquad \textbf{(A-7)}$$

where

β = steady state gain
β_{ac} = dynamic gain
ΔV_{CE} = change in collector-to-emitter voltage

Let us take for an example the difference in

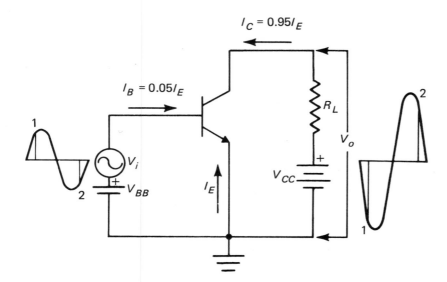

FIGURE A-7.
Common-Emitter
Circuit

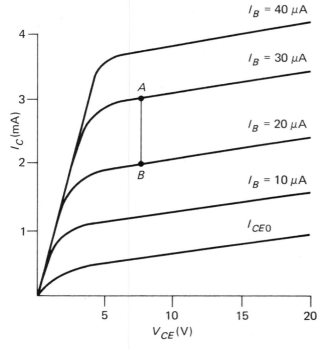

FIGURE A-8. Common-Emitter Characteristic
Curves

dynamic gain between points A and B on Figure
A-8. At these points, we have the following
values:

Point	Collector Current (mA)	Base Current (μA)	V_{CE} (V)
A	3	30	7.5
B	2	20	7.5

Then, we have

$$\beta_{ac} = \frac{3 \times 10^{-3} - 2 \times 10^{-3}}{30 \times 10^{-6} - 20 \times 10^{-6}} = 100$$

Here, we find that the dynamic gain is substantial; it is 100.

Let us also examine the steady state gain at
point A.

$$\beta = \frac{3 \times 10^{-3}}{30 \times 10^{-6}} = 100$$

Again, the gain is 100. (It is only a coincidence
that the dynamic and steady state gains are
equal. In most situations, they are different.)
Observe that β is many times larger than α, also.

Now, let us return to Figure A-7. We first
look at point 1 on the input, when V_i is aiding the
bias voltage. The increase in emitter current
causes both the base and the collector current to
increase. The output voltage, however, decreases.
The output is 180° out of phase with the input,
because a larger collector current produces more
voltage drop across the resistor. This effect is
shown on the figure, as is the amplification
caused by the large β gain. The output voltage
range is many times more than that of the input.
Conversely, when the input signal opposes the
emitter bias (point 2), the currents decrease, and
the output voltage becomes positive.

Returning to the curve of Figure A-8, we
see that collector current flows even when there is
no base current. This current is called the **leakage
current**, and it is caused by minority carriers in

the semiconductor for this circuit. The leakage current is designated I_{CE0}. (A similar, but much smaller, current, I_{CB0}, appears in Figure A-5.)

Gain Relationships

The gain equations that we have developed are quite useful in working with transistors. Most manufacturers specify the α or β parameters on their transistors. With a little algebra, we can readily convert one measure to another.

Recall that

$$I_B = I_E - I_C$$

and $\beta = \dfrac{I_C}{I_B}$

Then $\beta = \dfrac{I_C}{I_E - I_C}$

$$= \dfrac{I_C/I_E}{1 - I_C/I_E}$$

$$= \dfrac{\alpha}{1 - \alpha} \tag{A-8}$$

By a similar manipulation, we can demonstrate that

$$\alpha = \dfrac{\beta}{1 + \beta} \tag{A-9}$$

The dynamic equations yield corresponding results. That is,

$$\beta_{ac} = \dfrac{\alpha_{ac}}{1 - \alpha_{ac}} \tag{A-10}$$

and $\alpha_{ac} = \dfrac{\beta_{ac}}{1 + \beta_{ac}} \tag{A-11}$

By using these equations, we can find any of the three transistor currents given any one of them. Table A-2 lists these conversion factors. In the table, currents with lowercase letters are

dynamic values; uppercase letters indicate steady state values.

Suppose we know that steady state emitter current is 4 mA and we want to find the steady state collector current. Looking at the data sheet for this transistor, we see that $\alpha = 0.99$. Then, from Equation A-8, we have

$$\beta = \dfrac{0.99}{1 - 0.99} = 99$$

Now, we use Table A-2 to find I_C:

$$I_C = \left(\dfrac{\alpha\beta}{1 + \beta}\right) I_E$$
$$= \left[\dfrac{(0.99)(99)}{1 + 99}\right](4 \times 10^{-3})$$
$$= 1.97 \text{ mA}$$

Using the same transistor, let us find the dynamic collector current if the dynamic base current is 20 μA. From the table, we have

$$i_c = \beta\left(\dfrac{\alpha}{1 - \alpha}\right) i_b$$
$$= 99\left(\dfrac{0.99}{1 - 0.99}\right)(20 \times 10^{-6})$$
$$= 196 \text{ mA}$$

Note that the conversion factors in the table can be used for any transistor configuration, not just that of the common emitter.

Analysis of a Common-Emitter Amplifier

We will apply our basic principles of transistor operation to the common-emitter amplifier in Figure A-9. Assume, for this analysis, that we measured the voltages and currents listed in Table A-3.

TABLE A-2. Steady State and Dynamic Current Conversion Factors

Given	To Find $I_B(i_b)$	$I_C(i_c)$	$I_E(i_e)$
$I_B(i_b)$	1	$\beta\left(\dfrac{\alpha}{1 - \alpha}\right)$	$\dfrac{1 + \beta}{1 - \alpha}$
$I_C(i_c)$	$\left(\dfrac{1}{\beta}\right)\left(\dfrac{1 - \alpha}{\alpha}\right)$	1	$\dfrac{1 + \beta}{\alpha\beta}$
$I_E(i_e)$	$\dfrac{1 - \alpha}{1 + \beta}$	$\dfrac{\alpha\beta}{1 + \beta}$	1

TABLE A-3. Common-Emitter Amplifier Measurements

V_i (V)	I_B (μA)	I_C (mA)	V_{BE} (V)	V_{CE} (V)	V_o (V)
+0.05	40	3.96	0.2	8	12
0	30	2.97	0.15	11	9
−0.05	20	1.98	0.1	14	6

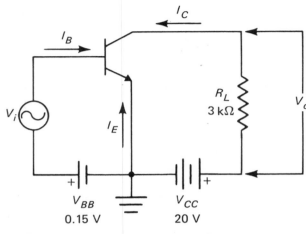

FIGURE A-9. Common-Emitter Amplifier

We compute the current gain from Equation A-6:

$$\beta = \frac{1.98 \times 10^{-3}}{20 \times 10^{-6}} = 99$$

We can then find α by using Equation A-9:

$$\alpha = \frac{99}{1 + 99} = 0.99$$

The voltage gain V_g is

$$V_g = \frac{\Delta V_o}{\Delta V_i} \qquad \text{(A-12)}$$

$$= \frac{12 - 6}{0.05 - (-0.05)}$$

$$= 60$$

The power gain P_g is

$$P_g = \beta V_g \qquad \text{(A-13)}$$
$$= (99)(60)$$
$$= 5940$$

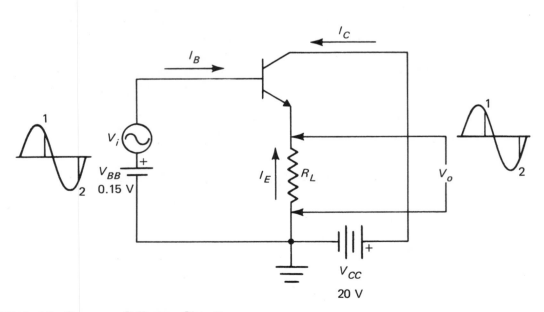

FIGURE A-10. Common-Collector Circuit

Common-Collector Circuit

The final transistor configuration, the **common-collector circuit**, is shown in Figure A–10. This circuit is also called an *emitter follower*. Here, the increasing input signal (point 1) aids the bias voltage. As the emitter current increases, it produces an in-phase output voltage. A decreasing input (point 2) decreases the output voltage.

Suppose we measure the currents and voltages in this circuit and find them to be those listed in Table A–3. When the input signal is zero, the emitter voltage is at a potential of the 9-V resistor drop above ground. Because V_{BE} is 0.15 V, the base-to-ground potential is 9.15 V. Figure A–11 shows the input and output voltages. Therefore, the voltage gain, computed by using Equation A–12, is

$$V_g = \frac{12 - 6}{12.2 - 6.1} = 0.98$$

which is less than unity. The current gain is

$$\beta = \frac{1.98 \times 10^{-3}}{20 \times 10^{-6}} = 99$$

And the power gain, from Equation A–13, is

$$P_g = (99)(0.98) = 97$$

A comparison of the three transistor amplifier configurations is provided in Table A–4. The common-base circuit has a large voltage gain but less-than-unity current gain. The common emitter offers high current and voltage gain, and it inverts the input signal. The common-collector output is in phase with the input, and current gain is high, but voltage gain is less than one.

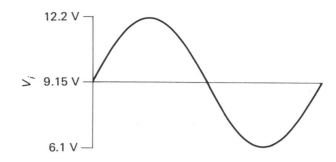
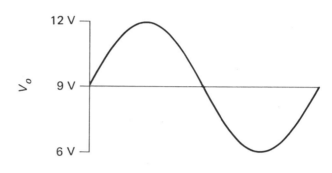

FIGURE A–11. Common-Collector Input and Output Voltages

□ BIASING CIRCUITS

Most of the time, we wish to bias a transistor with a single battery. Figure A–12a shows a simple **fixed-bias arrangement** for a common-emitter amplifier. The operating point on the load line with this design is shown in Figure A–12b with a

TABLE A–4. Transistor Amplifier Comparison

Parameter	Common Base	Common Emitter	Common Collector
Input voltage change	Small	Small	Large
Input current change	Large	Small	Small
Output voltage change	Medium	Medium	Medium
Output current change	Medium	Medium	Medium
Voltage gain	Large (in phase)	Large (out of phase)	Less than unity (in phase)
Current gain	Less than unity (α)	Large (β)	Large (β)
Power gain	Low	High	Low to medium

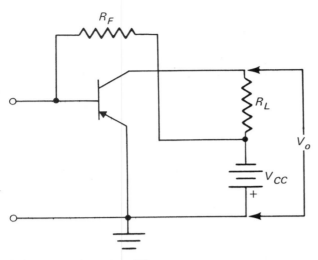

(a) *pnp* Transistor Amplifier

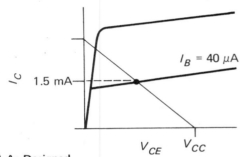

(b) As Designed

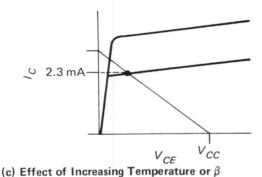

(c) Effect of Increasing Temperature or β

(d) Effect of Decreasing Temperature or β

FIGURE A-12. Fixed Biasing

collector current of 1.5 mA and a base current of 40 μA. We select the **biasing resistor** R_F so that

$$R_F = \frac{V_{CC}}{I_B} \qquad \text{(A-14)}$$

where I_B is the base current at the operating point. Suppose the desired base current is 40 μA, and V_{CC} is 20 V. Then, we have

$$R_F = \frac{20}{40 \times 10^{-6}} = 500 \text{ k}\Omega$$

This type of biasing is only satisfactory if the temperature is constant and the transistor parameters are known. (The β between two identical transistors frequently varies by 100 percent.) The effect that increasing temperature or replacing the transistor by one with a higher β has on the operating point is shown in Figure A-12c. The collector current at the operating point has increased. This result could be predicted from Table A-2, because

$$I_C = \beta \left(\frac{\alpha}{1 - \alpha} \right) I_B$$

As β gets larger, so does I_C. An opposite outcome is produced by lowering the temperature or using a replacement transistor with a smaller β (see Figure A-12d).

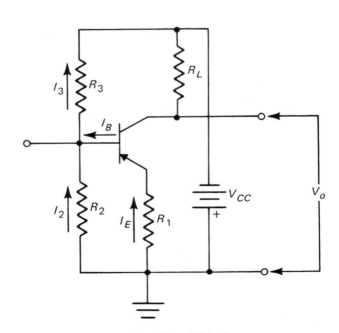

FIGURE A-13. Stabilized Biasing

An improvement in the biasing that largely eliminates these problems is shown in Figure A–13. The **stabilized bias** is less sensitive to changes in temperature or to the β of a transistor. In this circuit, R_2 and R_3 serve the same purpose as R_F in the previous circuit. The additional resistor, R_1, is used for stabilization. If there is no change in the base voltage, then an increase in the emitter current increases the voltage drop across R_1. This voltage drop, in turn, reduces the base-to-emitter voltage drop and, consequently, reduces the base current. An opposite effect results if the emitter current decreases. The size of R_1 should be relatively large in order to maintain collector circuit efficiency.

The voltage drop across R_3 is

$$V_3 = R_3(I_B + I_2)$$

To maintain a constant value of V_{BE}, we want I_2 to be much greater than I_B (three to five times). So small values for R_2 and R_3 are indicated.

Suggestions for Further Reading

Berlin, Howard M. *Design of Phase-Locked Loop Circuits.* Indianapolis: Howard W. Sams, 1978.

Grinich, Victor H., and Horace G. Jackson. *Introduction to Integrated Circuits.* New York: McGraw-Hill, 1975.

Jung, Walter G. *IC Converter Cookbook.* Indianapolis: Howard W. Sams, 1981.

Kershaw, John D. *Digital Electronics: Logic and Systems.* North Scituate, Mass.: Breton, 1976.

Millman, Jacob, and C. Halkias Christos. *Integrated Electronics: Analog and Digital Circuits and Systems.* New York: McGraw-Hill, 1972.

Mims, Forest M. *Engineer's Notebook: A Handbook of Integrated Circuit Applications.* Fort Worth, Tex.: Radio Shack, 1980.

Pasahow, Edward A. *Digital Integrated Circuits for Electronics Technicians.* New York: McGraw-Hill, 1979.

Answers to Odd Numbered Problems

1-1. Ohm's law, 40 ohms; temperature compensated, 35.2 ohms

1-3. 0.67 V

1-5. The base current must be approximately 22 μA.

1-7. off; on; off; on

1-9. cutoff; active; saturated; cutoff

2-1. low: 0–0.5 ms, 3.9–4 ms
undefined: 1.5–2 ms, 3.7–3.9 ms
high: 0.5–1.5 ms, 2–3.4 ms, 3.5–3.7 ms
forbidden: 3.4–3.5 ms

2-3. low

2-7. 180 mA; 0 mA

2-9. 4.3 V

2-11. 9.6 mA; 0 mA

2-13. 0.9 mA

2-15. an inverted square wave with a period of 200 ms

2-19. high: 20 ms; low: 50 ms; high: 40 ms; low: 30 ms; high: 80 ms

3-3. a.

F	$\overline{G}$	H	Output
0	0	0	0
0	0	1	0
0	1	0	0
0	1	1	0
1	0	0	0
1	0	1	0
1	1	0	0
1	1	1	1

b.

$\overline{M}$	$\overline{L}$	$\overline{J}$	Output
0	0	0	0
0	0	1	1
0	1	0	1
0	1	1	1
1	0	0	1
1	0	1	1
1	1	0	1
1	1	1	1

3-5. $x\overline{y} + \overline{x}y$

3-7. a. 0; b. 0

3-9. They are identical.

3-11. (3-11) $\overline{\overline{0}} = 0, \overline{\overline{1}} = 1$
(3-12) $0 \cdot \overline{0} = 0 \cdot 1 = 0, 1 \cdot \overline{1} = 1 \cdot 0 = 0$
(3-13) $0 + \overline{0} = 0 + 1 = 1,$
$\qquad 1 + \overline{1} = 1 + 0 = 1$

3-13. $= x\,(y + \overline{y}) + x(\overline{y} + Y)$
$= x + x$
$= x$

4-1. 4.0 ns

4-3. Both parameters are within specifications.

4-5. 0 mA; 0 mA

4-7. 1.10 mA; no change; 1.08 mA

4-9. 7.7 mW; 11.5 mW

5-1. 0.4 V; 0.4 V

5-3. all tied to V_{CC}

5-5. 77 percent

5-7. 2.7 ns; Schottky clamped

6-1. 3.2 ms

6-3. 797 ohms

6-5. 338 ohms

6-7. H for OR gates; L for AND gate

6-9. with low output, 18.8 mW

7-3. 0 V, 10^{10} ohms

7-5. 2.2 mW

7-7. D_1 and D_3 would conduct protecting the gate which would have an output of about -0.7 V.

7-9. 1.6 V

8-1. a. 45C; b. 7.A8; c. -56.F; d. 29.58

8-3. a. 1101 0010.1000 1110
b. -111 1100 0100 0101.0001 0010 0011
c. 1 0000.1010 0101
d. 0110 0100.0111 1000 1001 1100

8-5. a. 10 010 000
b. 1 011 100.110 011
c. 101 100 101.100 111
d. 1 010 011.01

8-7. a. 1111 0010.1101 0001
b. 111 000.011 11
c. 1 100 011.110 100 011

8-9. 110 0010.1110 011

9-1. a. 100 010
  b. 1 010 110.011
  c. 100 0110 1001
  d. 1 0111 0100.11

9-3. a. 11 0110 1011
  b. 101 101 011
  c. 1 0100 0000.0111 1001
  d. 1 011 010 110

9-5. a. 0101 0010
  b. 01 010 001
  c. 0011 1011
  d. 1100 0001

9-7. sum = 0111 1011; carry out = 0

9-9. 54_{16}

10-3. a. 1; b. 0

10-5. $D = 0$; $C = 1$; $B = 1$; $A = 1$

10-7. a. $F = \bar{B}$
  b. $F = A$
  c. $F = AB$

10-9. $S = 6_{16}$; $M = 1$; $\bar{C}_n = 0$

11-7. a. $Q = 1$; $\bar{Q} = 0$
  b. $Q = 0$; $\bar{Q} = 1$

11-9.

Pulse	T_1	T_2	Q_1	Q_2
1	1	1	0	1
2	1	0	1	1
3	1	1	0	0
4	1	0	1	0
5	1	1	0	1

12-3. The combined resistance is 50 ohms. The counter provides a step waveform for the first three inputs, then drops to 0 V and repeats.

12-7. 32

12-9. load a 4-stage 74192 counter with an initial count of 0049_{10}

13-1. a. 3; b. -30

13-3. 180 ohms

13-5. 2.7 μV

13-7. Yes, oscillations occur above 100 kHz. No, oscillations occur throughout the frequency range.

13-9. using 100 kHz for f_{-90}; $C = 1.6$ nF

14-1. The output of the op amp is 9.72 V of which 0.72 V is noise. The output of the instrumentation amplifier is 9 V with no noise.

14-3. $S3$ (level 1); $S4$ (level 2)

14-5. Pins 1 and 8 should be open.

14-7. $C_2 = 62.5$ pF; $R_1 = 1.27$ Mohms; $R_2 = 1.27$ Mohms; $R_3 = 900$ kohms; $R_4 = 1.54$ Mohms

14-9. BW = 200 Hz; $f_H = 1.1$ kHz

15-1. a. 1.87 V; b. 3.75 V; c. 4.5 V; d. 5.625 V

15-3. a. $1101\ 1111_2$; b. $0001\ 0001_2$;
  c. $0110\ 0101_2$; d. $1011\ 0110_2$

15-5. 4.375 V

15-7. 3.75 V

15-9. 2.4 mV

16-1. 22.5 kHz; fifth

16-3. 2.06 kHz; 0.14

16-5. 9 ms; 3.47 ms; 0.28

16-7. 285 Hz; 1426 Hz

16-9. square wave with a time high of 7 ms, period of 7.07 ms, amplitude of 5 V

16-11. $t = 0.511\ RC$

16-13. 227 nF

16-17. 8.5 ms

16-19. 0.9 V

17-1. a. 34.4; b. 68.8; c. 157.5; d. 540

17-3. 4.5 V

17-5. a. 0.6 V; b. 0.8 V; c. 2 V

17-7. $R_T = 12.9$ kohms; $C_L = 1.5$ uF

17-9. 1.2 nF

18-1. for $V_{CC} = 5$ V; $R_L = 120$ ohms (approximately)

18-3. Using a forward bias of 1.6 V and $V_{CC} = 5$ V, brightness is about 510 ft-L.

18-5. Using $V_{CC} = 5$ V, the resistor in the main leg is 120 ohms, in the green leg, 60 ohms (approximately).

18-7. 5

19-1. 35.7 ohms

19-3. using an operating current of half maximum, 10 ohms

19-5. $V_{dc} = 25.5$ V, $V_{rms} = 28.3$

19-7. $V_{out} = 19.5$ V; 5 percent

19-9. 5.8 V

Index

Index of Integrated Circuits